The Postal Service Guide to U.S. Stamps

25th Special Edition
1999 Stamp Values

United States Postal Service
Washington, D.C. 20260-2435
Item No. 8898

Library of Congress Catalog Card Number 87-656545
ISBN: 1-877707-08-2

Printed in the United States of America

Table of Contents

A PET PROJECT

Unleash the fun and learning of stamp collecting

Whether you're a dog lover or a feline afficionado, a bird watcher or an avid equestrian, the world of stamp collecting brings animals of all shapes and sizes into your home. What's more, it opens the door to an exciting world of history, sports, arts and science as well.

Stamps—both old and new—introduce you to statesmen and soldiers who changed the course of history. Spotlight scary movie monsters and glamourous Hollywood superstars. Help you discover rare flowers, natural wonders, jet planes and antique trains. And so much more.

But perhaps the best part about stamp collecting is that it's an affordable hobby that will truly last a lifetime. So, how do you start a collection of your own? Read on and find out.

4

How do I start collecting stamps?

It's easy. You can start by simply saving stamps from letters, packages and postcards. Ask your friends and family to save stamps from their mail. Neighborhood businesses that get a lot of mail—banks, stores, travel agencies—might save their envelopes for you, too.

Or, start your collection by choosing one or two favorite subjects. Then, collect only stamps that fit your theme—art, history, sports, transportation, science—whatever you choose! This is called topical collecting. See the stamps pictured in this feature article for ideas to get you started on a theme.

Definitive

Commemorative

Special

Airmail

Booklet

Coil

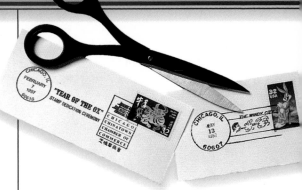

Will it cost me a lot to start a collection?

No! Start with used stamps and a few inexpensive accessories (such as a small album and a package of hinges), and you can have a great time on a limited budget. Remember to put stamps, albums and hinges on your birthday and holiday wish lists, too!

What kinds of stamps are there?

-*Definitive*
-*Commemorative*
-*Special*
-*Airmail*
-*Booklet format*
-*Coil format*

Definitive stamps are found on most mail. They feature former presidents, statesmen, prominent persons and national shrines. Their denominations range from 1 cent to 14 dollars. Definitives are usually available for several years, since they're printed in large quantities for specific postal rates.

Commemorative stamps are usually larger and more colorful than definitives. They honor important people, events or subjects. Only a limited number of each commemorative is printed, and most post offices only have them for a few months. The U.S. Postal Service's Philatelic Fulfillment Service Center also offers commemorative stamps by mail order for about one year after they are issued.

Special stamps supplement each year's regular stamp issues. They include the Christmas and Love stamps.

Airmail stamps are mainly used for sending mail overseas.

Booklet stamps come in small folders that contain panes of

3 to 20 stamps each. Gummed booklet stamps have at least one straight edge.

Coil stamps are issued in rolls. Each coil stamp has two straight edges and two edges with either slit-like cuts or little holes, called perforations.

How do I remove stamps from envelopes?

If you wish, you can save whole envelopes with stamps on them and store them anywhere—from shoe boxes to special albums. But if you want to remove stamps from envelopes, it pays to be careful. The best way to remove stamps from envelopes is to soak them. Here's how:

1. Tear or cut off the upper right-hand corner of the envelope.

2. Place it, stamp side down, in a small pan of warm water. After a few minutes, the stamp will sink to the bottom.

3. Wait a few more minutes for any remaining gum to dislodge from the stamp.

4. Lift the stamp out with tongs (a metal tool, like tweezers) if you have a pair. It's better to handle stamps with tongs because oil from your skin can damage stamps.

5. Place the stamp between two paper towels and put a heavy object, such as a book, on top. This will keep the stamp from curling as it dries. Leave the stamp there overnight.

6. If the stamp is a newer one with "invisible" gum, dry it face down with nothing touching the back and flatten it later if necessary. Otherwise, it may stick to the paper towel when drying.

How should I organize my stamps?

However you want to, of course—it's your collection. But be sure to protect them so they don't get damaged or lost. You can attach your stamps to loose-leaf paper and put them in a three-ring binder. Or, arrange them in a more formal album, which you can buy in stores.

How do I collect First Day Covers?

The fastest way to get a First Day Cover is to buy the stamp yourself (it will usually go on sale the day after the first day of issue), attach it to your own envelope (or cover), and send it to the first day post office for cancellation. You can submit up to 50 envelopes, up to 30 days after the stamp's issue date. Here's how:

1. Write your address in the lower right-hand corner of each first day envelope, at least 5/8" from the bottom. Leave plenty of room for the stamp(s) and cancellation. Use a peel-off label if you prefer.

2. Insert a piece of cardboard (about as thick as a postcard) into each envelope. You can tuck the flap in or seal the envelope.

3. Affix your stamp(s) to your first day envelope(s).

4. Put your first day envelope(s) inside another, larger envelope and mail it to "Customer-Affixed Envelopes" in care of the postmaster of the first day city. Your envelopes will be canceled and returned.

Or, you can purchase a plain envelope with the stamp(s) already affixed and canceled. These are now sold directly by mail order through the U.S. Postal Service.

What kinds of stamp albums can I buy?

Some stamp albums feature specific categories with pictures of the stamps that should appear on each page. You may want to select one with loose-leaf pages so you can add pages as your collection grows. A stock book is an album with plastic or paper pockets on each page. There are no pictures of stamps, so you can organize the album your way.

How do I put a stamp in the album?

It's best to use a hinge—a small strip of thin plastic with gum on one side. Unlike tape or glue, hinges let you peel the stamp off the page without damaging it. Hinges come either folded or unfolded. Here's how to use a folded hinge:

1.Moisten the short end of the hinge lightly. Press it to the back of the stamp, placing the fold about 1/8" from the top of the stamp.

2.Place the stamp in the album and press down to secure it.

3.Using your tongs, gently lift the corners of the stamp to make sure it's not stuck to the page.

Instead of a hinge, you can insert the entire stamp into a mount—a small, clear plastic sleeve. Mounts are more expensive than hinges, but they protect stamps from air, dirt and moisture.

Is there anything else I need?

Here's a list of other equipment you may find helpful:

Glassine envelopes are made of a special thin, see-through paper that protects stamps from grease and air. You can use them to keep stamps until you put them in your album.

A *stamp catalog* is a reference book with illustrations to help you identify stamps. It also lists the values of used and unused stamps.

A *magnifying glass* helps you examine stamps by making them appear larger.

A *perforation gauge* measures perforations along the edges of stamps. Sometimes the size and number of perforations (perfs) are needed to identify stamps.

A *watermark tray* and *watermark fluid* help make watermarks on stamps more visible. A watermark is a design or pattern that is pressed into some stamp paper during manufacturing.

How can I tell what a stamp is worth?

Ask yourself two questions: "How rare is it?" and "What condition is it in?" The price listed in a stamp catalog gives you some idea of how rare it is. However, the stamp may sell at more or less than the catalog price, depending on its condition.

Always try to find stamps in the best possible condition.

Light Cancel–Very Fine

Medium Cancel–Fine

Heavy Cancel

Superb

Very Fine

Fine

Good

How should I judge the condition of a stamp?

Stamp dealers put stamps into categories according to their condition. Look at the pictured examples to see the differences among categories. A stamp in mint condition is the same as when purchased from the post office. An unused stamp has no cancel but may not have any gum on the back. Mint stamps are usually worth more than unused stamps.

You can begin to judge the condition of a stamp by examining the front of it. Are the colors bright or faded? Is the stamp clean, dirty or stained? Is the stamp torn? Torn stamps are not considered "collectible." Is the stamp design centered on the paper, crooked or off to one side? Are all the perforations intact? Has the stamp been canceled? A stamp with a light cancellation is in better condition than one with heavy marks across it.

Now look at the back of the stamp. Is there a thin spot in the paper? If so, it may have been caused by careless removal from an envelope or hinge.

The values listed in this book are for used and unused stamps in Fine-Very Fine condition that have been hinged.

Where else can I find stamps?

Check the classified ads in philatelic newspapers and magazines at your local library. Also, there is a listing of philatelic publishers on page 51 of this book. These publishers will send you one free copy of their publications. Then you can decide if you'd like to subscribe.

What other stamp materials can I collect?

Postal stationery products are popular among some collectors. These have the stamp designs printed or embossed (printed with a raised design) directly on them.

Stamped Envelopes were first issued in 1853. More than 600 million of them are now printed each year.

Writers, Poets, Pet Lovers

They were some of America's most respected literary figures. They were also avid pet lovers whose affection for things furry was occasionally reflected in their work.

Jack London (1876-1916), for example, turned the exploits of a Saint Bernard dog into one of the century's most enduring adventure tales. "The Call of the Wild," published in 1903, tells the story of Buck, a young dog who's snatched from a pampered life and forced to survive in the unforgiving Klondike. The story—told from the canine's perspective—made London an international celebrity and remains a favorite in classrooms today.

T.S. Eliot (1888-1965) is best known for his influential Modernist poems like "The Waste Land" and "The Love Song of J. Alfred Prufrock." However, the staid and serious Nobel Prize winner also harbored a passion for felines. In fact, his playful collection of poems, "Old Possum's Book of Practical Cats," published in 1939, is a celebration of cats and the basis for Broadway's longest-running musical, Cats.

Mark Twain and Ernest Hemingway are two other literary giants whose collection of works include homages to house pets. Look for stamps honoring these and other famous pet lovers as you read The Postal Service Guide to U.S. Stamps.

Creature Features

The Bright Eyes stamps are the latest to pay tribute to our animal friends. As you make your way through The Postal Service Guide to U.S. Stamps, *be sure to watch for these and other pet-related stamps.*

Description	Scott Number
Humane Treatment of Animals	1307
Seeing Eye Dog	1787
Puppy and Kitten	2025
American Dogs	
Beagle, Boston Terrier	2098
Chesapeake Bay Retriever, Cocker Spaniel	2099
Alaskan Malamute, Collie	2100
Black and Tan Coonhound, American Foxhound	2101
American Horses	
Quarter Horse	2155
Morgan	2156
Saddlebred	2157
Appaloosa	2158
Love Stamp-Dog	2202
American Cats	
Siamese, Exotic Shorthair	2372
Abyssinian, Himalayan	2373
Maine Coon, Burmese	2374
American Shorthair, Persian	2375
Love Stamp-Lovebirds	2537

Postal Cards were first issued in 1873. The first U.S. multicolored commemorative postal cards came out in 1956. Several different postal cards are issued each year.

Aerogrammes (air letters) are designed to be letters and envelopes all in one. They are specially stamped, marked for folding and already gummed.

Other philatelic collectibles include:

Plate Blocks usually consist of four stamps from the corner of a pane, with the printing plate number in the margin (or selvage) of the pane.

Copyright Blocks feature the copyright symbol © followed by "United States Postal Service" or "USPS" in the margin of the pane. The USPS began copyrighting new stamp designs in 1978.

Booklet Panes are panes of three or more of the same stamp issue. Panes are affixed inside a thin folder to form a booklet. Usually, collectors of booklet panes save the entire pane.

First Day Covers are envelopes bearing new stamps that are postmarked on the first day of sale. For each new postal issue, the USPS selects one location, usually related to the stamp subject, as the place for the first day dedication ceremony and the first day postmark. There is even an annual First Day Cover Collecting Week. See the article on page 8 for information on how to collect these covers.

First Day Ceremony Programs are given to persons who attend first day ceremonies. They contain a list of participants, information on the stamp subject and the actual stamp attached and postmarked.

Are there any stamp groups I can join?

Yes! Stamp clubs can be a great source for new stamps and for stamp collecting advice. These clubs often meet at schools, YMCAs and community centers. Ask your local postmaster or librarian for the locations of stamp clubs in your area.

BRIGHT EYES, BEST FRIENDS

Household pets turn on the charm in 1998 stamp release

Furry, feathered or finned, pets have been our companions, our helpers and our friends for thousands of years. They've appeared in literature, music and art. They've been celebrated on the Broadway stage. Some were even worshipped by ancient cultures. In 1998, the United States Postal Service pays tribute to a few of these lovable critters with the release of "Bright Eyes," a series of five colorful commemorative stamps that gives everyone the chance to be a pet owner!

People and pets

Throughout history, animals were domesticated for a variety of reasons. Dogs, for example, were first made pets more than 14,000 years ago by cave-dwelling humans who valued them for their hunting skills. The ancient Egyptians revered cats as oracles and deities, adorning them with lavish earrings and collars. Chinese nobility viewed goldfish as symbols of wealth, while small songbirds were first kept by Europeans simply for entertainment.

Today, 58.2 million American households own pets. And while these pet lovers spend about $20 billion annually on them, pets offer humans much in return. Studies show people with pets actually live longer, less stressful lives. Pets have been known to increase medical patients's survival rates. Help children overcome behavioral problems. And maintain emotional support for the elderly. Here are a few household pets whose bright eyes make our world a little brighter too.

"Meow"

Cats have been pets since 3,000 B.C. and now outnumber dogs in the United States. While these felines have one of the keenest senses of hearing in the animal kingdom, their independent nature makes many believe they aren't very good listeners. City dwellers, in particular, enjoy cats because they

Animals in the Oval Office

Believe it or not, studies show that people with pets are assumed to be nicer than those without. A fact that may explain why American presidents are such avid pet lovers.

Perhaps no president had as many animals in the White House as our 35th president, John F. Kennedy. At one time or another, President Kennedy had seven dogs, a canary, two hamsters, a cat, a pony, and two parakeets named Bluebell and Maybell.

Other bird-loving chief executives included Calvin Coolidge and Andrew Jackson, who owned a parrot named Poor Poll. Harry Truman and Jimmy Carter kept cats.

Teddy Roosevelt had guinea pigs. And Richard Nixon, Franklin D. Roosevelt and Lyndon Johnson were just a few who were never far from their beloved pooches.

Look for stamps honoring these and other famous pet lovers as you read The Postal Service Guide to U.S. Stamps.

can be kept in small apartments, don't require outdoor walks and are good self-groomers. They also sleep about 16 hours a day, so they're ideal for people who lead busy lifestyles.

"Woof"

Dogs have earned their nickname "man's best friend" through centuries of service and companionship. Today, canines perform many indispensible roles. Seeing-eye dogs, for instance, and dogs for the hearing-impaired aid disabled people through their daily lives. Watch dogs, rescue dogs and scenthounds who sniff for illegal drugs or bombs play a vital role in ensuring our safety. And sporting dogs and herders are key helpers for

sportsmen and ranchers. Of all domestic animals, none are more versatile—or faithful—than dogs.

"Splash"

There are more than 100 varieties of goldfish—most of which aren't even gold! Unlike their tropical cousins, goldfish are simple to care for and don't require elaborate warm water aquariums. They do, however, prefer a hiding spot in their bowl or tank. Experts believe it helps eliminate stress and gives the fish a better sense of security.

USA 32

"Squeak"

Hamsters get their name from the German word for "hoard." And that's what these golden-haired rodents do best. They love stuffing their cheeks with food and hiding it throughout their cage. They also don't mind being alone, making them a good choice for children who want a pet, but may not have the attention for constant interaction.

"Chirp"

Canaries, parakeets, parrots and other housebirds make terrific pets. They're colorful, and full of personality, too. But how do you pick out a healthy bird? Just look for the four S's: Shiny, clear eyes; Sleek, smooth feathers; Self-confident stature; and Spirited movement.

BACK TO THE FRONTIER

Legendary Trans-Mississippi Stamps Return After 100 Years

No series of commemorative postage stamps captures the spirit and adventure of the American West like the 1898 Trans-Mississippi stamps. Often referred to as the "Omahas," the stamps were originally issued in support of the Trans-Mississippi Exposition held in Omaha, June 1-November 1, 1898, to further the development of resources and land west of the Mississippi River.

From the majesty of the great Mississippi River to the excitement of a buffalo hunt on the Great Plains, the stamps are considered by many to be some of the most beautiful of all time. In 1998, the United States Postal Service brings back this series in two eagerly-anticipated bicolor souvenir sheets.

Behind the Storm

The first reissued sheet features all nine original stamp designs from a century ago. The second bicolor sheet spotlights the most acclaimed stamp in the series—"Western Cattle in Storm," a one-dollar stamp considered a true classic.

Inspired by the 1897 painting "Vanguard" by J.A. MacWhirter, the engraving for "Western Cattle

in Storm" epitomizes the harsh reality of the cattle herd's life on the range. In the midst of a brutal and blinding storm, the herd looks to its leader to safely guide it through the treacherous winds. The poise and determination of the bull in the stamp's foreground symbolize the drive for survival in the wild West.

Behind the simple beauty on the stamp, however, is a story that's a little more complicated. First, the United States Post Office Department (as the United States Postal Service was known in 1898) discovered that the original painting depicted cattle in a storm in Scotland...not the American West.

Then, it was found that the artist had sold the painting to an Englishman, Lord Blythewood. In the meantime, without permission, an American cattle company used a reproduction of the painting on its letterhead. This reproduction was used by the Postal Department in the design of the stamp. When the mistake was discovered, hasty apologies were extended to Lord Blythewood, along with a gift of a die proof of the completed stamp design. Fortunately, the English gentleman graciously accepted the gift and all was forgiven. Today, this die proof hangs in the Offices of the Royal Mail in England.

A Colorful Addition to Stamp History

Originally, "Western Cattle in Storm" (and the eight other Trans-Mississippi designs) was to be printed in two colors. However, due to the increased demands of printing revenue stamps for the Spanish-American War, the Bureau of Engraving and Printing instead printed it in a single color. In 1998, the stamp finally appears in its intended black and red color scheme.

The reissue of the Trans-Mississippi series marks a once-in-a-lifetime addition to stamp collections everywhere. And its gritty depictions of America's westward expansion are sure to capture the imagination of anyone who's ever been intrigued by this era of discovery.

1998 Issues—New U.S. Postage Stamps

Lunar New Year (Year of the Tiger)
Date of Issue: January 5, 1998
Place of Issue: Seattle, WA

Winter Sports—Skiing
Date of Issue: January 22, 1998
Place of Issue: Salt Lake City, UT

Madam C. J. Walker
Date of Issue: January 28, 1998
Place of Issue: Indianapolis, IN

Lunar New Year (Year of the Tiger)

Started in 1993 with the Year of the Rooster stamp, the Lunar New Year series continues with the Year of the Tiger stamp, the sixth release in the series. The Chinese characters along the left edge of the stamp symbolize the words "Happy New Year." The set will be complete in 2004 with the issuance of the Year of the Monkey stamp.

Designer: Clarence Lee   Printing: Gravure
Date of Issue: January 5, 1998   Place of Issue: Seattle, WA

Winter Sports—Skiing

This 32¢ commemorative stamp celebrates one of the most daring and popular wintertime sports—alpine skiing, and was issued during the Utah Winter Games festivities in Salt Lake City. This Winter Sports stamp honors the more than nine million active skiers in the U.S. The modern alpine ski race began early this century through the combined efforts of Arnold Lunn of England and Hannes Schneider of Austria. Their Arlberg-Kandahar race evolved into a circuit of competitions held at resorts throughout the Alps and was the foundation for the ski events popular today.

Designer: Michael Schwab   Printing: Offset
Date of Issue: January 22, 1998   Place of Issue: Salt Lake City, UT

Madam C. J. Walker

Madam C. J. Walker, an early 20th century beauty product pioneer and one of the nation's first female millionaires, is honored by this self-adhesive 32¢ stamp. Walker was born to ex-slaves and spent her early life working in the cotton fields and the kitchen. After her marriage to Charles Joseph Walker in 1905, she developed the expertise in manufacturing hair goods and preparations which allowed her to amass her fortune. This stamp, the 21st in the U.S. Postal Service's Black Heritage Series, celebrates Walker as a philanthropist to African-American institutions like the NAACP and Bethune-Cookman College.

Designer: Richard Sheaff   Printing: Offset
Date of Issue: January 28, 1998   Place of Issue: Indianapolis, IN

Celebrate the Century 1900-1909
The Dawn of the Twentieth Century

Sixty percent of Americans lived on farms or in small towns. Immigrants were arriving on an average of 100 an hour. Railroads dominated land travel, but 1900 saw the first U.S. auto show and 1908 the first family transcontinental car trip. In 1908 Henry Ford made automobiles more affordable with the Model T. The Wright brothers stunned the world with their first airplane flight in 1903, and the game of baseball grew up.

President Theodore Roosevelt protected 148 million acres as national forests. The first daily comic strip, "Mutt and Jeff," appeared in the *San Francisco Chronicle*. The Ash Can School brought realism back to the art world.

Muckrakers exposed corruption: Ida Tarbell attacked monopoly in the oil industry, and Upton Sinclair revealed shocking conditions in the meat industry. In 1909 the newly formed NAACP promoted equal rights for African Americans.

New words: cheerleader, filmmaker, phony, psychoanalysis

Designer: Carl Herrman   Printing: Offset/Intaglio
Date of Issue: February 3, 1998   Place of Issue: Washington, D.C.

Celebrate the Century 1900-1909
Date of Issue: February 3, 1998
Place of Issue: Washington, D.C.

Celebrate the Century 1910-1919
Date of Issue: February 3, 1998
Place of Issue: Washington, D.C.

Spanish-American War
Date of Issue: February 15, 1998
Place of Issue: Key West, FL

Celebrate the Century 1910-1919
America Looks Beyond its Borders

Halley's comet lit up the sky to begin the decade. American workers began moving from farms to factories. The Ford Motor Co. refined the automobile assembly line. Traffic lights and white lane dividers became part of the American landscape.

Scientific and technological achievements changed society. In 1911, in New York, fingerprint evidence alone was used for the first time in the United States to arrest a burglar. Jim Thorpe was an international sports star, but Tarzan was an even more popular hero.

The accidental sinking of the luxury liner *Titanic* shocked the nation, but it was the sinking of another ship, the *Lusitania*, that upset society, leading to U.S. involvement in World War I. Two million American soldiers fought in Europe and more than 116,500 lost their lives.

Americans saw the light as the decade ended: Daylight saving time was instituted in 1918.

New words: camouflage, electronics, troublemaker

Designer: Howard Paine
Date of Issue: February 3, 1998
Printing: Offset/Intaglio
Place of Issue: Washington, D.C.

Spanish-American War

This stamp carrying the slogan "Remember the Maine" is a commemorative of the Spanish-American War. An explosion on the USS Maine caused it to sink in February 1898. Even though the investigation into the sinking of the USS Maine didn't determine the cause of the explosion that destroyed it, popular sentiment blamed the Spanish. The American press used the slogan "Remember the Maine" to stir sentiment in support of war against Spain.

Designer: Richard Sheaff
Date of Issue: February 15, 1998
Printing: Offset/Intaglio
Place of Issue: Key West, FL

Flowering Trees

Each of these five self-adhesive 32¢ stamps depicts the blossom of a magnificent flowering tree native to a different geographical region of the U.S.: Southern Magnolia, Blue Paloverde, Yellow Poplar, Prairie Crab Apple and Pacific Dogwood.

Designer: Howard Paine

Date of Issue: March 19, 1998

Printing: Offset

Place of Issue: New York, NY

Alexander Calder

This set of five commemorative 32¢ stamps honors the artist Alexander Calder and his innovative and influential sculptures. Featured on the stamps are photos of five of his sculptures.

Designer: Derry Noyes

Date of Issue: March 25, 1998

Printing: Gravure

Place of Issue: Washington, D.C.

Henry Luce

Part of the Postal Service's Great Americans series, this 32¢ stamp honors Henry R. Luce as one of America's most influential editors and publishers. Luce is best known as the co-founder of Time magazine.

Designer: Richard Sheaff

Date of Issue: April 3, 1998

Printing: Intaglio

Place of Issue: New York, NY

Cinco de Mayo

This 32¢ commemorative stamp colorfully celebrates the victory of Mexican troops over the French at the Battle of Puebla on May 5, 1862, and depicts two traditionally dressed Mexican dancers. The U.S. Postal Service in San Antonio, Texas, and the Mexican Postal Service in Mexico City issued the stamp jointly. In the U.S., Cinco de Mayo has become a popular celebration for Mexican Americans to show pride in their heritage.

Designer: Carl Herrman

Date of Issue: April 16, 1998

Printing: Gravure

Place of Issue: San Antonio, TX

Sylvester and Tweety

This fun-loving duo of Warner Bros., Sylvester and Tweety, appear on their own 1998 souvenir sheet of ten 32¢ stamps in line with the Bugs Bunny release of 1997. Bugs Bunny was appointed the ambassador of Stampers®, the Postal Service's youth stamp collecting program, and this release is aimed at encouraging children to join the cool world of stamp collecting.

Designer: Brenda Guttman,
          Warner Bros.

Date of Issue: April 27, 1998

Printing: Gravure

Place of Issue: New York, NY

Flowering Trees
Date of Issue: March 19, 1998
Place of Issue: New York, NY

Alexander Calder
Date of Issue: March 25, 1998
Place of Issue: Washington, D.C.

Henry R. Luce
Date of Issue: April 3, 1998
Place of Issue: New York, NY

Cinco De Mayo
Date of Issue: April 16, 1998
Place of Issue: San Antonio, TX

Sylvester and Tweety
Date of Issue: April 27, 1998
Place of Issue: New York, NY

Celebrate the Century 1920-1929
Date of Issue: May 28, 1998
Place of Issue: Chicago, IL

Wisconsin Statehood
Date of Issue: May 29, 1998
Place of Issue: Madison, WI

Diner
Date of Issue: June 5, 1998
Place of Issue: McLean, VA

Wetlands (Nonprofit)
Date of Issue: June 5, 1998
Place of Issue: McLean, VA

Celebrate the Century 1920-1929
The Roaring Twenties

Two Constitutional amendments went into effect in 1920, turning the nation upside down. The 18th Amendment prohibited the manufacture and sale of alcoholic beverages, and the 19th gave women the right to vote. Prohibition backfired, leading to widespread disrespect for the law. A federal highway system was organized and the number of automobiles nearly tripled. Spreading electrification spawned the golden age of radio.

The Roaring Twenties, as the decade came to be known, was an age of thrill seekers and heroes. In 1926 Gertrude Ederle swam the English Channel faster than any man had. The following year Charles Lindbergh flew nonstop across the Atlantic alone and Babe Ruth hit 60 home runs.

The first feature-length film with talking parts, *The Jazz Singer*, appeared in 1927 and the first Academy Awards were presented in 1929. The prosperous times ended with the stock market crash of Thursday, October 24, 1929.

New words: motel, robot, fan mail, teenage

Designer: Carl Herrman	Printing: Offset/Intaglio
Date of Issue: May 28, 1998	Place of Issue: Chicago, IL

Wisconsin Statehood

This 32¢ commemorative stamp celebrates the 150th anniversary of Wisconsin statehood. This particular stamp also contains a Scrambled Indicia®, a hidden image which can be viewed by using a special decoder lens. The hidden image is a badger, the state animal. Wisconsin was the 30th state admitted into the United States on May 29, 1848, by President James K. Polk.

Designer: Phil Jordan	Printing: Gravure
Date of Issue: May 29, 1998	Place of Issue: Madison, WI

Diner

This First-Class presort, nondenominated 25¢ stamp was issued to begin the NAPEX '98 stamp show in Northern Virginia. The Diner stamp is available only in gummed coils of 10,000 and offers businesses added convenience. The Diner stamp is third in the American Culture series.

Designer: Carl Herrman	Printing: Gravure
Date of Issue: June 5, 1998	Place of Issue: McLean, VA

Wetlands (Nonprofit)

Issued at the NAPEX '98 stamp show, this nondenominated, 5¢ nonprofit Wetlands stamp is available only in coils of 10,000. This stamp is third in the American Scenes series.

Designer: Phil Jordan	Printing: Gravure
Date of Issue: June 5, 1998	Place of Issue: McLean, VA

1898 Trans-Mississippi—All (Reissue)

This souvenir pane of nine commemorative stamps was reissued in the intended two-color design 100 years after the original printing. Because of cost considerations during the Spanish-American war, the Trans-Mississippi stamps were not issued in the original two-color design. The new stamps issued during the Mega-Event stamp show feature nine designs with different colors depicting American westward expansion. These stamps are now considered very popular in the stamp collecting community although when they were released in 1898 they received little attention.

1898 Designer: Raymond Ostrander Smith
1998 Designer: Richard Sheaff   Printing: Intaglio
Date of Issue: June 18, 1998   Place of Issue: Anaheim, CA

1898 Trans-Mississippi—Western Cattle in Storm

Considered one of the most popular stamps of all time, *Western Cattle in Storm* was reissued in a souvenir sheet of nine $1.00 stamps surrounded by a red border. The original stamp was issued in support of the Trans-Mississippi and International Exposition held in Omaha from June 1 to November 1, 1898. The exposition was held to further the progress and development of the resources and land west of the Mississippi River.

1898 Designer: Raymond Ostrander Smith
1998 Designer: Richard Sheaff   Printing: Intaglio
Date of Issue: June 18, 1998   Place of Issue: Anaheim, CA

Folk Musicians

The U.S. Postal Service issued this series during the annual Smithsonian Folklife Festival to celebrate the 50th anniversary of the historic Folkways record label. The featured folk musicians on the four separate stamps include Woody Guthrie, Sonny Terry, Huddie "Leadbelly" Ledbetter and Josh White. Woody Guthrie is probably the best known folk singer for his song, "This Land is Your Land." The Folk Musicians stamps were issued in part with the Legends of American Music series begun in 1993.

Designer: Howard Paine   Printing: Gravure
Date of Issue: June 26, 1998   Place of Issue: Washington, D.C.

Berlin Airlift

This 32¢ stamp commemorates the 50th anniversary of the Berlin Airlift, the massive aid effort during post-World War II which brought food and fuel to the war-torn citizens of Berlin by air after the Soviets had blocked all traffic in and out of Berlin by land or water. The stamp depicts a family of Berliners watching a C-54 aircraft carrying survival resources to Berlin with the words "Berlin Airlift delivers food and fuel in 1948-49 blockade." This historical event helped save Berlin from Soviet takeover. A U.S. Air Force plane that was part of one of the original deliveries brought over the special commemorative stamps as they were issued by the U.S. Postal Service in Berlin, Germany.

Designer: Howard Paine   Printing: Offset
Date of Issue: June 26, 1998   Place of Issue: Berlin, Germany

© USPS 1997

1898 Trans-Misssissippi—All (Reissue)
Date of Issue: June 18, 1998
Place of Issue: Anaheim, CA

1898 Trans-Misssissippi—Western Cattle in Storm
Date of Issue: June 18, 1998
Place of Issue: Anaheim, CA

Berlin Airlift
Date of Issue: June 26, 1998
Place of Issue: Berlin, Germany

Folk Musicians
Date of Issue: June 26, 1998
Place of Issue: Washington, D.C.

Spanish Settlement of the Southwest
Date of Issue: July 11, 1998
Place of Issue: Española, NM

Gospel Singers
Date of Issue: July 15, 1998
Place of Issue: New Orleans, LA

Lila and DeWitt Wallace
Date of Issue: July 16, 1998
Place of Issue: Pleasantville, NY

Stephen Vincent Benét
Date of Issue: July 22, 1998
Place of Issue: Harpers Ferry, WV

Tropical Birds
Date of Issue: July 29, 1998
Place of Issue: Puerto Rico

Spanish Settlement of the Southwest

In celebration of the 400th anniversary of the oldest European road in the U.S., El Camino Real de Tierra Adentro, and the founding of the Spanish settlement at San Gabriel, a 32¢ commemorative stamp was issued by the U.S. Postal Service. In 1598, the first European road was created in the U.S. by the Spanish expedition led by Don Juan de Onate. The stamp is a photograph of La Mision de San Miguel de San Gabriel, a replica of the church at San Gabriel which is located in present day Española, New Mexico.

Designer: Richard Sheaff Printing: Offset
Date of Issue: July 11, 1998 Place of Issue: Española, NM

Gospel Singers

Singers Roberta Martin, Sister Rosetta Tharpe, Clara Ward and Mahalia Jackson are immortalized on this pane of four 32¢ stamps. The Gospel Singers stamps join the Folk Musicians stamps as this year's additions to the Legends of American Music series. This series has recognized Broadway Musicals, Jazz Musicians, Big Band Leaders, Rock and Roll, Rhythm and Blues, Country and Western, Opera Singers and Classical Composers and Conductors.

Designer: Howard Paine Printing: Gravure
Date of Issue: July 15, 1998 Place of Issue: New Orleans, LA

Lila and DeWitt Wallace

This 32¢ definitive stamp is the newest addition to the Great Americans series and features Lila Acheson and DeWitt Wallace, noted philanthropists and founders of The Reader's Digest Association, Inc. and its flagship magazine. During their lifetimes, the Wallaces gave many millions to great charitable causes in the fields of education, arts, music and cultural heritage and were also awarded the Medal of Freedom by President Richard Nixon.

Designer: Howard Paine Printing: Intaglio
Date of Issue: July 16, 1998 Place of Issue: Pleasantville, NY

Stephen Vincent Benét

One hundred years after his birth, Stephen Vincent Benét, famous poet and writer, is immortalized on this 32¢ commemorative stamp. Benét wrote *John Brown's Body*, a book-length poem on the Civil War, which won him the Pulitzer Prize in 1929. He was awarded the Roosevelt Medal in 1933 and in 1938 was elected to the American Academy of Arts and Letters. The Stephen Vincent Benét stamp is the 15th in the Literary Arts series.

Designer: Carl Herrman Printing: Offset
Date of Issue: July 22, 1998 Place of Issue: Harpers Ferry, WV

Tropical Birds

These colorful 32¢ commemorative stamps celebrate tropical birds. Featured are the Antillean Euphonia, the Green-throated Carib, the Crested Honeycreeper and the Cardinal Honeyeater.

Designer: Phil Jordan Printing: Offset
Date of Issue: July 29, 1998 Place of Issue: Puerto Rico

Breast Cancer Research

The Breast Cancer Research stamp is the first U.S. stamp in history to have its net proceeds above the cost of postage earmarked for research organizations. Being heralded a "semipostal" stamp, this rainbow-colored, nondenominational stamp sells for 40¢ and is valid as postage for a standard first-class letter.

Designer: Ethel Kessler
Date of Issue: July 29, 1998

Printing: Gravure
Place of Issue: Washington, D.C.

Ring-Neck Pheasant

The new 20¢ stamp marks the third time that the ring-neck pheasant has appeared in a U.S. postage stamp design.

Designer: Terry McCaffrey
Date of Issue: July 31, 1998

Printing: Gravure
Place of Issue: Washington, D.C.

Alfred Hitchcock

Joining such Hollywood legends as Humphrey Bogart, Marilyn Monroe and James Dean, Alfred Joseph Hitchcock becomes part of the Postal Service's continuing tribute to individuals who made a major contribution to the legacy of American films on this 32¢ stamp. With a career that spanned six decades and more than 50 films and earned him the title, "Master of Suspense," Hitchcock becomes the fourth honoree in the Legends of Hollywood series.

Designer: Richard Sheaff
Date of Issue: August 3, 1998

Printing: Gravure
Place of Issue: Los Angeles, CA

Organ & Tissue Donation

Issued during the 30th anniversary of the first successful heart transplant in the U.S., this 32¢ stamp is intended to increase public awareness of the need for organ and tissue donors.

Designer: Richard Sheaff
Date of Issue: August 5, 1998

Printing: Gravure
Place of Issue: Columbus, OH

Green Bicycle

A non-denominated, presorted, standard-mail 10¢ stamp (formerly bulk rate).

Designer: Richard Sheaff
Date of Issue: August 14, 1998

Printing: Gravure
Place of Issue: Washington, D.C.

Red Fox

A self-adhesive $1.00 stamp issued in panes of 20.

Designer: Derry Noyes

Printing: Offset, with Scrambled Indicia®

Date of Issue: August 14, 1998

Place of Issue: Washington, D.C.

Bright Eyes

Honoring five of the most popular household pets, these 32¢ stamps feature fresh and original caricatures created by artist Bill Mayer of a dog, goldfish, cat, parakeet and hamster.

Designer: Carl Herrman
Date of Issue: August 20, 1998

Printing: Gravure
Place of Issue: Boston, MA

Breast Cancer Research
Date of Issue: July 29, 1998
Place of Issue: Washington, D.C.

Ring-Neck Pheasant
Date of Issue: July 31, 1998
Place of Issue: Washington, D.C.

Alfred Hitchcock
Date of Issue: August 3, 1998
Place of Issue: Los Angeles, CA

Organ & Tissue Donation
Date of Issue: August 5, 1998
Place of Issue: Columbus, OH

Green Bicycle
Date of Issue: August 14, 1998
Place of Issue: Washington, D.C.

Red Fox
Date of Issue: August 14, 1998
Place of Issue: Washington, D.C.

Bright Eyes
Date of Issue: August 20, 1998
Place of Issue: Boston, MA

Klondike Gold Rush
Date of Issue: August 21, 1998
Place of Issue: Nome and
                Skagway, AK

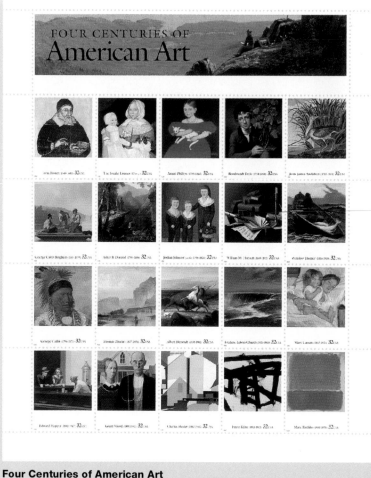

Four Centuries of American Art
Date of Issue: August 27, 1998
Place of Issue: Santa Clara, CA

Klondike Gold Rush

The Klondike Gold Rush which served as the catalyst for the birth of our 49th state is commemorated on this 32¢ stamp. This year is the 100th anniversary of the peak of the Klondike Gold Rush when over 60,000 Americans made the journey to discover their fortune. The stamp depicts men with dog sleds trudging through the Alaskan frontier in search of gold.

Designer: Howard Paine
Date of Issue: August 21, 1998

Printing: Offset
Place of Issue: Nome and Skagway, AK

Four Centuries of American Art

This pane of 20 stamps featuring American masterpieces created from the 17th through the mid-20th centuries provides a thumbnail view of works by some of America's finest artists. Presenting a mix of style and subject matter, the 20 works featured on the Four Centuries of American Art pane of 32¢ stamps come from 16 museums across the country. Works featured are John Foster's *Portrait of Richard Mather*, The Freake Limner's *Mrs. Elizabeth Freake and Baby Mary*, Ammi Phillips' *Girl in Red Dress with Cat and Dog*, Rembrandt Peale's *Rubens Peale with a Geranium*, John James Audubon's *Long-billed Curlew, Numenius Longrostris*, George Caleb Bingham's *Boatmen on the Missouri*, Asher B. Durand's *Kindred Spirits*, Joshua Johnson's *The Westwood Children*, William M. Harnett's *Music and Literature*, Winslow Homer's *Fog Warning*, George Catlin's *The White Cloud, Head Chief of the Iowas*, Thomas Moran's *Cliffs of Green River*, Albert Bierstadt's *The Last of the Buffalo*, Frederic Edwin Church's *Niagara*, Mary Cassatt's *Breakfast in Bed*, Edward Hopper's *Nighthawks*, Grant Wood's *American Gothic*, Charles Sheeler's *Two Against the White*, Franz Kline's *Mahoning* and Mark Rothko's *Number 22, 1949*.

Designer: Howard Paine
Date of Issue: August 27, 1998

Printing: Gravure
Place of Issue: Santa Clara, CA

Celebrate the Century 1930-1939
Depression, Dust Bowl, and a New Deal

By 1933 the average wage was 60 percent less than in 1929 and unemployment had skyrocketed to 25 percent. Dust storms forced many farmers to give up their land.

Americans escaped harsh realities by playing Monopoly, reading the adventures of "Buck Rogers" and "Flash Gordon" and listening to Hoagy Carmichael's "Stardust." Popular films included *King Kong* and *It Happened One Night*. For the first time, African-American athletes became national idols: Joe Louis in boxing and Jesse Owens in track and field.

Prohibition was repealed in 1933. President Franklin Roosevelt fought the Great Depression with his New Deal programs. The "Star-Spangled Banner" was chosen as the national anthem. The Empire State Building rose above the Manhattan skyline and the Golden Gate Bridge spanned the San Francisco Bay. Back on the ground, the parking meter made its first appearance in 1935.

As the decade closed, many Americans were anxious about the growing war in Europe.

New words: all-star, oops, pizza, racism

Designer: Howard Paine   Printing: Offset
Date of Issue: September 10, 1998   Place of Issue: Cleveland, OH

Ballet

The striking image on this 32¢ stamp is that of a ballerina *en pointe* in an *attitude derrière* pose. Celebrating the romance and beauty of ballet, a form of expression that captivates people worldwide, this stamp joins the Alexander Calder and Four Centuries of American Art issues honoring various art forms this year.

Designer: Derry Noyes   Printing: Offset
Date of Issue: September 16, 1998   Place of Issue: New York, NY

Celebrate the Century 1930-1939
Date of Issue: September 10, 1998
Place of Issue: Cleveland, OH

Ballet
Date of Issue: September 16, 1998
Place of Issue: New York, NY

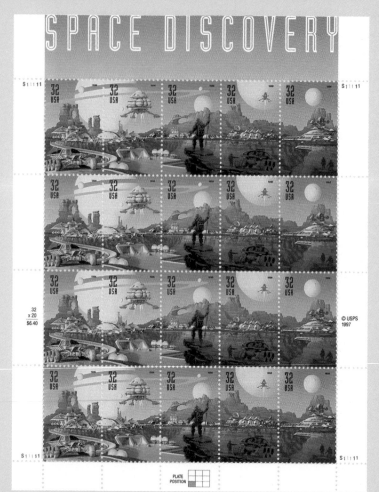

Space Discovery
Date of Issue: October 1, 1998
Place of Issue: Kennedy Space Center, FL

Philanthropy
Date of Issue: October 7, 1998
Place of Issue: Atlanta, GA

Space Discovery

October is the month that the Postal Service promotes National Stamp Collecting Month (NSCM). This promotion is designed to create awareness and enhance interest in stamps and stamp collecting among our youth audience (children ages 8-12) and their families. As part of this year's promotion, "Space Discovery" is the featured stamp issue. The theme is "Get Out of This World—Blast Off With Stamps!"

Designer: Phil Jordan

Printing: Gravure

Date of Issue: October 1, 1998

Place of Issue: Kennedy Space Center, FL

Philanthropy

This 32¢ stamp of goodwill honors the American tradition of giving and sharing. Pictured on the stamp are a bee and a flower, a graphic representation of a relationship where both parties are giving and benefiting.

Designer: Bob Dinetz

Printing: Gravure

Date of Issue: October 7, 1998

Place of Issue: Atlanta, GA

Holiday Traditional

Since 1966, with the issuance of a 5¢ stamp featuring the Madonna and Child by Hans Memling, these traditional Holiday stamps have attracted a devoted following. The design of this year's 32¢ stamp is based on a magnificent relief of Madonna and Child created around 1425 by an accomplished yet unknown art master.

Designer: Richard Scheaff   Printing: Offset

Date of Issue: October 15, 1998   Place of Issue: Washington, D.C.

Holiday Contemporary

Hanging a wreath on a home's front door during the holiday season is a sign of welcome and friendship in America. The wreaths depicted on these four 32¢ stamps express themes from various plant groupings common to different regions of the country: traditional, colonial, chili and tropical.

Designers: Chris Crinklaw   Printing: Offset
          George de Bruin
          Lillian Dinihanian
          Micheale Ttunin

Date of Issue: October 15, 1998   Place of Issue: Christmas, MI

Rate Change Scheduled for January 10, 1999

The United States Postal Service will issue a number of non-denominated stamps in support of the upcoming rate change taking effect January 10, 1999.

H-Series

Non-denominated, gummed and self-adhesive 33¢ first class stamps representing the new rate.

Date of Issue: To be determined sometime in late 1998

Place of Issue: To be determined sometime in late 1998

Make-Up Rate

A non-denominated 1¢ make-up rate stamp.

Date of Issue: To be determined sometime in late 1998

Place of Issue: To be determined sometime in late 1998

Express Mail

An $11.75 Express Mail stamp.

Date of Issue: To be determined sometime in late 1998

Place of Issue: To be determined sometime in late 1998

1998 Issues—Postal Cards

20¢ University of Mississippi	April 20, 1998
20¢ Girard College	May 1, 1998
20¢ Northeastern University	October 3, 1998
20¢ Brandeis University	October 17, 1998

Holiday Traditional
Date of Issue: October 15, 1998
Place of Issue: Washington, D.C.

Holiday Contemporay
Date of Issue: October 15, 1998
Place of Issue: Christmas, MI

H Series
Date of Issue: To be determined sometime in late 1998
Place of Issue: To be determined sometime in late 1998

Make-Up Rate
Date of Issue: To be determined
sometime in late 1998
Place of Issue: To be determined
sometime in late 1998

Express Mail
Date of Issue: To be determined
sometime in late 1998
Place of Issue: To be determined
sometime in late 1998

A *Successful Landing*

Space Exploration

Stamp Collecting Words and Phrases

Accessories
The tools used by stamp collectors, such as tongs, hinges, etc.

Adhesive
A gummed stamp made to be attached to mail.

Aerophilately
Stamp collecting that focuses on stamps or postage relating to airmail.

Album
A book designed to hold stamps and covers.

Approvals
Stamps sent by a dealer to a collector for examination. Approvals must either be bought or returned to the dealer within a specified time.

Auction
A sale at which philatelic material is sold to the highest bidder.

Black Jack
The nickname for the very popular U.S. two-cent black Andrew Jackson stamp, which was issued in various forms between 1863 and 1875.

Block
An unseparated group of stamps, at least two stamps high and two stamps wide.

Bluish Paper
Used to print portions of several issues in 1909; the paper was made with 35 percent rag stock instead of all wood pulp. The color goes through the paper, showing clearly on back and face.

Bogus
A completely fictitious, worthless "stamp," created only for sale to collectors. Bogus stamps include labels for nonexistent values added to regularly issued sets, issues for nations without postal systems, etc.

Booklet Pane
A small sheet of stamps specially cut to be sold in booklets.

Bourse
A marketplace, such as a stamp exhibition, where stamps are bought, sold or exchanged.

Cachet (ka-shay')
A design on an envelope describing an event. Cachets appear on first day of issue, first flight and stamp exhibition covers, etc.

Cancellation
A mark placed on a stamp by a postal authority to show that it has been used.

Centering
The position of the design on a postage stamp. On perfectly centered stamps the design is exactly in the middle.

Classic
An early stamp issue. Most people consider these to be rare stamps, but classic stamps aren't necessarily rare.

Coils
Stamps issued in rolls (one stamp wide) for use in dispensers or vending machines.

US Bicentennial 20 cents

Commemoratives
Stamps that honor anniversaries, important people or special events.

Compound Perforations
Different gauge perforations on different (normally adjacent) sides of a single stamp.

Condition

Condition is the most important characteristic in determining the value of a stamp. It refers to the state of a stamp regarding such details as centering, color and gum.

Cover

An envelope that has been sent through the mail.

Cracked Plate

A term used to describe stamps which show evidence that the plate from which they were printed was cracked.

Definitives

Regular issues of postage stamps, usually sold over long periods of time.

Denomination

The postage value appearing on a stamp, such as 5 cents.

Directory Markings

Postal markings that indicate a failed delivery attempt, stating reasons such as "No Such Number" or "Address Unknown."

Double Transfer

The condition on a printing plate that shows evidence of a duplication of all or part of the design.

Dry Printing

Begun as an experiment in 1953, this type of printing results in a whiter paper, a higher sheen on the surface, a thicker and stiffer feel and designs that stand out more clearly than on more standard "wet" printings.

Duplicates

Extra copies of stamps that can be sold or traded. Duplicates should be examined carefully for color and perforation variations.

Entire

An intact piece of postal stationery, in contrast to a cut-out of the printed design.

Error

A stamp with something incorrect in its design or manufacture.

Exploded

A stamp booklet is said to be "exploded" when it has been separated into its various components for show.

Face Value

The monetary value or denomination of a stamp.

Fake

A genuine stamp that has been altered in some way to make it more attractive to collectors. It may be repaired, reperfed or regummed to resemble a more valuable variety.

First Day Cover (FDC)

An envelope with a new stamp and cancellation showing the date the stamp was issued.

Foreign Entry

When original transfers are erased incompletely from a plate, they can appear with new transfers of a different design which are subsequently entered on the plate.

Franks

Marking on the face of a cover, indicating it is to be carried free of postage. Franks may be written, hand-stamped, imprinted or represented by special adhesives. Such free franking is usually limited to official correspondence, such as the President's mail.

Freak

An abnormal variety of stamps occurring because of paper fold, over-inking, perforation shift, etc., as opposed to a continually appearing variety or a major error.

Grill

A pattern of small, square pyramids in parallel rows impressed or embossed on the stamp to break paper fibers, allowing cancellation ink to soak in and preventing washing and reuse.

Gum

The coating of glue on the back of an unused stamp.

Hinges

Small strips of gummed material used by collectors to affix stamps to album pages.

Imperforate

Indicates stamps without perforations or separating holes. They usually are separated by scissors and collected in pairs.

Label

Any stamp-like adhesive that is not a postage stamp.

Laid Paper
When held to the light, the paper shows alternate light and dark crossed lines.

Line Pairs (LP)
Most coil stamp rolls prior to #1891 feature a line of ink printed between two stamps at varying intervals.

Miniature Sheet
A single stamp or block of stamps with a margin on all sides bearing some special wording or design.

On Paper
Stamps "on paper" are those that still have portions of the original envelope or wrapper stuck to them.

Overprint
Additional printing on a stamp that was not part of the original design.

Packet
A presorted unit of all different stamps. One of the most common and economical ways to begin a collection.

Pane
A full "sheet" of stamps as sold by a Post Office. Four panes typically make up the original sheet of stamps as printed.

Par Avion
French for mail transported "by air."

Perforations
Lines of small holes or cuts between rows of stamps that make them easy to separate.

Philately
The collection and study of postage stamps and other postal materials.

US Bicentennial 13cents

Pictorials
Stamps with a picture of some sort, other than portraits or static designs such as coats of arms.

Plate Block (PB) (or Plate Number Block)
A block of stamps with the margin attached that bears the plate number used in printing that sheet.

Plate Number Coils (PNC)
For most coil stamp rolls beginning with #1891, a small plate number appears at varying intervals in the roll in the design of the stamp.

Postage Due
A stamp issued to collect unpaid postage.

Postal Stationery
Envelopes, postal cards and aerogrammes with stamp designs printed or embossed on them.

Postmark
A mark put on envelopes or other mailing pieces showing the date and location of the post office where it was mailed.

Precancels
Cancellations applied to stamps before the stamps were affixed to mail.

Registered Mail
First class mail with a numbered receipt, including a valuation of the registered item. This guarantees customers will get their money back if an item is lost in the mail.

Reissue
An official reprinting of a stamp that was no longer being printed.

Replicas
Reproductions of stamps sold during the early days of collecting. Usually printed in one color on a sheet containing a number of different designs. Replicas were never intended to deceive either the post office or the collector.

Reprint
A stamp printed from the original plate after the issue is no longer valid for postage. Official reprints are sometimes made for presentation purposes, official collections, etc., and are often distinguished in some way from the "real" ones.

Revenue Stamps
Stamps not valid for postal use but issued for collecting taxes.

Ribbed Paper
Paper which shows fine parallel ridges on one or both sides of a stamp.

Se-tenant
An attached pair, strip or block of stamps that differ in design, value or surcharge.

Speculative
A stamp or issue released primarily for sale to collectors, rather than to meet any legitimate postal need.

Strip
Three or more unseparated stamps in a row.

Topicals
Indicates a group of stamps with the same theme—space travel, for example.

Unhinged
A stamp without hinge marks, but not necessarily with original gum.

Unused
The condition of a stamp that has no cancellation or other sign of use.

Secret Marks
Many stamps have included tiny reference points in their designs to foil attempts at counterfeiting and to differentiate issues.

Selvage
The unprinted paper around panes of stamps, sometimes called the margin.

Series
All the variations of design and value of a particular issue.

Set
A unit of stamps with a common design or theme issued at one time for a common purpose or over an extended period.

Souvenir Sheet
A small sheet of stamps with a commemorative inscription of some sort.

Surcharge
An overprint that changes the denomination of a stamp from its original face value.

Sweatbox
A closed box with a grill over which stuck-together unused stamps are placed. A wet, sponge-like material under the grill creates humidity so the stamps can be separated without removing the gum.

Thematic
A stamp collection that relates to a specific theme and is arranged to present a logical story and progression.

Tied On
Indicates a stamp whose postmark touches the envelope.

Tongs
A tool, used to handle stamps, that resembles a tweezers with rounded or flattened tips.

Used
The condition of a stamp that has been canceled.

Want List
A list of philatelic material needed by a collector.

Watermark
A design pressed into stamp paper during its manufacture.

Wet Printing
Has a moisture content of 15-35 percent, compared to 5-10 percent for "dry" printings; also, has a duller look than "dry" printings.

Wove Paper
A uniform paper which, when held to the light, shows no light or dark figures.

Organizations, Publications and Resources

For Your Information ...

Here's a list of philatelic resources that can increase your knowledge of stamps as well as your collecting enjoyment.

Organizations

Please enclose a stamped, self-addressed envelope when writing to these organizations.

American Air Mail Society
Stephen Reinhard
PO Box 110
Mineola, NY 11501-0110

Specializes in all phases of aerophilately. Membership services include Advance Bulletin Service, Auction Service, free want ads, Sales Department, monthly journal, discounts on Society publications, translation service.

American First Day Cover Society
Douglas Kelsey
Executive Director
PO Box 65960
Tucson, AZ 85728-5960

A full-service, not-for-profit, noncommercial society devoted exclusively to First Day Covers and First Day Cover collecting. Publishes 90-page magazine, First Days, eight times per year. Offers information on 300 current cachet producers, expertizing, foreign covers, translation service, color slide programs and archives covering First Day Covers.

American Philatelic Society
Robert E. Lamb
Executive Director
PO Box 8000
Dept. PG
State College, PA
16803-8000

A full complement of services and resources for stamp collectors. Annual membership offers: library services, educational seminars and correspondence courses, expertizing service, estate advisory service, translation service, a stamp theft committee that functions as a clearinghouse for philatelic crime information, intramember sales service and a monthly journal, The American Philatelist, sent to all members. Membership 57,000 worldwide.

American Society for Philatelic Pages and Panels
Gerald Blankenship
PO Box 475
Crosby, TX 77532-0475

American Stamp Dealers' Association
Joseph B. Savarese
3 School St.
Glen Cove, NY 11542-2517

Association of dealers engaged in every facet of philately, with 11 regional chapters nationwide. Sponsors national and local shows. Will send you a complete listing of dealers in your area or collecting specialty. A #10 SASE must accompany your request.

American Topical Association
Douglas Kelsey
Executive Director
PO Box 65749
Tucson, AZ 85728-5730

A service organization concentrating on the specialty of topical stamp collecting. Offers handbooks and checklists on specific topics; exhibition awards; Topical Time, a bimonthly publication dealing with topical interest areas; a slide loan service, and information, translation and sales services.

Booklet Collectors Club
Jim Natele
PO Box 2461-U
Cinnaminson, NJ
08077-2461

Devoted to the study of worldwide booklets and booklet collecting, with special emphasis on U.S. booklets. Publishes The Interleaf, a quarterly journal.

Bureau Issues Association
PO Box 23707
Belleville, IL 62223-0707

Devoted to the study of all U.S. stamps, principally those produced by the Bureau of Engraving and Printing.

Ebony Society of Philatelic Events and Reflections
Sheryl A. Byrd
2112 Lambros Dr.
Midland, MI 48642-4059

Telephone: (517) 839-0037.

**Junior Philatelists
of America**
Central Office
PO Box 850
Boalsburg, PA 16827-0850

*Publishes a bimonthly
newsletter,* The Philatelic
Observer, *and offers auction,
exchange, pen pal and other
services to young stamp
collectors. Adult supporting
membership and gift
memberships are available.
The Society also publishes
various brochures on stamp
collecting.*

**Mailer's Postmark
Permit Club**
Florence M. Sugarberg
PO Box 5793
Akron, OH 44372-5793

*Publishes bimonthly
newsletter,* Permit Patter,
*which covers all aspects
of mailer's precancel
postmarks, as well as a
catalog and two checklists.*

**Modern Postal
History Society**
Bill DiPaolo
404 Dorado Ct.
High Point, NC 27265-9650

*Emphasizes the collection
and study of postal history,
procedures and rates
beginning with the early
20th century and including
rates as shown by use of
definitive stamps on
commercial covers, modern
markings such as bar codes
and ink-jet postmarks, and
auxiliary markings such as
"Return to Sender," etc.
Publishes the quarterly*
Modern Postal History
Journal.

Philatelic Foundation
501 Fifth Ave. Rm. 1901
New York, NY 10017-6103

*A nonprofit organization
known for its excellent
expertization service.
The Foundation's broad
resources, including
extensive reference
collections, 5,000-volume
library and Expert
Committee, provide
collectors with comprehen-
sive consumer protection.
Slide and cassette programs
are available on such
subjects as the Pony Express,
classic U.S. stamps,
Confederate Postal History
and collecting basics for
beginners. Book series
include expertizing case
histories in* Opinions,
*Foundation seminar
subjects in "textbooks" and
specialized U.S. subjects in
monographs.*

Postal History Society
Kalman V. Illyefalvi
8207 Daren Ct.
Pikesville, MD 21208-2211

*Devoted to the study of
various aspects of the
development of the mails
and local, national and
international postal systems;
UPU treaties; and means of
transporting mail.*

**Souvenir Card
Collectors Society**
Dana M. Marr
PO Box 4155
Tulsa, OK 74159-4155

*Provides member auctions,
a quarterly journal and
access to limited-edition
souvenir cards.*

Stamp Services
United States Postal Service
475 L'Enfant Plaza SW
Washington, D.C.
20260-2439

**United Postal
Stationery Society**
Mrs. Joann Thomas
PO Box 48
Redlands, CA 92373-0601

**Universal Ship
Cancellation Society**
David Kent
PO Box 127
New Britain, CT
06050-0127

*Specializes in naval ship
postmarks.*

Free Periodicals

*The following publications
will send you a free copy of
their magazine or newspaper
upon request.*

Linn's Stamp News
PO Box 29
Sidney, OH 45365-0029

*The largest weekly stamp
newspaper.*

**Mekeel's Weekly Stamp
News and Market Report**
PO Box 5050-fa
White Plains, NY 10602

*World's oldest stamp weekly,
for intermediate and
advanced collectors.*

Stamp Collector
Rick Groth
700 E. State St.
Iola, WI 54990-0001

*For beginning and advanced
collectors of all ages.*

Stamps Auction News
85 Canisteo St.
Hornell, NY 14843-1544

*The monthly financial journal
of the stamp market.*

Stamps Magazine
85 Canisteo St.
Hornell, NY 14843-1544

*The weekly magazine of
philately.*

USA Philatelic
Stamp Fullfillment Services
United States Postal Service
8300 NE Underground Drive
Pillar 210
Kansas City, MO
64144-0001

U.S. Stamp News
PO Box 5050-fb
White Plains, NY 10602

*Monthly magazine for all
collectors of U.S. stamps,
covers and postal history.*

Museums, Libraries and Displays

There is no charge to visit any of the following institutions. Please contact them before visiting because their hours may vary.

American Philatelic Research Library

PO Box 8000
State College, PA
16803-8000

Founded in 1968; now the largest philatelic library in the U.S. Currently receives more than 400 worldwide periodical titles and houses extensive collections of bound journals, books, auction catalogs and dealer pricelists. Directly serves members of the APS and APRL (library members also receive the quarterly Philatelic Literature Review). The public may purchase photocopies directly or borrow materials through the national interlibrary loan system.

Cardinal Spellman Philatelic Museum

235 Wellesley St.
Weston, MA 02193-1538

America's first fully accredited museum devoted to the display, collection and preservation of stamps and postal history. It has three galleries of rare stamps, a philatelic library and a post office/philatelic counter. Telephone: (617) 894-6735.

The Collectors Club

22 E. 35th St.
New York, NY 10016-3806

Bimonthly journal, publication of various reference works, one of the most extensive reference libraries in the world, reading and study rooms. Regular meetings on the first and third Wednesdays of each month at 6:30 p.m., except July and August. Telephone: (212) 683-0559.

Friends of the Western Philatelic Library

P.O. Box 2219
Sunnyvale, CA 94087-2219

Hall of Stamps

United States Postal Service
475 L'Enfant Plaza
Washington, DC
20260-0001

Located at USPS headquarters, this exhibit features more than $500,000 worth of rare U.S. stamps, a moon rock and letter canceled on the moon, original stamp design art, etc.

National Postal Museum

Smithsonian Institution
2 Massachusetts Ave. NE
Washington, DC
20560-0001

Houses more than 16 million items for exhibition and study purposes. Research may be conducted by appointment only on materials in the collection and library. This new museum, which is housed in the old Washington, D.C. Post Office next to Union Station, opened to the public in mid-1993. Telephone: (202) 633-9360.

The Postal History Foundation

PO Box 40725
Tucson, AZ 85717-0725

Regular services include a library, USPS contract post office, philatelic sales, archives, artifacts and collections and a Youth Department. Membership includes subscription to a quarterly journal, The Heliograph. Telephone: (602) 623-6652.

San Diego County Philatelic Library

4133 Poplar St.
San Diego, CA 92105-4541

Western Philatelic Library

Sunnyvale Public Library
665 W. Olive Ave.
Sunnyvale, CA 94087

Wineburgh Philatelic Research Library

University of Texas at Dallas
PO Box 830643
Richardson, TX 75083-0643

Open Monday-Thursday, 9 a.m.– 6 p.m.; Friday, 9 a.m. – 5 p.m.; first Saturday each month (except May and June), 1 p.m. – 5 p.m.

Exchange Service

Stamp Master

PO Box 17
Putnam Hall, FL 32685

An "electronic connection" for philatelists via modem and computer to display/ review members' stamp inventories for trading purposes, etc.

Literature

Basic Philately
Stamp Collector
Rick Groth
700 E. State St.
Iola, WI 54990-0001

Brookman Disney, Baseball & Entertainment Topical Price Guide
Arlene Dunn
Brookman Stamp Company
10 Chestnut Dr.
Bedford, NH 03110-5566

Illustrated, 128-page, perfect-bound book.

1995 Brookman Price Guide of U.S., U.N. and Canada Stamps and Postal Collectibles
Arlene Dunn
Brookman Stamp Company
10 Chestnut Dr.
Bedford, NH 03110-5566

Illustrated, 304-page, perfect-bound catalog.

Catalogue of U.S. Souvenir Cards
Washington Press
2 Vreeland Rd.
Florham Park, NJ
07932-1587

Commemorative Cancellation Catalog
General Image, Inc.
PO Box 335
Maplewood, NJ 07040-0335

Catalog covering all pictorial cancellations used in the U.S. during 1988 to 1990 is available. Please send self-addressed, stamped envelope for prices and description.

Compilation of U.S. Souvenir Cards
PO Box 4155
Tulsa, OK 74159-4155

Durland Plate Number Catalog
c/o: Bureau Issues Association
PO Box 23707
Belleville, Il 62223-0707

ArtCraft First Day Cover Price List
Washington Press
2 Vreeland Rd.
Florham Park, NJ
07932-1587

Includes Presidential Inaugural covers.

Fleetwood's Standard First Day Cover Catalog
Fleetwood
Cheyenne, WY 82008-0001

The Fun of Stamp Collecting
Arlene Dunn
Brookman Stamp Company
10 Chestnut Dr.
Bedford, NH 03110-5566

Illustrated, 96-page, perfect-bound book.

The Hammarskjold Invert
Washington Press
2 Vreeland Rd.
Florham Park, NJ
07932-1587

Tells the story of the Dag Hammarskjold error/invert. FREE for #10 SASE.

Linn's U.S. Stamp Yearbook
PO Box 29
Sidney, OH 45365-0029

A series of books providing facts and annual figures on every collectible variety of U.S. stamps, postal stationery and souvenir cards issued since 1983.

Linn's World Stamp Almanac
P.O. Box 29
Sidney, OH 45365-0029

The most useful single reference source for stamp collectors. Contains detailed information on U.S. stamps.

19th Century Envelopes Catalog
PO Box 48
Redlands, CA 92373-0601

Postage Stamp Identifier and Dictionary of Philatelic Terms
Washington Press
2 Vreeland Rd.
Florham Park, NJ
07932-1587

1992 edition, with new country listings.

Precancel Stamp Society Catalog of U.S. Bureau Precancels
108 Ashwamp Rd.
Scarborough, ME 04074

Precancel Stamp Society Catalog of U.S. Local Precancels
108 Ashwamp Rd.
Scarborough, ME 04074

Scott Specialized Catalogue of U.S. Stamps
PO Box 828
Sidney, OH 45365-8959

Scott Stamp Monthly
PO Box 828
Sidney, OH 45365-0828

Scott Standard Postage Stamp Catalogue
PO Box 828
Sidney, OH 45365-0828

Stamp Collecting Made Easy
PO Box 29
Sidney, OH 45365-0029

An illustrated, easy-to-read, 96-page booklet for beginning collectors.

The 24c 1918 Air Mail Invert
Washington Press
2 Vreeland Rd.
Florham Park, NJ
07932-1587

Tells all there is to know about this famous stamp. FREE for #10 SASE.

20th Century Envelopes Catalog
PO Box 48
Redlands, CA 92373-0601

U.S. Postal Card Catalog
PO Box 48
Redlands, CA 92373-0601

The U.S. Transportation Coils
Washington Press
2 Vreeland Rd.
Florham Park, NJ
07932-1587

FREE for #10 SASE.

Philatelic Centers

In addition to the more than 20,000 postal facilities authorized to sell philatelic products, the U.S. Postal Service also maintains more than 300 Philatelic Centers located in major population centers.

These Philatelic Centers have been established to serve stamp collectors and make it convenient for them to acquire an extensive range of current postage stamps, postal stationery and philatelic products issued by the Postal Service.

Centers are located at Main Post Offices unless otherwise indicated.

Note: Zip + 4 is 9998 unless otherwise indicated.

Alabama
351--24th St. N.
Birmingham, AL
  35203-9816

615 Clinton Ave. W.
Huntsville, AL
  35801-

250 St. Joseph
Mobile, AL 36601-

Downtown Station
135 Catoma St.
Montgomery, AL
  36104-

6701 Winton Blount
Blvd.
Montgomery, AL
  36124-

Alaska
Downtown Station
3rd & C Streets
Anchorage, AK
  99510-

Arizona
2400 N. Postal Blvd.
Flagstaff, AZ
  86004-

Osborne Station
3905 N. 7th Ave.
Phoenix, AZ
  85013-9995

General Mail
Facility
4949 E. Van Buren
Phoenix, AZ 85026-

1501 S. Cherrybell
Strav
Tucson, AZ 85726-

Arkansas
600 E. Capitol
Little Rock, AR
  72202-

California
Holiday Station
1180 W. Bull Road
Anaheim, CA 92812-

2730 W. Tregallas
Road
Antioch, CA 94509-

3400 Pegasus Drive
Bakersfield, CA
  93380-

2000 Allston Way
Berkeley, CA 94704-

18122 Carmenita
Road
Cerritos, CA 90703-

6330 Fountains S.
Citrus Heights, CA
  95621-

2121 Meridian Park
Blvd.
Concord, CA 94520-

2020 Fifth Street
Davis, CA 95616-

8111 Firestone Blvd.
Downey, CA 90241-

401 W. Lexington
Ave.
El Cajon, CA
  92020-

Cutten Station
3901 Walnut Dr.
Eureka, CA 95501-

600 Kentucky St.
Fairfield, CA 94533-

1900 E St.
Fresno, CA
  93706-

339 N. Central Ave.
Glendale, CA
  91209-

Hillcrest Station
300 E. Hillcrest
Blvd.
Inglewood, CA
  50301-

300 N. Long Beach
Blvd.
Long Beach, CA
  90802-

Alameda Station
760 N. Main St.
Los Angeles, CA
  90012-

407 C St.
Marysville, CA
  95901-001

415 W. 18th St.
Merced, CA 95341-

715 Kearney Ave
Modesto, CA
  95350-

Civic Center Annex
201 13th St.
Oakland, CA
  94612-9991

211 Brooks St.
Oceanside, CA
  92054-

281 E. Colorado
Blvd.
Pasadena, CA 91101-

4300 Black Ave.
Pleasanton, CA
  94566-2323

Churn Creek Rd.
Redding, CA 96049-

1201 N. Catalina
Redondo Beach, CA
  90277-

2535 Midway Dr.
San Diego, CA
  92186-

180 Steuart St.
San Francisco, CA
  94105-

1750 Maridian Ave.
San Jose, CA 95125-

40 Bellum Blvd.
San Rafael, CA
  94901-

836 Anacapa St.
Santa Barbara, CA
  93102-

201 E. Battles Rd.
Santa Maria, CA
93454-

730 Second St.
Santa Rosa, CA
95402-

Hammer Ranch
Station
7554 Pacific Ave.
Stockton, CA 95210-

200 Prairie Ct.
Vacaville, CA 95687-

15701 Sherman Way
Van Nuys, CA
91409-

Colorado

16890 E. Alameda
Pkwy.
Aurora, CO 80017-

1905 15th St.
Boulder, CO 80302-

201 E. Pikes Peak
Ave.
Rm. 205
Colorado Springs, CO
80901-

951 20th St.
Denver, CO 80202-

222 W. Eighth St.
Durango, CO 81301-

241 N. 4th St.
Grand Junction, CO
81501-

Connecticut

115 Boston Ave.
Bridgeport, CT
06610-

141 Weston St.
Hartford, CT 06101-

11 Silver St.
Middletown, CT
06457-

50 Brewery St.
New Haven, CT
06511-

26 Catoonah St.
Ridgefield, CT
06877-

135 Grand St.
Waterbury, CT
06701-

Delaware

55 The Plaza
Dover, DE 19901-

110 E. Main St.
Newark, DE 19711-

Wilmington P&DC
147 Quigley Blvd.
New Castle, DE
19720-

Rodney Square
Station
1101 N. King St.
Wilmington, DE
19801-

Florida

100 South Belcher Rd.
Clearwater, FL
34625-

General Mail Facility
500 Bill France
Daytona Beach, FL
32114-

1900 W. Oakland Pk.
Fort Lauderdale, FL
33310-

8695 College Pkwy.,
Ste. 301
Fort Myers, FL
33919-4892

5000 W. Midway Rd.
Fort Pierce, FL
34981-

4600 SW. 34th St.
Gainesville, FL
32608-9996

1801 Polk St.
Hollywood, FL
33022-

1100 Kings Rd.
Jacksonville, FL
32203-

210 N. Missouri Ave.
Lakeland, FL
33801-9996

2200 NW. 72nd Ave.
Miami, FL 33152-

1200 Goodlette Rd.
Naples, FL 34102-

6550 Nebraska Ave.
New Port Richey, FL
34653-

400 SW. 1st Ave.
Ocala, FL 34478-

1335 Kingsley Ave.
Orange Park, FL
32073-

1400 West Jordan St.
Pensacola, FL 32501-

Open Air Station
76 Fourth St. N.
St. Petersburg, FL
33701-

1661 Ringling Blvd.
Sarasota, FL
34230-9649

2800 S. Adams St.
Tallahassee, FL
32301-

850 E. Lime St.
Tarpon Springs, FL
34689-

Georgia

101 Marietta St.
NW.
Atlanta, GA 30301-

Parimeter Branch
4707 Ashford
Dunwoody Rd.
Atlanta, GA 31146-

3470 McClure Bridge
Road
Duluth, GA 30136-

364 Green St. NE
Gainesville, GA
30501-

451 College St.
Macon, GA
31213-9812

257 Lawrence St.
Marietta, GA 30060-

2 N. Farm St.
Savannah, GA
31402-

Hawaii

335 Merchant St.
Honolulu, HI 96813-

Idaho

770 S. 13th St.
Boise, ID 83708-

220 E. 5th St.
Moscow, ID 83843-

730 E. Clark St.
Pocatello, ID 83201-

Illinois

909 W. Euclid Ave.
Arlington Heights, IL
60004-

525 N. Broadway
Aurora, IL 60507-

Moraine Valley
Station
7401 100th Place
Bridgeview, IL
60455-

1301 E. Main St.
Carbondale, IL
62901-

Loop Station
211 S. Clark St.
Chicago, IL 60604-

433 W. Harrison St.
2nd Fl.
Chicago, IL
60607-9208

1000 E. Oakton St.
Des Plaines, IL
60018-

1101 Davis St.
Evanston, IL 60201-

2350 Madison Ave.
Granite City, IL
62040-

1750 W. Ogden Ave.
Naperville, IL 60540-

123 Indianwood
Blvd.
Park Forest, IL
60466-

N. University Station
6310 N. University
Peoria, IL
61614-3454

401 William
River Forest, IL
60305-1900

5225 Harrison Ave.
Rockford, IL 61125-

1956 2nd Ave.
Rock Island, IL
61201-9700

2105 E. Cook St.
Springfield, IL
62703-9995

Edison Square Station
1519 N. Lewis Ave.
Waukegan, IL
60085-1700

In addition to these Philatelic Centers, some larger Post Offices have dedicated "Philatelic" Windows with many current stamps and products.

Indiana

North Park Branch
4490 1st Ave. Arcade
Evansville, IN
47710-3688

Fort Wayne Postal
Facility
1501 S. Clinton St.
Fort Wayne, IN
46802-

5530 Sohl St.
Hammond, IN
46320-

125 W. South Street
Indianapolis, IN
46206-

3450 State Rd. 26
East
Lafayette, IN 47901-

424 S. Michigan St.
South Bend, IN
46624-

Cross Roads Station
70 Rose Ave.
Terre Haute, IN
47803-

Iowa

615 6th Ave. SE.
Cedar Rapids, IA
52401-9806

1165 Second Ave.
Des Moines, IA
50318-9755

214 Jackson St.
Sioux City, IA 51101-

Kansas

6029 Broadmoor St.
Shawnee Mission, KS
66202-9608

Santa Fe Room
424 S. Kansas Ave.
Topeka, KS 66603-

Downtown Station
330 W. 2nd Street
Wichita, KS 67202-

Kentucky

1088 Nandino Blvd.
Lexington, KY
40511-00017

Okolona Branch
7400 Jefferson Blvd.
Louisville, KY 40219-

St. Mathews Station
4600 Shelbyville Rd.
Louisville, KY 40207-

Louisiana

3401 Government St.
Alexandria, LA
71302-

3301 7th St.
Metairie, LA 70009-

Vieux Carre Station
1022 Iberville St.
New Orleans, LA
70112-3145

2400 Texas Ave.
Shreveport, LA
71102-

Maine

40 Western Ave.
Augusta, ME 04330-

202 Harlow St.
Bangor, ME 04401-

125 Forest Ave.
Portland, ME 04101-

Maryland

1 Church Cir.
Annapolis, MD
21401-

900 E. Fayette St.
Baltimore, MD
21233-9715

Chevy Chase
Finance Unit
5910 Connecticut Ave.
Bethesda, MD
20815-

215 Park St.
Cumberland, MD
21502-

201 E. Patrick St.
Frederick, MD
21701-

44 W. Franklin St.
Hagerstown, MD
21740-

816 E. Salisbury
Pkwy.
Salisbury, MD
21801-

Massachusetts

120 Commercial St.
Brockton, MA
02402-9997

2 Government Center
Fall River, MA
02722-

431 Common St.
Lawrence, MA
01842-0665

Main Post Office
PO Box 9998
Lowell, MA 01853-

695 Pleasant St.
New Bedford, MA
02740-

212 Fenn St.
Pittsfield, MA
01201-

2 Margin St.
Salem, MA 01270-

Main St. Station
1883 Main St.
Springfield, MA
01101-

Turner Falls Post
Office
178 Ave. A
Turner Falls, MA
01376-

4 E. Central St.
Worcester, MA
01613-

Michigan

2075 W. Stadium
Blvd.
Ann Arbor, MI
48106-

90 S. McCamly
Battle Creek, MI
49016-

26200 Ford Rd.
Dearborn Hgts., MI
48127-

1401 W. Fort St.
Detroit, MI 48233-

250 E. Boulevard Dr.
Flint, MI 48502-

225 Michigan NW
Grand Rapids, MI
49599-9818

200 S. Otsego Ave.
Jackson, MI 49201-

General Mail Facility
4800 Collins Rd.
Lansing, MI 48924-

735 W. Huron St.
Pontiac, MI
48343-0001

1300 Military St.
Port Huron, MI
48060-

30550 Gratiot St.
Roseville, MI 48066-

200 W. 2nd St.
Royal Oak, MI
48068-

1233 S. Washington
St.
Sangrian, MI 48605-

6300 Wayne Rd.
Westland, MI
48185-3169

Minnesota

Burnsville Branch
12212 12th Avenue S.
Burnsville, MN
55337-

2800 W. Michigan
Duluth, MN 55806-

Mississippi

401` E. South St.
Jackson, MS 39205-

Missouri

401 S. Washington St.
Chillicothe, MO
64601-

2300 Bernadette Dr.
Columbia, MO
65203-4607

315 W. Pershing Rd.
Kansas City, MO
64108-

Northwest Plaza
Station
44 Northwest Plaza
St. Ann, MO 63074-

201 S. 8th St.
St. Joseph, MO
64501-

Clayton Branch
7750 Moneyland Ave.
St. Louis, MO 63105-

500 W. Chestnut
Expwy.
Springfield, MO
65801

Montana

841 S. 26th
Billings, MT 59101-

215 First Ave. N.
Great Falls, MT
59401-

1100 W. Kent Ave.
Missoula, MT 59801-

Nebraska

W. South Front St.
Grand Island, NE
68801-

700 R St.
Lincoln, NE
68501-9804

300 E. Third St.
North Platte, NE
69101-

1124 Pacific St.
Omaha, NE
68108-9630

Nevada

1001 Sunset Rd.
Las Vegas, NV
89199-

2000 Vassar St.
Reno, NV 89510-

New Hampshire

955 Goffs Falls Rd.
Manchester, NH
03103-9713

80 Daniel St.
Portsmouth, NH
03801-

New Jersey

21 Kilmer Rd.
Adison, NJ
08899-9706

1701 Pacific Ave.
Atlantic City, NJ
08401-

421 Benigno Blvd.
Bellmawr, NJ 08031-

25 Veterans Plaza
Bergenfield, NJ
07621-

1 Convent Rd.
Convent, NJ
07961-9999

3 Miln St.
Cranford, NJ 07016-

229 Main St.
Fort Lee, NJ 07024-

65 Hazlet Ave
Hazlet, NJ 07730-

5 Wannamaker
Municipal Complex
Island Heights, NJ
08732-0001

160 Maplewood Ave.
Maplewood, NJ
07040-

Nutley Branch
372 Franklin Ave.
Nutley, NJ 07110-

171 Broad St.
Red Bank, NJ 07701-

680 US Highway
Rt 130
Trenton, NJ 08650-

Sheffield Station
150 Pompton Plains
Cross Rd.
Wayne, NJ
07470-9994

411 Greenwood Ave.
Wyckoff, NJ 07481-

New Mexico

1135 Broadway NE.
Albuquerque, NM
87101-

200 E. Las Cruces Ave.
Las Cruces, NM
88001-

415 N. Pennsylvania
Ave.
Roswell, NM 88201-

New York

30 Old Karner Rd.
Albany, NY 12288-

Empire State Plaza
Station
Albany, NY 12220-

115 Henry St.
Binghamton, NY
13902-

Bronx General P.O.
558 Grand Concourse
Bronx, NY 10451-

Throggs Neck Station
3630 East Tremont
Ave.
Bronx, NY 10465-

Homecrest Station
2302 Ave. U
Brooklyn, NY 11229-

1200 William St.
Buffalo, NY 14240-

960460 Baron
DeHirsch Rd.
Crompond, NY
10517-

Downtown Station
255 Clemens Center
Pkwy.
Elmira, NY 14902-

41-65 Main St.
Flushing, NY
11351-0001

77 Old Glenham Rd.
Glenham, NY 12527-

185 W. John St.
Hicksville, NY
11801-

8840 164th St.
Jamaica, NY 11431-

300 E. 3rd St.
Jamestown, NY
14701-

324 Broadway
Monticello, NY
12701-

Bowling Green
Station
25 Broadway
New York, NY
10094-

Church St. Station
90 Church St.
New York, NY
10007-

Madison Square
Station
149 E. 23rd St.
New York, NY
10010-

New York General
P.O.
421 8th Ave.
New York, NY
10001-

Rockefeller Center
610 Fifth Ave.
New York, NY
10920-9991

352 Main St.
Oneonta, NY 13820-

35 S. Main St.
Pearl River, NY
10965-

Branch Office
407 East Main St.
Port Jefferson, NY
11777-

55 Mansion St.
Poughkeepsie, NY
12601-

1335 Jefferson Rd.
Rochester, NY
14692-9205

250 Merrick Rd.
Rockville Ctr., NY
11570-

29 Jay St.
Schenectady, NY
12305-

25 Route 111
Smithtown, NY
11787-

100 Pitcher St.
Utica, NY
13504-9603

108 Main St.
Warwick, NY 10990-

100 Fisher Ave.
White Plains, NY
10602-

79-81 Main St.
Yonkers, NY 10701-

North Carolina

1302 Patton Ave.
Asheville, NC 28806-

6241 S. Boulevard
Charlotte, NC
20224-9798

Four Seasons Station
301 Four Seasons
Town Ctr.
Greensboro, NC
27427-

North Dakota

220 E. Rosser Ave.
Bismarck, ND 58502-

675 2nd Ave. N.
Fargo, ND 58102-

In addition to these Philatelic Centers, some larger Post Offices have dedicated "Philatelic" Windows with many current stamps and products.

Ohio

675 Wolf Ledges Pky.
Akron, OH 44309-

4420 Dressler Rd. NW
Canton, OH 44718-

2400 Orange Ave.
Cleveland, OH 44101-

6316 Nicholas Dr.
Columbus, OH 43235-

1111 E. 5th St. Rm. 212A
Dayton, OH 45401-

345 E. Bridge St.
Elyria, OH 44035-

200 N. Diamond St.
Mansfield, OH 44901-

435 S. St. Clair St.
Toledo, OH 43601-

99 S. Walnut St.
Youngstown, OH 44501-9713

Oklahoma

115 W. Broadway
Enid, OK 73701-

525 W. Okmulgee
Muskogee, OK 74401-

129 W. Gray
Norman, OK 73069-

333 W. 4th St.
Tulsa, OK 74103-9612

Oregon

520 Willamette St.
Eugene, OR 97401-

751 NW. Hoyt St.
Portland, OR 97208-3480

Pennsylvania

442 Hamilton St.
Allentown, PA 18101-1611

535 Wood St.
Bethlehem, PA 18016-

Lehigh Valley Post Office
17 S. Commerce St.
Bethlehem, PA 18002-

115 Boylston St.
Bradford, PA 16701-

44 N. Brady St.
Du Bois, PA 15801-

1314 Griswold Plaza
Erie, PA 16501-

1025 Valley Forge Road
Fairview Village, PA 19409-

115 Buford Ave.
Gettysburg, PA 12325-9990

238 S. Pennsylvania
Greensburg, PA 15601-

813 Market St.
Harrisburg, PA 17105-

Downtown Station
48-50 W. Chestnut St.
Lancaster, PA 17603-

980 Wheeler Way
Langhorne, PA 19047-

435 S. Cascade St.
New Castle, PA 16108-

501 11th St.
New Kensington, PA 15068-

William Penn Annex Station
900 Market St.
Philadelphia, PA 19107-

General Mail Facility
1001 California Ave.
Rm. 1002
Pittsburgh, PA 15233-

701 Ann St.
Stroudsburg, PA 18360-

300 S. Main St.
Wilkes Barre, PA 18701-9602

Center City Finance Station
240 West Third St.
Williamsport, PA 17703-

200 S. George St.
York, PA 17405-

Puerto Rico

General Post Office
585 Roosevelt Ave.
San Juan, PR 00936-9711

Rhode Island

320 Thames St.
Newport, RI 02840-

40 Montgomery St.
Pawtucket, RI 02860-

24 Corliss St.
Providence, RI 02904-9713

South Carolina

7075 Cross County Road
Charleston, SC 29423-

1601 Assembly St.
Columbia, SC 29201-9713

600 W. Washington St.
Greenville, SC 29602-9918

South Dakota

500 E. Boulevard
Rapid City, SD 57701-

320 S. 2nd Ave.
Sioux Falls, SD 57104-

Tennessee

5424 Bell Forge Lane E.
Antioch, TN 37013-

General Mail Facility
6050 Shallowford Road
Chattanooga, TN 37421-

200 Martin Luther King Dr.
Jackson, TN 38301-

530 E. Main St.
Johnson City, TN 37601-

General Mail Facility
1237 E. Weisgarber Road
Knoxville, TN 37950-

901 Broadway
Nashville, TN 37203-

Texas

2301 S. Ross
Amarillo, TX 79120-9604

2121 E. Wm. J. Bryan Pky.
Bryan, TX 77801-

809 Nueces Bay Blvd.
Corpus Christi, TX 78469-0703

400 N. Ervay St.
Dallas, TX 75201-

Olla Podrida Post Office
12215 Coit Rd.
Dallas, TX 75251-

5300 E. Paisano Dr.
El Paso, TX 79910-

251 W. Lancaster Ave.
Fort Worth, TX 76102-8108

401 Franklin Ave.
Houston, TX 77201-

300 N. 10th
Killeen, TX 76541-

601 E. Pecan
McAllen, TX 78501-

Your local Post Office may be able to direct you to the nearest "Philatelic" Window, Philatelic Center or Postal Store (new, state-of-the-art facilities formerly called "Store of the Future").

100 E. Wall
Midland, TX 79701-

433 Belle Grove Dr.
Richardson, TX
75080-

1 N. Abe St.
San Angelo, TX
76902-

Downtown Station
615 E. Houston
San Antonio, TX
78205-

10410 Perrin Beitel
Rd.
San Antonio, TX
78284-

202 E. Erwin St.
Tyler, TX 75702-

1000 Lamar St.
Wichita Falls, TX
26301-

Utah

3680 Pacific Ave.
Ogden, UT 84401-

1760 W. 2100 S.
Salt Lake City, UT
84199-

Vermont

204 Main St.
Brattleboro, VT
05301-

11 Elmwood Ave.
Burlington, VT
05401-9711

10 Sykes Ave.
White River Junction,
VT 05001-

Virginia

111 Sixth St.
Bristol, VA
24201-9996

1425 Battlefield
Blvd. N.
Chesapeake, VA
23327-

700 Main St.
Danville, VA 24541-

809 Aberdeen Rd.
Hampton, VA
23670-

300 Odd Fellows Rd.
Lynchburg, VA
24506-

600 Church St.
Norfolk, VA 23501-

1801 Brook Rd.
Richmond, VA
23232-

419 Rutherford Ave.
NE.
Roanoke, VA 24022-

1430 N. Augusta
Staunton, VA 24401-

Washington

11 3rd St. NW.
Auburn, WA 98002-

PO Box 9998
Bellevue, WA 98009-

315 Prospect St.
Bellingham, WA
98225-

3500 W. Court
Pasco, WA
99301-4532

424 E. 1st St.
Port Angeles, WA
98362-

301 Union St.
Seattle, WA 98101-

1102 A St.
Tacoma, WA 98402-

205 W. Washington
Ave.
Yakima, WA 98903-

West Virginia

301 North St.
Bluefield, WV
24701-

Charleston Town
Center
Charleston, WV
25357-

500 W. Pike St.
Clarksburg, WV
26301-

1000 Virginia Ave.
W. Huntington, WV
25704-1726

217 W. King St.
Martinsburg, WV
25401-

Wisconsin

126 N. Barstow St.
Eau Claire, WI
54703-

425 State St.
La Crosse, WI
54601-

3902 Milwaukee St.
Madison, WI 53714-

345 W. St. Paul Ave.
Milwaukee, WI
53203-

1025 W. 20th Ave.
Oshkosh, WI 54901

235 Forrest St.
Wausau, WI 54403-

Wyoming

150 E. B Street
Casper, WY 82602-

2120 Capitol Ave.
Cheyenne, WY
82001-

FOREIGN CENTERS

Australia

Max Stern
234 Flinders St.
Box 997H GPO
Melbourne 3001

Denmark

Nordfrim
DK 5450 Otterup
Denmark

Germany

Hermann Sieger
Venusberg 32-34
D73545
Lorch Wurttemberg

Italy

DeRosa S.P.A.
Via Privata Maria
Teresa 11
1-20123 Milan

Alberto Bolaffi
Via Cavour 17
10123 Torino

Japan

Japan Philatelic
Agency
P.O. Box 96
Toshima
Tokyo 170-91

Thailand

International House
of Stamps and Coins
(Siam) Co. Ltd.
434 Thadindeang
Road
Bangkok 10600

United Kingdom

Harry Allen
P.O. Box 5
Watford Herts
WD2 5SW

Explanation of Catalog Prices

The United States Postal Service sells only the commemoratives released during the past few years, current regular and special stamps, and current postal stationery.

Prices in this book are called "catalog prices" by stamp collectors. Collectors use catalog prices as guidelines when buying or trading stamps. It is important to remember the prices are simply guidelines to the stamp values. Stamp condition (see pp 10-11) is very important in determining the actual value of a stamp.

Condition Affects Value

The catalog prices are given for unused (mint) stamps and used (canceled) stamps, which have been hinged and are in Very Fine condition. Stamps in Superb condition that have never been hinged may cost more than the listed price. Stamps in less than Fine condition may cost less.

The prices for used stamps are based on a light cancellation; a heavy cancellation lessens a stamp's value. Canceled stamps may be worth more than uncanceled stamps. This happens if the cancellation is of a special type or for a significant date. Therefore, it is important to study an envelope before removing a stamp and discarding its "cover."

Prices are Estimated

Listed prices are estimates of how much you can expect to pay for a stamp from a dealer. **A 15-cent minimum valuation has been established which represents a fair-market price to have a dealer locate and provide a single stamp to a customer. Dealers may charge less per stamp to provide a group of such stamps, and may charge less for such a single stamp. Similarly, a $1.00 minimum has been established for First Day Covers (FDCs). If you sell a stamp to a dealer, he or she may offer you much less than the catalog** price. Dealers pay based on their interest in owning a particular stamp. If they already have a full supply, they may only buy additional stamps at a low price.

Sample Listing

				Un	U	PB/LP/PNC	#	FDC	Q(M̄)
3069	32¢	Georgia O'Keefe	05/23/96	.60	.15	2.40	(4)	1.25	156

Scott Catalog Number (bold type indicates stamp is pictured)

Description Denomination

Date of Issue

Unused Catalog Price

Used Catalog Price

Plate Block Price, Line Pair Price or Plate Number Coil Price

# of stamps in Plate Block, Line Pair or Plate Number Coil

First Day Cover Price

Quantity Issued in Millions (where known)

3069

Understanding the Listings

- Prices in regular type for single unused and used stamps are taken from the *Scott 1999 Standard Postage Stamp Catalogue, Volume 1A-B* ©1998, whose editors have based these prices on **actual retail values** as they found them in the marketplace. The Scott numbering system for stamps is used in this book. Prices quoted for unused and used stamps are for "Very Fine" condition, except where Very Fine is not available.

- Stamp values in *italic* generally refer to items difficult to value accurately.

- A dash (—) in a value column means the item is known to exist but information is insufficient for establishing a value.

- The stamp listings contain a number of additions designated "a," "b," "c," etc. These represent recognized variations of stamps as well as errors. These listings are as complete as space permits.

- Occasionally, a new stamp or major variation may be inserted by the catalog editors into a series or sequence where it was not originally anticipated. These additions are identified by capital letters "A," "B" and so forth. For example, a new stamp which logically belonged between 1044 and 1045 is designated 1044A, even though it is entirely different from 1044. The insertion was preferable to a complete renumbering of the series.

- Prices for Plate Blocks, First Day Covers, American Commemorative Panels and Souvenir Pages are taken from *Scott's Specialized Catalogue of U.S. Stamps*, 1998 Edition, ©1997.

Sample Variation Listing

			Un	U	PB/PNC	#	FDC	Q($\overline{M}$)
2281	25¢ Honeybee	09/02/88	.45	.15	3.25	(3)	1.25	
a	Imperf. pair		*40.00*					
b	Black omitted		*65.00*					
d	Pair, imperf. between		*1,000.00*					

Scott Catalog Number (bold type indicates stamp is pictured) | Description | Denomination | Date of Issue | Unused Catalog Price | Used Catalog Price | Plate Block Price, Line Pair Price or Plate Number Coil Price | # of stamps in Plate Block, Line Pair or Plate Number Coil | First Day Cover Price | Quantity Issued in Millions (where known)

2281

Commemorative and Definitive Stamps

1847-1861

1

2

3

4

5

11

12

14

17

For additional details and distinguishing characteristics of stamps, see pages 64 and 65. This information has now been positioned near the appropriate stamp listings for better, quicker reference.

Issues of 1847	Un	U
Thin, Bluish Wove Paper, July 1, Imperf., Unwmkd.		
1 5¢ Benjamin Franklin	5,000.00	600.00
b 5¢ orange brown	6,250.00	700.00
c 5¢ red orange	*12,500.00*	*5,000.00*
Pen cancel		300.00
Double transfer of top or top and bottom frame lines		725.00
Double transfer of top, bottom and left frame lines and numerals		2,600.00
2 10¢ George Washington	*26,000.00*	1,400.00
Pen cancel		625.00
Vertical line through second "F" of "OFFICE"	—	1,600.00
With "stick pin" in tie, or with "harelip"	—	1,900.00
Double transfer in lower right "X," or of left and bottom frame lines	—	2,000.00
Double transfer in "POST OFFICE"	—	2,300.00

Issues of 1875, Reproductions of 1 and 2, Bluish Paper, Without Gum

3	5¢ Franklin	800.00	—
4	10¢ Washington	1,000.00	—

5¢. On the originals, the left side of the white shirt frill touches the oval on a level with the top of the "F" of "Five." On the reproduction, it touches the oval about on a level with the top of the figure "5."

10¢. On the reproductions, line of coat at left points to right of "X" and line of coat at right points to center of "S" of CENTS. On the originals, line of coat points to "T" of TEN and between "T" and "S" of CENTS.

On the reproductions, the eyes have a sleepy look, the line of the mouth is straighter and in the curl of hair near the left cheek is a strong black dot, while the originals have only a faint one.

Issues of 1851-57, Imperf.

5	1¢ Franklin, type I	*175,000.00*	*30,000.00*
5A	1¢ blue, type Ib	*11,500.00*	*4,500.00*
	#6-9: Franklin (5), 1851		
6	1¢ dark blue, type Ia	*30,000.00*	*8,000.00*
7	1¢ blue, type II	950.00	150.00
	Cracked plate	1,150.00	350.00
8	1¢ blue, type III	*9,000.00*	2,250.00
8A	1¢ blue, type IIIa	*4,000.00*	900.00
9	1¢ blue, type IV	650.00	125.00
	Triple transfer, one inverted	800.00	175.00

Issues of 1851-57 Imperf.	Un	U
#10-11, 25-26a all had plates on which at least four outer frame lines (and usually much more) were recut, adding to their value.		
10 3¢ orange brown Washington, type I (11)	2,500.00	85.00
3¢ copper brown	3,000.00	150.00
On part-India paper	—	500.00
11 3¢ Washington, type I	225.00	10.00
3¢ deep claret	300.00	18.00
Double transfer, "GENTS" for "CENTS"	350.00	35.00
12 5¢ Jefferson, type I	*15,000.00*	1,100.00
13 10¢ green Washington, type I (14)	*13,000.00*	775.00
14 10¢ green, type II	3,000.00	225.00
15 10¢ Washington, type III	3,000.00	225.00
16 10¢ green, type IV (14)	*18,000.00*	1,500.00
17 12¢ Washington	4,000.00	325.00

Issues of 1857-61, Perf. 15.5 (Issued in 1857 except #18, 27, 28A, 29, 30, 30A, 35, 36b, 37, 38, 39)

	#18-24: Franklin (5)		
18	1¢ blue, type I	1,300.00	475.00
19	1¢ blue, type Ia	*15,000.00*	*4,000.00*
20	1¢ blue, type II	850.00	225.00
21	1¢ blue, type III	*8,500.00*	1,600.00
22	1¢ blue, type IIIa	1,500.00	400.00
23	1¢ blue, type IV	5,000.00	525.00
24	1¢ blue, type V	175.00	40.00
	"Curl" on shoulder	240.00	67.50
	"Earring" below ear	350.00	95.00
	Long double "curl" in hair	300.00	80.00
b	Laid paper		—
	#25-26a: Washington (11)		
25	3¢ rose, type I	1,800.00	70.00
	Major cracked plate	3,000.00	500.00
26	3¢ dull red, type II	75.00	5.00
	3¢ brownish carmine	140.00	16.00
	3¢ claret	170.00	21.00
	Left or right frame line double	110.00	15.00
	Cracked plate	*750.00*	225.00
26a	3¢ dull red, type IIa	200.00	45.00
	Double transfer	300.00	100.00
	Left frame line double	—	140.00

The stamp listings contain a number of "a," "b," "c," etc., additions which include recognized varieties and errors. These listings are as complete as space permits.

1¢ Franklin Types I-V, series 1851-57, 1857-61, 1875

5

Bust of Benjamin Franklin

Detail of **#7, 20** Type II

Lower scrollwork incomplete (lacks little balls and lower plume ornaments). Side ornaments are complete.

Detail of **#9, 23** Type IV

Similar to Type II, but outer lines recut top, bottom or both.

Detail of **#5, 18, 40** Type I

Has curved, unbroken lines outside labels. Scrollwork is substantially complete at top, forms little balls at bottom.

Detail of **#8, 21** Type III

Outer lines broken in the middle. Side ornaments are substantially complete.

Detail of **#8A, 22** Type IIIa

Outer lines broken top or bottom but not both.

Detail of **#24** Type V

Similar to Type III of 1851-57 but with side ornaments partly cut away.

Detail of **#6, 19** Type Ia

Same as Type I at bottom but top ornaments and outer line partly cut away. Lower scrollwork is complete.

Detail of **#5A** Type Ib

Lower scrollwork is incomplete, the little balls are not so clear.

3¢ Washington Types I-IIa, series 1851-57, 1857-61, 1875

10

Bust of George Washington

Detail of **#10, 11, 25, 41**
Type I

There is an outer frame line
at top and bottom.

Detail of **#26** Type II

The outer frame line
has been removed at top
and bottom. The side frame
lines were recut so as to be
continuous from the top to
the bottom of the plate.

Detail of **#26a** Type IIa

The side frame lines ex-
tended only to the bottom
of the stamp design.

5¢ Jefferson Types I-II, Series 1851-57, 1857-61

12

Portrait of Thomas Jefferson

Detail of **#12, 27-29** Type I

There are projections on all
four sides.

Detail of **#30-30A** Type II

The projections at top and
bottom are partly cut away.

10¢ Washington Types I-IV, series 1851-57, 1857-61, 1875

15

Portrait of George
Washington

Detail of **#13, 31, 43** Type I

The "shells" at the lower
corners are practically
complete. The outer line
below the label is very
nearly complete. The outer
lines are broken above the
middle of the top label and
the "X" in each upper corner.

Detail of **#14, 32** Type II

The design is complete at
the top. The outer line at the
bottom is broken in the
middle. The shells are partly
cut away.

Detail of **#15, 33** Type III

The outer lines are broken
above the top label and the
"X" numerals. The outer line
at the bottom and the shells
are partly cut away, as in
Type II.

Detail of **#16, 34** Type IV

The outer lines have been recut at top or bottom or both.
Types I, II, III and IV have
complete ornaments at the
sides of the stamps and
three pearls at each outer
edge of the bottom panel.

Detail of **#35** Type V

(Two typical examples).
Side ornaments slightly cut
away. Outer lines complete
at top except over right "X."
Outer lines complete at bottom and shells nearly so.

1857-1875

Issues of 1857-61		Un	U
Perf. 15.5			
#27-29: Jefferson (12)			
27	5¢ brick red, type I	*14,000.00*	950.00
28	5¢ red brown, type I	2,750.00	425.00
b	5¢ brt. red brn., type I	3,000.00	600.00
28A	5¢ Indian red, type I	*19,000.00*	2,500.00
29	5¢ brown, type I	1,750.00	300.00
	Defective transfer	—	—
30	5¢ orange brown, type II	1,100.00	1,100.00
30A	5¢ brown, type II (30)	1,500.00	260.00
b	Printed on both sides	*4,000.00*	*4,250.00*
	#31-35: Washington (15)		
31	10¢ green, type I	12,000.00	700.00
32	10¢ green, type II	3,750.00	275.00
33	10¢ green, type III	3,750.00	275.00
	"Curl" on forehead or in left "X"	—	350.00
34	10¢ green, type IV	*25,000.00*	*2,000.00*
35	10¢ green, type V	275.00	65.00
	Small "curl" on forehead	325.00	77.50
	"Curl" in "e" or "t" of "Cents"	350.00	90.00
	Plate I—Outer frame lines complete.		
36	12¢ blk. Washington (17), plate I	1,100.00	180.00
	Triple transfer	1,300.00	—
36b	12¢ black, plate III	675.00	160.00
	Vertical line through rosette	825.00	240.00
37	24¢ gray lilac	1,200.00	300.00
a	24¢ gray	1,200.00	300.00
b	24¢ red lilac	1,000.00	
38	30¢ orange Franklin	1,500.00	400.00
	Recut at bottom	1,750.00	525.00
39	90¢ blue Washington	2,350.00	*5,500.00*
	Double transfer at top or bottom	2,400.00	—
	90¢ Same, with pen cancel		1,250.00

Note: Beware of forged cancellations of #39. Genuine cancellations are rare.

Issues of 1875		Un	U
Government Reprints, White Paper, Without Gum, Perf. 12			
40	1¢ bright blue Franklin (5)	*525.00*	
41	3¢ scarlet Wash. (11)	2,200.00	
42	5¢ orange brown Jefferson (30)		950.00
43	10¢ blue green Washington (14)		1,900.00
44	12¢ greenish black Washington (17)		2,250.00
45	24¢ blackish violet Washington (37)		2,250.00
46	30¢ yellow orange Franklin (38)		2,250.00
47	90¢ deep blue Washington (39)		3,500.00
48-54	Not assigned		
Issue of 1861, Thin, Semi-Transparent Paper			

#55-62 are no longer considered postage stamps. Many experts consider them to be essays and/or trial color proofs.

		Un	U
55	1¢ Franklin (see #63)		
56	3¢ Washington (see #65)		
58	10¢ Washington (see #68)		
59	12¢ Washington (see #69)		
60	24¢ Washington (see #70)		
61	30¢ Franklin (see #71)		
62	90¢ Washington (see #72)		
62B	10¢ dark green Washington (58)	5,500.00	675.00
	Double transfer	*5,500.00*	525.00

30   37

38   39

40

62B

Pacific '97 1847 Franklin
Date of Issue: May 29, 1997
Place of Issue: San Francisco, CA

Pacific '97 1847 Washington
Date of Issue: May 30, 1997
Place of Issue: San Francisco, CA

Have you noticed? The Perf listings have changed from fractions to decimals. For example, Perf 10-1/2 is now 10.5. This is the first step taken toward giving you a more precise perf gauge which currently may only be precise to the nearest 0.5.

63   **64**   **65**   **67**

68   **69**   **70**   **71**

72   **73**   **77**

Details

Issues of 1861-62, 1861-66, 1867 and 1875

Detail of **#63, 86, 92**

There is a dash in 63, 86 and 92 added under the tip of the ornament at the right of the numeral in upper left corner.

Detail of **#67, 75, 80, 95**

There is a leaf in 67, 75, 80 and 95 added to the foliated ornaments at each corner.

Detail of **#69, 85E, 90, 97**

In 69, 85E, 90 and 97, ovals and scrolls have been added at the corners.

Detail of **#64-66, 74, 79, 82-83, 85, 85C, 88, 94**

In 64-66, 74, 79, 82-83, 85, 85C, 88 and 94, ornaments at corners have been enlarged and end in a small ball.

Detail of **#68, 85D, 89, 96**

There is an outer line in 68, 85D, 89 and 96 cut below the stars and an outer line added to the ornaments above them.

Detail of **#72, 101**

In 72 and 101, parallel lines form an angle above the ribbon containing "U.S. Postage"; between these lines a row of dashes has been added, along with a point of color to the apex of the lower line.

Issues of 1861-62		Un	U
Perf. 12			
63	1¢ blue Franklin	240.00	25.00
a	1¢ ultramarine	600.00	225.00
b	1¢ dark blue	450.00	55.00
c	Laid paper	—	—
d	Vert. pair, imperf. horiz.		—
e	Printed on both sides	—	2,500.00
	Double transfer	—	37.50
	Dot in "U"	260.00	30.00
64	3¢ pink Washington	5,750.00	650.00
a	3¢ pigeon blood pink	14,000.00	3,100.00
b	3¢ rose pink	450.00	110.00
65	3¢ rose Washington	125.00	2.50
b	Laid paper	—	—
d	Vertical pair, imperf. horizontally	3,500.00	750.00
e	Printed on both sides	2,000.00	1,600.00
f	Double impression		6,000.00
	Cracked plate	—	—
	Double transfer	140.00	5.50
66	3¢ lake Washington	2,000.00	
	Double transfer	2,250.00	
67	5¢ buff Jefferson	13,000.00	650.00
68	10¢ yellow green Washington	475.00	47.50
	10¢ deep yellow green on thin paper	600.00	55.00
a	10¢ dark green	500.00	50.00
b	Vert. pair, imperf. horiz.		3,500.00
	Double transfer	525.00	52.50
69	12¢ blk. Washington	850.00	85.00
	12¢ intense black	875.00	90.00
	Double transfer of top or bottom frame line	900.00	100.00
	Double transfer of top and bottom frame lines	925.00	105.00
70	24¢ red lilac Washington	1,250.00	125.00
a	24¢ brown lilac	1,200.00	115.00
b	24¢ steel blue	6,500.00	425.00
c	24¢ violet	9,000.00	850.00
d	24¢ grayish lilac	2,250.00	500.00
	Scratch under "A" of "POSTAGE"		—
71	30¢ orange Franklin	975.00	120.00
a	Printed on both sides		—
72	90¢ bl. Washington	2,100.00	350.00
a	90¢ pale blue	2,100.00	350.00
b	90¢ dark blue	2,300.00	400.00
	Issues of 1861-66		
73	2¢ blk. Andrew Jackson	300.00	45.00
	Double transfer	350.00	45.00
	Major double transfer of top left corner and "POSTAGE"		7,500.00
	Cracked plate	—	—

Issues of 1861-66		Un	U
Perf. 12			
	#74 was not regularly issued.		
74	3¢ scarlet Washington (65)	7,000.00	
75	5¢ red brown Jefferson (67)	3,500.00	400.00
76	5¢ brown Jefferson (67)	800.00	95.00
a	5¢ dark brown	900.00	110.00
	Double transfer of top or bottom frame line	875.00	110.00
77	15¢ blk. Lincoln	1,100.00	120.00
	Double transfer	1,150.00	130.00
78	24¢ lilac Washington (70)	650.00	80.00
c	24¢ blackish violet	21,000.00	1,750.00
	Scratch under "A" of "POSTAGE"	—	—

Grills on U.S. Stamps

Between 1867 and 1870, postage stamps were embossed with pyramid-shaped grills that absorbed cancellation ink to prevent reuse of canceled stamps.

Issues of 1867, With Grills			
Grills A, B and with C: Points Up			
A. Grill Covers Entire Stamp			
79	3¢ rose Washington (56)	3,750.00	800.00
b	Printed on both sides		—
80	5¢ brown Jefferson (57)	—	—
a	5¢ dark brown		50,000.00
81	30¢ orange Franklin (61)		—
B. Grill about 18 x 15mm			
82	3¢ rose Washington (56)		100,000.00
C. Grill about 13 x 16mm			
83	3¢ rose Washington (56)	4,000.00	750.00
	Double grill	5,250.00	1,850.00
Grills, D, Z, E, F with Points Down			
D. Grill about 12 x 14mm			
84	2¢ black Jackson (73)	12,000.00	2,000.00
85	3¢ rose Washington (56)	4,250.00	750.00
	Split grill		825.00
Z. Grill about 11 x 14mm			
85A	1¢ blue Franklin (55)		—
85B	2¢ black Jackson (73)	4,750.00	750.00
	Double transfer	5,250.00	800.00
85C	3¢ rose Washington (56)	7,750.00	2,000.00
	Double grill	9,250.00	
85D	10¢ grn. Washington (58)		45,000.00
85E	12¢ blk. Washington (59)	6,750.00	950.00
	Double transfer of top frame line		1,050.00
85F	15¢ black Lincoln (77)		100,000.00
E. Grill about 11 x 13mm			
86	1¢ blue Franklin (55)	1,900.00	400.00
	Double grill	—	525.00
	Split grill	2,000.00	450.00

	Issues of 1867	Un	U
	With Grills, Perf. 12		
87	2¢ black Jackson (73)	800.00	100.00
	2¢ intense black	875.00	120.00
	Double grill	—	—
	Double transfer	850.00	110.00
88	3¢ rose Washington (65)	575.00	15.00
a	3¢ lake red	625.00	19.00
	Double grill	—	—
	Very thin paper	600.00	16.00
89	10¢ grn. Washington (68)	2,750.00	275.00
	Double grill	3,750.00	475.00
90	12¢ blk. Washington (69)	3,000.00	300.00
	Double transfer of top or bottom frame line	3,100.00	325.00
91	15¢ black Lincoln (77)	6,000.00	575.00
	Double grill	—	875.00
	F. Grill about 9 x 13mm		
92	1¢ blue Franklin (63)	800.00	150.00
	Double transfer	800.00	180.00
	Double grill	—	290.00
93	2¢ black Jackson (73)	300.00	35.00
	Double grill	—	140.00
	Very thin paper	350.00	42.50
94	3¢ red Washington (65)	260.00	4.25
c	Vertical pair, imperf. horizontally	1,000.00	
d	Printed on both sides	1,100.00	
	Double grill	—	
	End roller grill		325.00
	Quadruple split grill	475.00	125.00
95	5¢ brown Jefferson (67)	2,250.00	550.00
a	5¢ dark brown	2,500.00	600.00
	Double transfer of top frame line	—	—
	Double grill	—	—
96	10¢ yellow green Washington (68)	1,750.00	175.00
	Double transfer	—	—
	Quadruple split grill		500.00
97	12¢ blk. Washington (69)	2,100.00	200.00
	Double transfer of top or bottom frame line	2,100.00	190.00
	Triple grill		—
98	15¢ black Lincoln (77)	2,200.00	275.00
	Double transfer of upper right corner	—	—
	Double grill	—	425.00
	Quadruple split grill	2,750.00	575.00
99	24¢ gray lilac Washington (70)	3,500.00	625.00
100	30¢ orange Franklin (71)	4,000.00	600.00
	Double grill	4,750.00	1,050.00
101	90¢ bl. Washington (72)	6,500.00	1,100.00
	Double grill	9,000.00	

	Issues of 1875	Un	U
	Reissue of 1861-66 Issues, Without Grill, Perf. 12		
102	1¢ blue Franklin (63)	650.00	950.00
103	2¢ black Jackson (73)	2,500.00	4,500.00
104	3¢ brown red Washington	2,750.00	4,750.00
105	5¢ brown Jefferson (67)	2,100.00	2,500.00
106	10¢ grn. Washington (68)	2,250.00	4,250.00
107	12¢ blk. Washington (69)	3,000.00	5,000.00
108	15¢ black Lincoln (77)	3,000.00	5,250.00
109	24¢ deep violet Washington (70)	3,750.00	6,750.00
110	30¢ brownish orange Franklin (71)	4,000.00	7,000.00
111	90¢ bl. Washington (72)	5,250.00	22,500.00
	Issues of 1869, With Grill		
	G. Grill about 9½ x 9mm		
112	1¢ Franklin, Mar. 27	525.00	125.00
b	Without grill	3,500.00	
	Double grill	750.00	225.00
113	2¢ br. Post Rider, Mar. 27	450.00	45.00
	Split grill	450.00	60.00
	Double transfer		55.00
114	3¢ Locomotive, Mar. 27	275.00	15.00
a	Without grill	750.00	
d	Double impression		3,500.00
	Triple grill	—	—
	Sextuple grill	—	3,250.00
	Gray paper	—	85.00
115	6¢ Washington	1,750.00	160.00
	Quadruple split grill	—	650.00
116	10¢ Shield and Eagle	1,500.00	120.00
	End roller grill	—	—
117	12¢ S.S. Adriatic, Apr. 5	1,500.00	130.00
	Split grill	1,800.00	140.00
118	15¢ Columbus Landing, type I, Apr. 2	5,500.00	550.00
119	15¢ type II (118)	2,250.00	225.00
b	Center inverted	275,000.00	17,500.00
c	Center double, one inverted		—
120	24¢ Declaration of Independence, Apr. 7	4,750.00	650.00
b	Center inverted	275,000.00	20,000.00
121	30¢ Shield, Eagle and Flags, May 15	5,250.00	500.00
b	Flags inverted	210,000.00	57,500.00
	Double grill	—	900.00
122	90¢ Lincoln	7,250.00	2,000.00
	Split grill	—	—
	Issues of 1875, Reissue of 1869 Issue, Without Grill, Hard, White Paper		
123	1¢ buff (112)	425.00	290.00
124	2¢ brown (113)	525.00	400.00
125	3¢ blue (114)	4,250.00	12,500.00
126	6¢ blue (115)	1,100.00	1,250.00

112

113

114

115

116

117

118

120

121

122

Details

15¢ Landing of Columbus, Types I-III, Series 1869-75

Detail of **#118** Type I

Picture unframed.

Detail of **#119** Type II

Picture framed.

#**129** Type III

Same as Type I but
without fringe of brown
shading lines around
central vignette.

134   **135**   **136**   **137**

138   **139**   **140**   **141**

142   **143**   **144**

156   **157**   **158**

Details

Detail of #**134, 145**

Detail of #**135, 146**

Detail of #**136, 147**

Detail of #**156, 167, 182, 192**

Detail of #**157, 168, 178, 180, 183, 193**

Detail of #**158, 169, 184, 194**

1¢. In the pearl at the left of the numeral "1" there is a small crescent.

2¢. Under the scroll at the left of "U.S." there is small diagonal line. This mark seldom shows clearly.

3¢. The under part of the upper tail of the left ribbon is heavily shaded.

	Issues of 1875, Perf. 12	Un	U
127	10¢ yellow (116)	1,750.00	1,400.00
128	12¢ green (117)	1,900.00	2,250.00
129	15¢ brown and blue, type III (118)	1,600.00	900.00
a	Imperf. horizontally	2,500.00	—
130	24¢ grn. & violet (120)	1,600.00	1,050.00
131	30¢ bl. & carmine (121)	2,100.00	2,000.00
132	90¢ car. & black (122)	4,750.00	4,500.00

Issue of 1880, Reissue of 1869 Issue, Soft, Porous Paper

		Un	U
133	1¢ buff (112)	250.00	170.00
a	1¢ brown orange, issued without gum	210.00	150.00

Issues of 1870-71

With Grill, White Wove Paper, No Secret Marks

H. Grill about 10 x 12mm

		Un	U
134	1¢ Franklin, April 1870	1,300.00	90.00
	End roller grill		425.00
135	2¢ Jackson, April 1870	800.00	52.50
136	3¢ Washington	550.00	15.00
	Cracked plate	—	75.00
137	6¢ Lincoln, April 1870	3,000.00	425.00
	Double grill	—	725.00
138	7¢ Edwin M. Stanton	2,100.00	375.00
139	10¢ Jefferson	3,250.00	600.00
140	12¢ Henry Clay	18,000.00	2,750.00
141	15¢ Daniel Webster	4,000.00	950.00
142	24¢ Gen. Winfield Scott	—	8,000.00
143	30¢ Alexander Hamilton	8,500.00	1,400.00
144	90¢ Commodore Perry	9,500.00	1,200.00
	Split grill		1,250.00

	Issues of 1870-71	Un	U

Without Grill, White Wove Paper, No Secret Marks

		Un	U
145	1¢ ultra. Franklin (134)	325.00	12.00
146	2¢ red brn. Jackson (135)	240.00	7.50
147	3¢ grn. Washington (136)	240.00	1.10
148	6¢ carmine Lincoln (137)	500.00	20.00
	6¢ violet carmine	525.00	25.00
149	7¢ verm. Stanton (138)	575.00	80.00
150	10¢ brown Jefferson (139)	500.00	17.50
151	12¢ dull violet Clay (140)	1,200.00	110.00
152	15¢ brt. or. Webster (141)	1,200.00	110.00
153	24¢ purple Scott (142)	1,200.00	120.00
154	30¢ black Hamilton (143)	2,500.00	145.00
155	90¢ carmine Perry (144)	2,500.00	240.00

Comparison of Issue of 1870-71: Printed by National Bank Note Company. Issued without secret marks (#134-41, 145-52, 187) and Issues of 1873-80: Printed by Continental and American Bank Note Companies. Issued with secret marks (156-63, 167-74, 178, 180, 182-184, 186, 188-90, 192-99).

Issues of 1873, Without Grill, White Wove Paper, Thin to Thick, Secret Marks

		Un	U
156	1¢ ultra. Franklin	180.00	2.50
	Paper with silk fibers	—	20.00
f	Imperf. pair	—	550.00
157	2¢ br. Jackson	325.00	15.00
	Double paper	425.00	30.00
c	With grill	1,500.00	700.00
158	3¢ gr. Washington	110.00	.30
	3¢ olive green	130.00	3.00
	Cracked plate	—	32.50

Remembering a naval hero

On September 10, 1813, during the War of 1812, U.S. naval officer Oliver Perry strategically orchestrated a fleet of nine American vessels a few miles northwest of Put-in-Bay—defeating and capturing a flotilla of six British ships. This victory in the Battle of Lake Erie caused a major momentum shift in the war as it greatly deflated the British naval power on Lake Erie and brought new life to the struggling American defense after a series of defeats. A century later, a monument constructed in Commodore Perry's honor was finished just 10 miles southeast of the battlesite. Perry's Victory and International Peace Memorial was declared a national monument on June 2, 1936, by proclamation of President Franklin D. Roosevelt, symbolizing nearly two centuries of peace between the United States and Canada. **(#144)**

Issues of 1873	Un	U
Without Grill, White Wove Paper, Thin to Thick, Secret Marks		
159 6¢ dull pk. Lincoln	375.00	15.00
b With grill	1,400.00	
160 7¢ or. verm. Stanton	800.00	75.00
Ribbed paper	—	90.00
161 10¢ br. Jefferson	525.00	16.00
162 12¢ bl. vio. Clay	1,350.00	85.00
163 15¢ yel. or. Webster	1,350.00	85.00
a With grill	4,000.00	
164 24¢ pur. Scott		—
165 30¢ gray blk. Hamilton	1,500.00	80.00
166 90¢ rose carm. Perry	2,250.00	230.00
Issues of 1875, Special Printing, Hard, White Wove Paper, Without Gum, Secret Marks		
Although perforated, these stamps were usually cut apart with scissors. As a result, the perforations are often much mutilated and the design is frequently damaged.		
167 1¢ ultra. Franklin (156)	8,500.00	
168 2¢ dk. br. Jackson (157)	3,900.00	
169 3¢ blue green Washington (158)	10,500.00	—
170 6¢ dull rose Lincoln (159)	9,250.00	
171 7¢ reddish vermilion Stanton (160)	2,200.00	
172 10¢ pale brown Jefferson (161)	9,000.00	
173 12¢ dark vio. Clay (162)	3,250.00	

Issues of 1875	Un	U
174 15¢ bright orange Webster (163)	9,000.00	
175 24¢ dull pur. Scott (142)	2,000.00	—
176 30¢ greenish black Hamilton (143)	6,500.00	
177 90¢ vio. car. Perry (144)	8,250.00	
Regular Issue, Yellowish Wove Paper		
178 2¢ verm. Jackson (157)	300.00	7.50
c With grill	400.00	
179 5¢ Zachary Taylor, June	400.00	14.00
Cracked plate	—	130.00
Double paper	475.00	
c With grill	750.00	
Paper with silk fibers	—	22.50
Special Printing, Hard, White Wove Paper, Without Gum		
180 2¢ carmine vermilion Jackson (157)	24,000.00	
181 5¢ br. bl. Taylor (179)	36,500.00	
Issues of 1879, Soft, Porous Paper, Thin to Thick		
182 1¢ dark ultramarine Franklin (156)	225.00	2.00
183 2¢ verm. Jackson (157)	110.00	2.00
a Double impression	—	500.00

Who is famous for the words, "Liberty *and* Union, now and forever, one and inseparable!"?

Daniel Webster was one of the early 19th century's strongest advocates of American nationalism. He graduated from Dartmouth College in 1801 and opened his law practice in Portsmouth, New Hampshire, in 1807. As a Federalist Party leader, Webster served in the House of Representatives from 1813 to 1817. He returned to government in 1827 as a senator from Massachusetts, and it was in 1830 during a Senate debate over a high-tariff bill that Webster defended the Union with the words, "Liberty *and* Union, now and forever, one and inseparable!"

In a speech before the Senate on March 7, 1850, he supported the Compromise of 1850, denouncing the Southern threats of secession but urging Northern support for a stronger law for the recovery of fugitive slaves. Webster's stand alienated antislavery forces but helped preserve the Union. **(#163)**

159

160

161

162

163

179

Details

Detail of **#137, 148**

Detail of **#138, 149**

Detail of **#139, 150, 187**

Detail of **#159, 170, 186, 195**

6¢.The first four vertical lines of the shading in the lower part of the left ribbon have been strengthened.

Detail of **#160, 171, 196**

7¢. Two small semicircles are drawn around the ends of the lines that outline the ball in the lower righthand corner.

Detail of **#161, 172, 188, 197**

10¢. There is a small semi-circle in the scroll at the right end of the upper label.

Detail of **#140, 151**

Detail of **#141, 152**

Detail of **#143, 154, 165, 176**

Detail of **#162, 173, 198**

12¢. The balls of the figure "2" are crescent-shaped.

Detail of **#163, 174, 189, 199**

15¢. In the lower part of the triangle in the upper left corner two lines have been made heavier, forming a "V". This mark can be found on some of the Continental and American (1879) printings, but not all

Detail of **#143, 154, 165, 176**

Detail of **#190**

30¢. In the "S" of "CENTS," the vertical spike across the middle section of the letter has been broadened.

75

205 **206** **207** **208**

209 **210** **211** **212**

219 **220** **221** **222** **223** **224**

225 **226** **227** **228** **229**

Details

Issues of 1881-82, Re-engravings of 1873 Designs

Detail of **#206**

1¢. Upper vertical lines have been deepened, creating a solid effect in parts of background. Upper arabesques shaded.

Detail of #207

3¢. Shading at sides of central oval is half its previous width. A short horizontal dash has been cut below th "TS" of "CENTS."

Detail of **#208**

6¢. Has three vertical lines instead of four between the edge of the panel and the outside of the stamp.

Detail of #209

10¢. Has four vertical lines instead of five between left side of oval and edge of the shield. Horizontal lines in lower part of background strengthened.

Issues of 1879, Perf. 12	Un	U
184 3¢ grn. Washington (158)	85.00	.25
Double transfer	—	4.25
Short transfer	—	5.50
185 5¢ blue Taylor (179)	425.00	12.00
186 6¢ pink Lincoln (159)	750.00	17.50
187 10¢ brown Jefferson (139) (no secret mark)	1,450.00	22.50
188 10¢ brown Jefferson (161) (with secret mark)	1,100.00	22.50
10¢ black brown	1,200.00	35.00
Double transfer		40.00
189 15¢ red or. Webster (163)	300.00	21.00
190 30¢ full blk. Hamilton (143)	850.00	50.00
191 90¢ carmine Perry (144)	1,750.00	220.00

Issues of 1880, Special Printing, Soft, Porous Paper, Without Gum

	Un	U
192 1¢ dark ultramarine Franklin (156)	11,000.00	
193 2¢ blk. br. Jackson (157)	6,500.00	
194 3¢ blue green Washington (158)	16,250.00	
195 6¢ dull rose Lincoln (159)	12,500.00	
196 7¢ scarlet vermilion Stanton (160)	2,450.00	
197 10¢ deep brown Jefferson (161)	11,000.00	
198 12¢ blk. pur. Clay (162)	4,000.00	
199 15¢ or. Webster (163)	12,500.00	
200 24¢ dk. vio. Scott (142)	4,000.00	
201 30¢ greenish black Hamilton (143)	9,000.00	
202 90¢ dull carmine Perry (144)	10,000.00	
203 2¢ scarlet vermilion Jackson (157)	20,000.00	
204 5¢ dp. bl. Taylor (179)	35,000.00	

Issues of 1882

	Un	U
205 5¢ Garfield, Apr. 10	190.00	6.00

Special Printing, Soft, Porous Paper, Without Gum

	Un	U
205C 5¢ gray brown Garfield (205)	20,000.00	

Issues of 1881-82, Designs of 1873 Re-engraved

	Un	U
206 1¢ Franklin, Aug. 1881	55.00	.60
Double transfer	70.00	4.00
207 3¢ Washington, July 16, 1881	60.00	.30
Double transfer	—	7.50
Cracked plate	—	
208 6¢ Lincoln, June 1882	400.00	60.00
a 6¢ brown red	350.00	85.00
209 10¢ Jefferson, Apr. 1882	120.00	3.50
10¢ pur. or olive brown	130.00	3.75
b 10¢ black brown	275.00	22.50

Issues of 1883, Perf. 12	Un	U
210 2¢ Washington, Oct. 1	45.00	.25
Double transfer	50.00	1.30
211 4¢ Jackson, Oct. 1	200.00	10.00
Cracked plate	—	

Special Printing, Soft, Porous Paper

	Un	U
211B 2¢ pale red brown Washington (210)	650.00	—
c Horizontal pair, imperf. between	2,250.00	
211D 4¢ deep blue green Jackson (211) no gum	17,000.00	

Issues of 1887

	Un	U
212 1¢ Franklin, June	90.00	1.00
Double transfer		—
213 2¢ green Washington (210), Sept. 10	35.00	.30
b Printed on both sides		—
Double transfer	—	3.00
214 3¢ vermilion Washington (207), Oct. 3	65.00	45.00

Issues of 1888

	Un	U
215 4¢ carmine Jackson (211), Nov.	200.00	15.00
216 5¢ indigo Garfield (205), Feb.	200.00	8.50
217 30¢ orange brown Hamilton (165), Jan.	425.00	90.00
218 90¢ pur. Perry (166), Feb. 1	1,100.00	190.00

Issues of 1890-93

	Un	U
219 1¢ Franklin, Feb. 22, 1890	25.00	.25
Double transfer	—	—
219D 2¢ lake Washington (220), Feb. 22, 1890	190.00	.60
Double transfer	—	—
220 2¢ Washington, 1890	20.00	.25
a Cap on left "2"	65.00	2.00
c Cap on both "2s"	190.00	15.00
Double transfer	—	3.00
221 3¢ Jackson, Feb. 22, 1890	65.00	6.00
222 4¢ Lincoln, June 2, 1890	67.50	2.25
Double transfer	82.50	—
223 5¢ Grant, June 2, 1890	65.00	2.25
Double transfer	80.00	2.50
224 6¢ Garfield, Feb. 22, 1890	67.50	18.00
225 8¢ Sherman, Mar. 21, 1893	52.50	11.00
226 10¢ Webster, Feb. 22, 1890	140.00	2.75
Double transfer	—	—
227 15¢ Clay, Feb. 22, 1890	180.00	18.00
Double transfer	—	—
Triple transfer	—	
228 30¢ Jefferson, Feb. 22, 1890	300.00	25.00
Double transfer	—	—
229 90¢ Perry, Feb. 22, 1890	450.00	115.00
Short transfer at bottom	—	—

	Issues of 1893, Perf. 12		Un	U	PB	#	FDC	Q(M̄)
	Columbian Exposition Issue, Printed by The American Bank Note Co.							
230	1¢ Columbus in Sight of Land	01/02/93	25.00	.40	350.00	(6)	*3,500.00*	449
	Double transfer		30.00	.75				
	Cracked plate		95.00					
231	2¢ Landing of Columbus	01/02/93	22.50	.20	275.00	(6)	3,000.00	1,464
	Double transfer		27.50	.30				
	Triple transfer		67.50	—				
	Quadruple transfer		100.00					
	Broken hat on third figure left of Columbus		65.00	.30				
	Broken frame line		24.00	.25				
	Recut frame lines		24.00	—				
	Cracked plate		95.00	—				
232	3¢ *Santa Maria,* Flagship	01/02/93	62.50	15.00	750.00	(6)	6,000.00	12
	Double transfer		82.50	—				
233	4¢ ultramarine, Fleet	01/02/93	87.50	7.50	1,050.00	(6)	9,500.00	19
a	4¢ blue (error)		*16,000.00*	*5,500.00*	*72,500.00*	(4)		
	Double transfer		125.00	—				
234	5¢ Columbus Soliciting Aid from Isabella	01/02/93	95.00	8.00	1,400.00	(6)	*16,000.00*	35
	Double transfer		145.00	—				
235	6¢ Columbus Welcomed at Barcelona	01/02/93	90.00	22.50			*20,000.00*	5
a	6¢ red violet		90.00	22.50	1,250.00	(6)		
	Double transfer		115.00	30.00				
236	8¢ Restored to Favor	03/93	80.00	11.00	875.00	(6)		11
	Double transfer		92.50	—				
237	10¢ Presenting Natives	01/02/93	135.00	8.00	3,250.00	(6)	—	17
	Double transfer		175.00	12.50				
	Triple transfer		—					
238	15¢ Columbus Announcing His Discovery	01/02/93	240.00	65.00	*3,750.00*	(6)		2
	Double transfer		—	—				
239	30¢ Columbus at La Rábida	01/02/93	300.00	85.00	*8,500.00*	(6)		0.6
240	50¢ Recall of Columbus	01/02/93	600.00	160.00	*13,000.00*	(6)		0.2
	Double transfer		—	—				
	Triple transfer		—	—				
241	$1 Isabella Pledging Her Jewels	01/02/93	1,500.00	650.00	*45,000.00*	(6)		0.05
	Double transfer		—	—				
242	$2 Columbus in Chains	01/02/93	1,550.00	600.00	*65,000.00*	(6)	*50,000.00*	0.05
243	$3 Columbus Describing His Third Voyage	01/02/93	2,400.00	975.00				0.03
a	$3 olive green		2,400.00	975.00	*85,000.00*	(6)		
244	$4 Isabella and Columbus	01/02/93	3,250.00	1,350.00				0.03
a	$4 rose carmine		3,250.00	1,350.00	*240,000.00*	(6)		
245	$5 Portrait of Columbus	01/02/93	3,750.00	1,600.00	*190,000.00*	(6)		0.03

230   231   232

233   234   235

236   237   238

239   240   241

242   243   244

245

246   **248**   **253**

254   **255**   **256**

257   **258**   **259**

Details

2¢ Washington Types I-III, Series 1894-98

Triangle of **#248-50, 265**
Type I

Horizontal lines of
uniform thickness run
across the triangle.

Triangle of **#251, 266**
Type II

Horizontal lines cross the
triangle, but are thinner
within than without.

Triangle of **#252, 267,
279B-279Be** Type III

The horizontal lines do
not cross the double
frame lines of the triangle.

Issues of 1894		Un	U	PB	#
Unwmkd., Perf. 12					

Bureau Issues Starting in 1894 and continuing until 1979, the Bureau of Engraving and Printing in Washington produced all U.S. postage stamps except #909-21, 1335, 1355, 1410-18 and 1789. Beginning in 1979, security printers in addition to the Bureau of Engraving and Printing started producing postage stamps under contract with the U.S. Postal Service.

#	Description	Date	Un	U	PB	#
246	1¢ Franklin	10/94	27.50	4.00	300.00	(6)
	Double transfer		32.50	5.00		
247	1¢ blue Franklin (246)	11/94	60.00	2.00	575.00	(6)
	Double transfer		—	3.50		
248	2¢ pink Washington, type I	10/94	25.00	3.00	225.00	(6)
	Double transfer		—	—		
249	2¢ carmine lake, type I (248)	10/94	125.00	2.25	1,250.00	(6)
	Double transfer		—	2.75		
250	2¢ carmine, type I (248)		27.50	.50	275.00	(6)
a	Vertical pair, imperf. horizontally		*1,500.00*			
b	Horizontal pair, imperf. between		*1,500.00*			
	Double transfer		—	1.50		
251	2¢ carmine, type II (248)		200.00	3.50	2,100.00	(6)
252	2¢ carmine, type III (248)		110.00	3.75	1,250.00	(6)
a	Horizontal pair, imperf. horizontally		*1,350.00*			
b	Horizontal pair, imperf. veritcally		*1,500.00*			
253	3¢ Jackson	09/94	95.00	8.00	1,000.00	(6)
254	4¢ Lincoln	09/94	120.00	3.75	1,200.00	(6)
255	5¢ Grant	09/94	85.00	4.75	825.00	(6)
c	Vertical pair, imperf. horiz.		*1,350.00*		—	
	Worn plate, diagonal lines missing in oval background		100.00	5.50		
	Double transfer		105.00	5.50		
256	6¢ Garfield	07/94	135.00	21.00	2,100.00	(6)
a	Vertical pair, imperf. horizontally		*850.00*		12,500.00	(6)
257	8¢ Sherman	03/94	130.00	14.00	1,200.00	(6)
258	10¢ Webster	09/94	200.00	10.00	2,100.00	(6)
	Double transfer		230.00	11.50		
259	15¢ Clay	10/94	260.00	45.00	3,400.00	(6)

Who is considered one of the most hated men in Georgia's history?

Union General William Tecumseh Sherman, who created mass destruction during the Civil War with his 1864 "Atlanta Campaign," is known to be one of the most unpopular men in the history of Georgia. General Sherman and his men captured Atlanta and then Savannah on their "March to the Sea" in late 1864, which split the Confederate army and ensured a quick Union victory. Born on February 8, 1820, in Lancaster, Ohio, Sherman graduated from the U.S. Military Academy at West Point in 1840. Records show that during their campaign through South Carolina, Union soldiers spared a particular home from destruction when they learned the mistress of the home was the daughter of an old friend of Sherman's. **(#257)**

	Issues of 1894, Unwmkd., Perf. 12		Un	U	PB	#
260	50¢ Jefferson	11/94	375.00	95.00	5,000.00	(6)
261	$1 Perry, type I	11/94	800.00	250.00	*15,000.00*	(6)
261A	$1 black Perry, type II (261)	11/94	1,900.00	550.00	*25,000.00*	(6)
262	$2 James Madison	12/94	2,600.00	825.00	*32,500.00*	(6)
263	$5 John Marshall	12/94	4,000.00	1,750.00	*18,500.00*	(4)
	Issues of 1895, Wmkd. (191)					
264	1¢ blue Franklin (246)	04/95	5.50	.25	175.00	(6)
265	2¢ carmine Washington, type I (248)	05/95	27.50	.80	340.00	(6)
	Double transfer		40.00	3.25		
266	2¢ carmine, type II (248)		27.50	3.00	340.00	(6)
267	2¢ carmine, type III (248)		4.50	.25	135.00	(6)
	Triple transfer		—			
	Triangle at right without shading		22.50	6.00		
268	3¢ purple Jackson (253)	10/95	35.00	1.10	500.00	(6)
	Double transfer		42.50	2.75		
269	4¢ dark brown Lincoln (254)	06/95	37.50	1.60	525.00	(6)
	Double transfer		42.50	3.00		
270	5¢ chocolate Grant (255)	06/11/95	35.00	1.90	475.00	(6)
	Double transfer		42.50	3.25		
	Worn plate, diagonal lines missing in oval background		37.50	2.50		
271	6¢ dull brown Garfield (256)	08/95	75.00	4.25	1,400.00	(6)
	Very thin paper		85.00	4.50		
a	Wmkd. USIR		*2,250.00*	400.00		
272	8¢ violet brown Sherman (257)	07/95	55.00	1.25	625.00	(6)
a	Wmkd. USIR		1,750.00	110.00	*5,500.00*	(3)
	Double transfer		67.50	2.75		
273	10¢ dark green Webster (258)	06/95	75.00	1.50	1,000.00	(6)
	Double transfer		90.00	3.50		
274	15¢ dark blue Clay (259)	09/95	190.00	9.00	2,500.00	(6)
275	50¢ orange Jefferson (260)	11/95	260.00	20.00	5,000.00	(6)
a	50¢ red orange		290.00	24.00	5,250.00	(6)
276	$1 black Perry, type I (261)	08/95	600.00	65.00	*10,000.00*	(6)
276A	$1 black Perry, type II (261)	08/95	1,200.00	140.00	*22,500.00*	(6)
277	$2 bright blue Madison (262)	08/95	975.00	300.00	*16,000.00*	(6)
a	$2 dark blue		975.00	300.00		
278	$5 dark green Marshall (263)	08/95	2,250.00	425.00	*67,500.00*	(6)

260   261

262   263

277

Watermark 191
Double-line "USPS"
in capital letters;
detail at right.

Details

$1 Perry, Types I-II, Series 1894

Detail of **#261, 276** Type I

The circles enclosing $1 are broken.

Detail of **#261A, 276A** Type I

The circles enclosing $1 are complete.

	Issues of 1898-1900		Un	U	PB	#	FDC	Q(M)
	Wmkd. (191), Perf. 12							
279	1¢ deep grn. Franklin (246)	01/98	9.00	.25	175.00	(6)		
	Double transfer		12.00	.85				
279B	2¢ red Washington, type III (248)	01/98	9.00	.25	175.00	(6)		
c	2¢ rose carmine, type III		225.00	65.00	2,500.00	(6)		
d	2¢ orange red, type III		10.00	.30	190.00	(6)		
e	Booklet pane of 6	04/16/00	400.00	350.00				
f	2¢ deep red, type III		13.50	1.00	260.00	(6)		
280	4¢ rose brn. Lincoln (254)	10/98	30.00	.90				
a	4¢ lilac brown		30.00	.90				
b	4¢ orange brown		30.00	.90	550.00	(6)		
	Extra frame line at top		50.00	4.00				
281	5¢ dark blue Grant (255)	03/98	35.00	.75	550.00	(6)		
	Double transfer		45.00	2.00				
	Worn plate, diagonal lines missing in oval background		40.00	.90				
282	6¢ lake Garfield (256)	12/98	45.00	2.50	800.00	(6)		
a	6¢ purple lake		55.00	3.50	950.00	(6)		
	Double transfer		57.50	3.50				
282C	10¢ brown Webster (258), type I	11/98	180.00	2.50	2,000.00	(6)		
	Double transfer		200.00	4.25				
283	10¢ orange brown Webster (258), type II		110.00	2.00	1,150.00	(6)		
284	15¢ olive grn. Clay (259)	11/98	150.00	7.50	2,000.00	(6)		
	Issues of 1898, Trans-Mississippi Exposition Issue							
285	1¢ Marquette on the Mississippi	06/17/98	27.50	6.00	300.00	(6)	*11,000.00*	71
	Double transfer		40.00	7.25				
286	2¢ Farming in the West	06/17/98	25.00	1.50	275.00	(6)	*11,000.00*	160
	Double transfer		37.50	2.25				
	Worn plate		27.50	1.75				
287	4¢ Indian Hunting Buffalo	06/17/98	140.00	21.00	1,400.00	(6)	*27,500.00*	5
288	5¢ Frémont on the Rocky Mountains	06/17/98	130.00	19.00	1,300.00	(6)	*16,000.00*	8
289	8¢ Troops Guarding Wagon Train	06/17/98	175.00	37.50	2,750.00	(6)	—	3
a	Vertical pair, imperf. horizontally		*17,500.00*		*70,000.00*	(4)		
290	10¢ Hardships of Emigration	06/17/98	170.00	22.50	3,000.00	(6)	*27,500.00*	5
291	50¢ Western Mining Prospector	06/17/98	550.00	170.00	*20,000.00*	(6)	—	0.5
292	$1 Western Cattle in Storm	06/17/98	1,250.00	500.00	*45,000.00*	(6)	—	0.06
293	$2 Mississippi River Bridge	06/17/98	2,100.00	850.00	*130,000.00*	(6)		0.06

282C

285

286

287

288

289

290

291

292

293

Details

10¢ Webster Types I-II, Series 1898

Detail of **#282C** Type I

The tips of the foliate ornaments do not impinge on the white curved line below "TEN CENTS."

Detail of **#283** Type II

The tips of the ornaments break the curved line below the "E" of "TEN" and the "T" of "CENTS."

The United States Postal Service is proudly celebrating 25 years of service to the collecting community with this 25th edition of *The Postal Service Guide to U.S. Stamps (The Guide)*.

For more than a quarter of a century, The Guide—known as *Stamps & Stories* until the name was changed in 1983—has provided illustrated stories of some of the important people, places and events shown on stamps. Originally, *Stamps & Stories* was edited and published for the Postal Service by Scott Publishing. At that time, *Stamps & Stories* displayed all U.S. stamps as well as stamps issued by the United Nations, the Confederate States of America, the Canal Zone, Guam, Hawaii, Puerto Rico and the Philippines. Since the Postal Service assumed complete responsibility for production of *The Guide*, listings for stamps other than U.S. stamps have gradually been eliminated.

Over the years, the responsibility for editing *The Guide* has fallen to Bill LaFevre, Cathy Caggiano, Bill Halstead, Joe Brockert and Louise Smith. Almost since the beginning, the responsibility for printing *The Guide* has been assumed by R.R. Donnelley & Sons.

294

295

296

297

298

299

300

301

302

303

304

305

306

307

308

309

310

311

312

313

	Issues of 1901-03		Un	U	PB	#	FDC	Q(M̄)
	Issues of 1901, Pan-American Exposition Issue							
294	1¢ Great Lakes Steamer	05/01/01	19.00	3.00	250.00	(6)	*4,500.00*	91
a	Center inverted		*10,000.00*	*6,500.00*	*42,500.00*	(4)		
295	2¢ An Early Locomotive	05/01/01	18.00	1.00	250.00	(6)	*2,750.00*	210
a	Center inverted		*37,500.00*	*16,000.00*	*275,000.00*	(4)		
296	4¢ Automobile	05/01/01	85.00	15.00	2,500.00	(6)	*4,250.00*	6
a	Center inverted		*17,000.00*		*90,000.00*	(4)		
297	5¢ Bridge at Niagara Falls	05/01/01	100.00	14.00	2,750.00	(6)	*15,000.00*	7
298	8¢ Canal Locks at Sault Ste. Marie	05/01/01	125.00	50.00	*4,500.00*	(6)	*12,500.00*	5
299	10¢ American Line Steamship	05/01/01	175.00	25.00	7,250.00	(6)		5
	Wmkd. (191), Perf. 12 (All issued in 1903 except #300b, 306, 308)							
300	1¢ Franklin	02/03	9.00	.20	160.00	(6)		
b	Booklet pane of 6	03/06/07	550.00	—				
	Double transfer		12.00	1.00				
	Worn plate		9.00	.30				
	Cracked plate		9.00	.30				
301	2¢ Washington	01/17/03	12.50	.20	185.00	(6)	*2,750.00*	
c	Booklet pane of 6	01/24/03	450.00	—				
	Double transfer		19.00	1.00				
	Cracked plate		—	1.00				
302	3¢ Jackson	02/03	50.00	2.75	650.00	(6)		
	Double transfer		70.00	3.75				
	Cracked plate		—	—				
303	4¢ Grant	02/03	55.00	1.25	675.00	(6)		
	Double transfer		67.50	2.75				
304	5¢ Lincoln	01/03	55.00	1.50	675.00	(6)		
305	6¢ Garfield	02/03	65.00	2.50	775.00	(6)		
	6¢ brownish lake		62.50	2.50				
	Double transfer		67.50	3.50				
306	8¢ M. Washington	12/02	40.00	2.00	600.00	(6)		
	8¢ lavender		47.50	2.75				
307	10¢ Webster	02/03	60.00	1.40	825.00	(6)		
308	13¢ B. Harrison	11/18/02	45.00	7.50	560.00	(6)		
309	15¢ Clay	05/27/03	150.00	4.75	2,500.00	(6)		
	Double transfer		180.00	9.00				
310	50¢ Jefferson	03/23/03	400.00	22.50	*6,000.00*	(6)		
311	$1 David G. Farragut	06/05/03	700.00	55.00	*13,000.00*	(6)		
312	$2 Madison	06/05/03	1,100.00	170.00	*24,000.00*	(6)		
313	$5 Marshall	06/05/03	2,750.00	650.00	*50,000.00*	(6)		

For listings of #312 and 313 with perf. 10, see #479 and 480.

Issues of 1906-08			Un	U	PB/LP	#	FDC	Q(M̄)
	Imperf. (All issued in 1908 except #314)							
314	1¢ bl. grn. Franklin (300)	10/02/06	21.00	15.00	180.00	(6)		
314A	4¢ brown Grant (303)	04/08	25,000.00	20,000.00				
	#314A was issued imperforated, but all copies were privately perforated at the sides.							
315	5¢ blue Lincoln (304)	05/12/08	325.00	425.00	3,000.00	(6)		
	Coil Stamps, Perf. 12 Horizontally							
316	1¢ bl. grn. pair Franklin (300)	02/18/08	90,000.00	—	125,000.00	(2)		
317	5¢ blue pair Lincoln (304)	02/24/08	10,000.00	—	22,500.00	(2)		
	Coil Stamp, Perf. 12 Vertically							
318	1¢ bl. grn. pair Franklin (300)	07/31/08	6,500.00	—	12,500.00	(2)		
	Issues of 1903, Perf. 12							
319	2¢ Washington	11/12/03	4.75	.15	85.00	(6)		
a	2¢ lake, type I		—	—				
b	2¢ carmine rose, type I		6.50	.35	125.00	(6)		
c	2¢ scarlet, type I		4.75	.25	75.00	(6)		
d	Vertical pair, imperf. horizontally		3,000.00					
e	Vertical pair, imperf. between		950.00					
f	2¢ lake, type II		6.25	.25	175.00	(6)		
g	Booklet pane of 6, carm., type I,	12/03/03	110.00	150.00				
h	Booklet pane of 6, carm., type II		225.00					
i	2¢ carmine, type II		22.50	50.00				
q	Booklet pane of 6, lake, type II		175.00	250.00				
	Issues of 1906, Washington (319), Imperf.							
320	2¢ carmine	10/02/06	20.00	12.00	225.00	(6)		
a	2¢ lake, die II		50.00	40.00	750.00	(6)		
b	2¢ scarlet		19.00	12.50	225.00	(6)		
	Double transfer		27.50	16.00				
	Issues of 1908, Coil Stamp (319), Perf. 12 Horizontally							
321	2¢ carmine pair	02/18/08	100,000.00	110,000.00	—			
	Coil Stamp, Perf. 12 Vertically							
322	2¢ carmine pair	07/31/08	7,500.00	5,000.00	8,500.00	(2)		
	Issues of 1904, Louisiana Purchase Exposition Issue, Perf. 12							
323	1¢ Robert R. Livingston	04/30/04	30.00	3.75	275.00	(6)	6,000.00	80
	Diagonal line through left "1"		50.00	11.00				
324	2¢ Thomas Jefferson	04/30/04	27.50	1.50	275.00	(6)	4,500.00	193
325	3¢ James Monroe	04/30/04	90.00	30.00	950.00	(6)	5,000.00	5
326	5¢ William McKinley	04/30/04	95.00	20.00	1,000.00	(6)	22,500.00	7
327	10¢ Map of Louisiana Purchase	04/30/04	180.00	27.50	2,250.00	(6)	24,000.00	4
	Issues of 1907, Jamestown Exposition Issue, Wmkd. (191), Perf. 12							
328	1¢ Captain John Smith	04/26/07	27.50	4.00	250.00	(6)	4,500.00	78
	Double transfer		32.50	5.00				
329	2¢ Founding of Jamestown, 1607	04/26/07	32.50	3.50	350.00	(6)	6,000.00	149
330	5¢ Pocahontas	04/26/07	130.00	27.50	2,500.00	(6)		8

319

323

324

325

326

325   326   327

328   329

330

Details

2¢ Washington Die I-II, Series 1903

Detail of **#319a, 319b, 319g** Die I

Detail of **#319c, 319f, 319h, 319i** Die II

331

332

333

334

335

337

338

339

340

341

342

Details

3¢ Washington Types I-IV, Series 1908-19

Detail of #**333, 345, 359, 376, 389, 394, 426, 445, 456, 464, 483, 493, 501-01b** Type I

Top line of toga rope is weak and rope shading lines are thin. Fifth line from left is missing. Line between lips is thin.

Detail of #**484, 494, 502, 541** Type II

Top line of toga rope is strong and rope shading lines are heavy and complete. Line between lips is heavy.

Detail of #**529** Type III

Top row of toga rope is strong but fifth shading line is missing as in Type I. Toga button center shading line consists of two dashes, central dot. "P," "O" of "POSTAGE" are separated by line of color.

Detail of #**530, 535** Type IV

Toga rope shading lines are complete. Second, fourth toga button shading lines are broken in middle, third line is continuous with dot in center. "P," "O" of "POSTAGE" are joined.

	Issues of 1908-09		Un	U	PB/LP	#
	Wmkd. (191) Perf. 126 (All issued in 1908 except #336, 338-42, 345-47)					
331	1¢ Franklin	12/08	6.50	.15	70.00	(6)
a	Booklet pane of 6	12/02/08	150.00	*125.00*		
	Double transfer		8.50	.60		
332	2¢ Washington	11/08	6.00	.15	62.50	(6)
a	Booklet pane of 6	11/16/08	130.00	*125.00*		
	Double transfer		11.00	—		
	Cracked plate		—	—		
333	3¢ Washington, type I	12/08	30.00	2.50	300.00	(6)
334	4¢ Washington	12/08	37.50	1.00	375.00	(6)
	Double transfer		50.00	—		
335	5¢ Washington	12/08	47.50	2.00	475.00	(6)
336	6¢ Washington	01/09	60.00	5.00	700.00	(6)
337	8¢ Washington	12/08	45.00	2.50	450.00	(6)
	Double transfer		52.50	—		
338	10¢ Washington	01/09	65.00	1.40	775.00	(6)
a	"China Clay" paper		*900.00*			
	Very thin paper		—			
339	13¢ Washington	01/09	37.50	19.00	450.00	(6)
	Line through "TAG" of "POSTAGE"		60.00	—		
340	15¢ Washington	01/09	62.50	5.50	575.00	(6)
a	"China Clay" paper		*900.00*			
341	50¢ Washington	01/13/09	300.00	17.50	*6,500.00*	(6)
342	$1 Washington	01/29/09	475.00	70.00	*13,000.00*	(6)
	Imperf.					
343	1¢ green Franklin (331)	12/08	6.50	4.50	60.00	(6)
	Double transfer		12.50	7.00		
344	2¢ carmine Washington (332)	12/10/08	8.00	3.00	95.00	(6)
	Double transfer		13.50	4.00		
	Foreign entry, design of 1¢		*1,250.00*	—		
	#345-47: Washington (333-35)					
345	3¢ deep violet, type I	1809	15.00	20.00	190.00	(6)
	Double transfer		25.00	—		
346	4¢ orange brown	02/25/09	25.00	22.50	220.00	(6)
	Double transfer		45.00	—		
347	5¢ blue	02/25/09	45.00	32.50	375.00	(6)
	Cracked plate		—			
	Issues of 1908-10, Coil Stamps, Perf. 12 Horizontally					
	#350-51, 354-56: Washington (Designs of 334-35, 338)					
348	1¢ green Franklin (331)	12/29/08	27.50	14.00	210.00	(2)
349	2¢ carmine Washington (332)	01/09	50.00	8.00	350.00	(2)
	Foreign entry, design of 1¢		—	*1,750.00*		
350	4¢ orange brown	08/15/10	120.00	85.00	875.00	(2)
351	5¢ blue	01/09	130.00	110.00	900.00	(2)
	Issues of 1909, Coil Stamps, Perf. 12 Vertically					
352	1¢ green Franklin (331)	01/09	60.00	32.50	450.00	(2)
	Double transfer		—	—		

	Issues of 1909		Un	U	PB/LP	#	FDC	Q(M̄)
	Coil Stamps, Perf. 12 Vertically							
353	2¢ carmine Washington (332)	01/12/09	60.00	9.00	450.00	(2)		
354	4¢ orange brown	02/23/09	150.00	65.00	1,100.00	(2)		
355	5¢ blue	02/23/09	160.00	85.00	1,100.00	(2)		
356	10¢ yellow	01/07/09	2,150.00	1,000.00	8,500.00	(2)		
	Bluish Paper, Perf. 12, #359-66: Washington (Designs of 333-40)							
357	1¢ green Franklin (331)	02/16/09	95.00	95.00	1,000.00	(6)		
358	2¢ carmine Washington (332)	02/16/09	90.00	80.00	975.00	(6)		
	Double transfer		—					
359	3¢ deep violet, type I	1909	1,800.00	2,000.00	17,500.00	(6)		
360	4¢ orange brown	1909	17,500.00		80,000.00	(3)		
361	5¢ blue	1909	4,500.00	5,000.00	35,000.00	(6)		
362	6¢ red orange	1909	1,350.00	1,500.00	15,000.00	(6)		
363	8¢ olive green	1909	18,500.00		80,000.00	(3)		
364	10¢ yellow	1909	1,600.00	1,750.00	17,000.00	(6)		
365	13¢ blue green	1909	2,800.00	1,900.00	20,000.00	(6)		
366	15¢ pale ultramarine	1909	1,350.00	1,500.00	10,000.00	(6)		
	Lincoln Memorial Issue, Wmkd. (191)							
367	2¢ Bust of Abraham Lincoln	02/12/09	5.50	1.75	150.00	(6)	400.00	148
	Double transfer		7.50	2.50				
	Imperf.							
368	2¢ carmine (367)	02/12/09	22.50	20.00	200.00	(6)	10,000.00	1
	Double transfer		45.00	27.50				
	Bluish Paper							
369	2¢ carmine (367)	02/09	225.00	240.00	2,900.00	(6)		0.6
	Alaska-Yukon Pacific Exposition Issue							
370	2¢ Willam H. Seward	06/01/09	9.00	2.00	225.00	(6)	1,800.00	153
	Double transfer		11.00	4.50				
	Imperf.							
371	2¢ carmine (370)	06/09	30.00	22.50	250.00	(6)		0.5
	Double transfer		42.50	27.50				
	Hudson-Fulton Celebration Issue, Wmkd. (191)							
372	2¢ *Half Moon & Clermont*	09/25/09	13.00	4.50	300.00	(6)	700.00	73
	Double transfer		16.00	4.75				
	Imperf.							
373	2¢ carmine (372)	09/25/09	35.00	25.00	280.00	(6)	—	0.2
	Double transfer		47.50	30.00				
	Issues of 1910-11, Wmkd. (190) #376-82: Washington (Designs of 333-38, 340)							
374	1¢ green Franklin (331)	11/23/10	6.50	.20	75.00	(6)		
a	Booklet pane of 6	10/07/10	140.00	100.00				
	Double transfer		13.00	—				
	Cracked plate		—	—				
375	2¢ carmine Washington (332)	11/23/10	6.50	.20	82.50	(6)		
	2¢ lake		250.00					
a	Booklet pane of 6	11/30/10	95.00	85.00				
	Cracked plate		—	—				
	Double transfer		11.00	—				
	Foreign entry, design of 1¢		—	1,000.00				
376	3¢ deep violet, type I	01/16/11	17.50	1.40	210.00	(6)		

367

370

372

Watermark 190
Single-line "USPS"
in capital letters;
detail at right.

In the face of adversity

President Abraham Lincoln (1809-1865), 16th president of the United States, is considered one of the nation's most influential presidents because of his role in the Civil War and the emancipation of the slaves. However, Lincoln's great accomplishments are especially outstanding in light of the challenges of his personal life during his presidency. He was the father of four sons, and his wife, Mary Todd, was considered high strung and mentally unstable. Less than a year after the start of the Civil War, the President's son, William Wallace, died of typhoid. While Mrs. Lincoln was incapacitated by grief, President Lincoln took care of his family, led the nation through war and worked on the Emancipation Proclamation. A preliminary proclamation was issued only six months after his son's untimely death. (#367)

Interesting Fact: Of Lincoln's four sons, only one, Robert Todd, lived to maturity.

Have you noticed? We expanded the stamp listings. They are now grouped according to historical eras.

Bay for about 200 years before the bay was discovered. (Sir Francis Drake, who landed on the California coast in 1579, may have visited the bay.) Gaspar de Portolá and his scouting party were the first Europeans to see San Francisco Bay, which they discovered by land in 1769. It wasn't until several years later that the bay, one of the world's most impressive natural harbors, was entered from the ocean. In 1775, Juan Manuel de Ayala sailed his ship, the *San Carlos*, through the Golden Gate and proceeded to conduct a preliminary survey of the bay area. Some of the names he assigned to designate sites are still in use today—Sausalito (*Saucelito* or "little thicket of willows") and Alcatraz (*Isla de los Alcatraces* or "island of the pelicans"). (#400)

We redesigned and expanded the new issues just for you! Read about the newest issues in the "New Issues" section.

Additional Information on Stamp Collecting Products

You can expand your stamp collection and keep it updated with philatelic products from the USPS. Check the box next to the products you'd like to learn more about.

Item #8898 Price $12.95

- ❏ *American Commemorative Panels*
- ❏ *Commemorative Stamp Collections*
- ❏ *Commemorative Stamp Club*
- ❏ *Personalized Stamped Envelopes*
- ❏ *Souvenir Pages Program*
- ❏ *Standing Order Service*
- ❏ *First Day Covers*

...And a Free Offer!

Let us know if you're interested in receiving:
- ❏ *A copy of* **USA Philatelic,** *our catalog which contains details and mail-order information on all stamps and stamp products currently available from the Postal Service.*

Neatly print your name and address below, and drop this card in the mail—no postage necessary. (Information that you provide is protected and only disclosed in accordance with the Privacy Act of 1974.)

Mr./Mrs./Ms.

Street Address
(Include P.O. Box, Apt. no.,R.D. Route, etc. where appropriate)

City   State   ZIP Code

Please detach at perforation.

Please detach at perforation.

PHILATELIC FULFILLMENT SERVICE CENTER
KANSAS CITY MO 64179-0997

Official Business

BUSINESS REPLY MAIL
FIRST CLASS MAIL   PERMIT NO 73026   WASHINGTON DC

POSTAGE WILL BE PAID BY THE ADDRESSEE

UNITED STATES POSTAL SERVICE
PHILATELIC FULFILLMENT SERVICE CENTER
CUSTOMER SERVICE
BOX 419424
KANSAS CITY MO 64179-1009

	Issues of 1911		Un	U	PB/LP	#	FDC	Q(M̄)
	Wmkd. (190), Perf. 12							
377	4¢ brown	01/20/11	27.50	.50	265.00	(6)		
	Double transfer		—	—				
378	5¢ blue	01/25/11	27.50	.50	320.00	(6)		
	Double transfer		—	—				
379	6¢ red orange	01/25/11	32.50	.70	460.00	(6)		
380	8¢ olive green	02/08/11	110.00	12.50	1,050.00	(6)		
381	10¢ yellow	01/24/11	100.00	3.75	1,100.00	(6)		
382	15¢ pale ultramarine	03/01/11	260.00	15.00	2,250.00	(6)		
	Issues of 1910, Imperf.							
383	1¢ green Franklin (331)	12/10	2.60	2.00	47.50	(6)		
	Double transfer		6.50	—				
384	2¢ carmine Washington (332)	12/10	4.25	2.50	140.00	(6)		
	Foreign entry, design of 1¢		1,500.00					
	Double transfer		8.00	—				
	Rosette plate, crack on head		100.00	—				
	Issues of 1910, Coil Stamps, Perf. 12 Horizontally							
385	1¢ green Franklin (331)	11/01/10	25.00	13.00	310.00	(2)		
386	2¢ carmine Washington (332)	11/01/10	45.00	17.50	550.00	(2)		
	Issues of 1910-11, Coil Stamps, Wmkd. (190), Perf. 12 Vertically							
387	1¢ green Franklin (331)	11/01/10	100.00	42.50	425.00	(2)		
388	2¢ carmine Washington (332)	11/01/10	750.00	300.00	5,000.00	(2)		
389	3¢ deep violet Washington, type I (333)	01/24/11	37,500.00	10,000.00	90,000.00	(2)		
	Issues of 1910-13, Coil Stamps, Perf. 8.5 Horizontally							
390	1¢ green Franklin (331)	12/12/10	4.25	5.00	30.00	(2)		
	Double transfer		—	—				
391	2¢ carmine Washington (332)	12/23/10	30.00	10.00	190.00	(2)		
	Coil Stamps, Perf. 8.5 Vertically #394-96: Washington (Designs of 333-35)							
392	1¢ green Franklin (331)	12/12/10	20.00	19.00	150.00	(2)		
	Double transfer		—	—				
393	2¢ carmine Washington (332)	12/16/10	35.00	7.75	225.00	(2)		
394	3¢ deep violet, type I	09/18/11	45.00	47.50	325.00	(2)		
395	4¢ brown	04/15/12	45.00	42.50	325.00	(2)		
396	5¢ blue	03/13	45.00	42.50	325.00	(2)		
	Issues of 1913, Panama Pacific Exposition Issue, Wmkd. (190), Perf. 12							
397	1¢ Vasco Nunez de Balboa	01/01/13	17.50	1.50	175.00	(6)	5,000.00	167*
	Double transfer		22.50	2.50				
398	2¢ Pedro Miguel Locks, Panama Canal	01/13	20.00	.50	275.00	(6)		251*
	2¢ carmine lake		575.00					
	Double transfer		40.00	2.00				
399	5¢ Golden Gate	01/01/13	77.50	9.50	1,900.00	(6)	21,000.00	14*
400	10¢ yellow Discovery of San Francisco Bay	01/01/13	125.00	20.00	2,400.00	(6)	—	8*
400A	10¢ orange (400)	08/13	210.00	16.00	13,500.00	(6)		
	*Includes perf. 10 printing quantities.							

1912-1915

	Issues of 1914-15, Perf. 10		Un	U	PB/LP	#
401	1¢ green (397)	12/14	25.00	5.50	340.00	(6)
402	2¢ carmine (398)	01/15	75.00	1.50	1,500.00	(6)
403	5¢ blue (399)	02/15	175.00	15.00	4,000.00	(6)
404	10¢ orange (400)	07/15	950.00	62.50	*12,000.00*	(6)
	Issues of 1912-14, Wmkd. (190), Perf. 12					
405	1¢ green	02/12	5.25	.15	75.00	(6)
a	Vertical pair, imperf. horizontally		*650.00*	—		
b	Booklet pane of 6	02/08/12	60.00	*35.00*		
	Cracked plate		12.50	—		
	Double transfer		6.00	—		
406	2¢ carmine, type I	02/12	5.00	.15	95.00	(6)
	2¢ lake		*350.00*	—		
a	Booklet pane of 6	02/08/12	60.00	*60.00*		
b	Double impression		—			
	Double transfer		6.75	—		
407	7¢ black	04/14	80.00	11.00	1,100.00	(6)
	Imperf. #408-13: Washington (Designs of 405-6)					
408	1¢ green	03/12	1.15	.55	20.00	(6)
	Double transfer		2.50	1.00		
	Cracked plate		—	—		
409	2¢ carmine, type I	02/12	1.40	.60	40.00	(6)
	Cracked plate		15.00	—		
	Coil Stamps, Perf. 8.5 Horizontally					
410	1¢ green	03/12	6.00	4.00	30.00	(2)
	Double transfer		—	—		
411	2¢ carmine, type I	03/12	9.00	3.75	47.50	(2)
	Double transfer		11.00	—		
	Coil Stamps, Perf. 8.5 Vertically					
412	1¢ green	03/18/12	22.50	5.50	105.00	(2)
413	2¢ carmine, type I	03/12	37.50	1.10	220.00	(2)
	Double transfer		42.50	—		
	Perf. 12					
414	8¢ Franklin	02/12	45.00	1.25	450.00	(6)
415	9¢ Franklin	04/14	55.00	12.50	625.00	(6)
416	10¢ Franklin	01/12	45.00	.40	475.00	(6)

405 406 407 414 415 416

Details

2¢ Washington, Types I-VII, Series 1912-21

Detail of **#406-06a, 411, 413, 425-25e, 442, 444, 449, 453, 461, 463-63a, 482, 499-99f** Type I

One shading line in first curve of ribbon above left "2" and one in second curve of ribbon above right "2". Toga button has only a faint outline. Top line of toga rope, from button to front of the throat, is very faint. Shading lines of face end in the front of the ear, with little or no joining, to form lock of hair.

Detail of **#482a, 500** Type Ia

Similar to Type I but all lines are stronger.

Detail of **#454, 487, 491, 539** Type II

Shading lines in ribbons as in Type I. Toga button, rope and rope shading lines are heavy. Shading lines of face at lock of hair end in strong vertical curved line.

Detail of **#450, 455, 488, 492, 540, 546** Type III

Two lines of shading in curves of ribbons.

Detail of **#526, 532** Type IV

Top line of toga rope is broken. Toga button shading lines form "DID". Line of color in left "2" is very thin and usually broken.

Detail of **#527, 533** Type V

Top line of toga is complete. Toga button has five vertical shading lines. Line of color in left "2" is very thin and usually broken. Nose shading dots are as shown.

Detail of **#528, 534** Type Va

Same as Type V except third row from bottom of nose shading dots has four dots instead of six. Overall height of design is 1/3mm shorter than Type V.

Detail of **#528A, 534A** Type VI

Generally same as Type V except line of color in left "2" is very heavy.

Detail of **#528B, 534B** Type VII

Line of color in left "2" is continuous, clearly defined and heavier than in Type V or Va but not as heavy as Type VI. An additional vertical row of dots has been added to upper lip. Numerous additional dots appear in hair at top of head.

417

418

419

420

421

423

434

Benjamin Franklin, philanthropist

A man of many talents, Benjamin Franklin (1706-1790) influenced our nation and the world through politics, science, philosophy, music and economics. Franklin didn't stop there, however, and also brought safety to daily life. In 1736, he organized the Union Fire Company in Philadelphia to help people survive fires. And in 1752, he set up America's first fire insurance company. He even organized a night watch and militia to help keep peace and safety in Philadelphia. Other institutions Franklin organized include a library, an academy and a hospital. Many of these foundations were the first of their kind in North America. (#419)

After 1915 (from 1916 to date), all postage stamps, except #519 and 832b, are on unwatermarked paper.

	Issues of 1912-14, Perf. 12		Un	U	PB	#
417	12¢ Franklin	04/14	50.00	4.25	525.00	(6)
	Double transfer		55.00	—		
	Triple transfer		72.50	—		
418	15¢ Franklin	02/12	85.00	3.50	725.00	(6)
	Double transfer		—	—		
419	20¢ Franklin	04/14	200.00	15.00	1,800.00	(6)
420	30¢ Franklin	04/14	125.00	15.00	1,450.00	(6)
421	50¢ Franklin	08/14	425.00	17.50	9,500.00	(6)
	Wmkd. (191)					
422	50¢ Franklin (421)	02/12/12	250.00	15.00	4,500.00	(6)
423	$1 Franklin	02/12/12	500.00	60.00	10,500.00	(6)
	Double transfer		525.00	—		
	Issues of 1914-15, Wmkd. (190), Perf.10 #424-30: Wash. (Designs of 405-06, 333-36, 407)					
424	1¢ green	09/05/14	2.20	.20	40.00	(6)
	Cracked plate		—	—		
	Double transfer		4.25	—		
	Experimental precancel, New Orleans			—		
a	Perf. 12 x 10		850.00	750.00		
b	Perf. 10 x 12			375.00		
c	Vertical pair, imperf. horizontally		425.00	250.00		
d	Booklet pane of 6		4.75	2.00		
e	Vertical pair, imperf. between and at top		—			
425	2¢ rose red, type I	09/05/14	2.10	.20	27.50	(6)
	Cracked plate		9.00	—		
	Double transfer		—	—		
c	Perf. 10 x 12			—		
d	Perf. 12 x 10		—	800.00		
e	Booklet pane of 6	01/06/14	15.00	10.00		
426	3¢ deep violet, type I	09/18/14	13.50	1.25	180.00	(6)
427	4¢ brown	09/07/14	32.50	.50	500.00	(6)
	Double transfer		42.50	—		
428	5¢ blue	09/14/14	30.00	.50	400.00	(6)
a	Perf. 12 x 10			2,250.00		
429	6¢ red orange	09/28/14	45.00	1.40	525.00	(6)
430	7¢ black	09/10/14	80.00	4.00	950.00	(6)
	#431-33, 435, 437-40: Franklin (414-21, 423)					
431	8¢ pale olive green	09/26/14	32.50	1.50	475.00	(6)
	Double impression		—			
432	9¢ salmon red	10/06/14	47.50	7.50	700.00	(6)
433	10¢ orange yellow	09/09/14	45.00	.40	825.00	(6)
434	11¢ Franklin	08/11/15	21.00	7.50	250.00	(6)
435	12¢ claret brown	09/10/14	24.00	4.00	300.00	(6)
a	12¢ copper red		27.50	4.00	325.00	(6)
	Double transfer		30.00	—		
	Triple transfer		35.00	—		
436	Not assigned					
437	15¢ gray	09/16/14	120.00	7.25	1,100.00	(6)
438	20¢ ultramarine	09/19/14	200.00	4.00	3,250.00	(6)
439	30¢ orange red	09/19/14	250.00	16.00	4,000.00	(6)
440	50¢ violet	12/10/15	550.00	16.00	13,500.00	(6)

Issues of 1914		Un	U	PB/LB	#
Coil Stamps, Perf. 10 Horizontally #441-59: Wash. (Designs of 405-06, 333-35; Flat Press, 18½-19 x 22mm)					
441	1¢ green	11/14/14	1.00	1.00	7.75	(2)
442	2¢ carmine, type I	07/22/14	8.00	6.00	47.50	(2)
Coil Stamps, Perf. 10 Vertically					
443	1¢ green	05/29/14	22.50	5.00	135.00	(2)
444	2¢ carmine, type I	04/25/14	30.00	1.50	200.00	(2)
445	3¢ violet, type I	12/18/14	220.00	125.00	1,200.00	(2)
446	4¢ brown	10/02/14	120.00	42.50	675.00	(2)
447	5¢ blue	07/30/14	42.50	27.50	240.00	(2)
Issues of 1915-16, Coil Stamps, Perf. 10 Horizontally (Rotary Press, Designs 18½-19 x 22½mm)					
448	1¢ green	12/12/15	6.00	3.25	40.00	(2)
449	2¢ red, type I	12/05/15	2,250.00	400.00	*11,000.00*	(2)
450	2¢ carmine, type III	02/16	9.50	3.00	55.00	(2)
451	Not assigned					
Issues of 1914-16, Coil Stamps, Perf. 10 Vertically (Rotary Press, Designs 19½-20 x 22mm)					
452	1¢ green	11/11/14	9.50	2.00	70.00	(2)
453	2¢ carmine rose, type I	07/03/14	110.00	4.25	550.00	(2)
	Cracked plate		—	—		
454	2¢ red, type II	06/15	87.50	10.00	460.00	(2)
455	2¢ carmine, type III	12/15	9.00	1.00	52.50	(2)
456	3¢ violet, type I	02/02/16	230.00	85.00	1,100.00	(2)
457	4¢ brown	02/18/16	25.00	17.50	150.00	(2)
	Cracked plate		35.00	—		
458	5¢ blue	03/09/16	30.00	17.50	180.00	(2)
Issue of 1914, Horizontal Coil Stamp, Imperf.					
459	2¢ carmine, type I	06/30/14	250.00	*900.00*	1,350.00	(2)
Issues of 1915, Wmkd. (191), Perf. 10					
460	$1 violet black Franklin (423)	02/08/15	800.00	80.00	*12,000.00*	(6)
	Double transfer		850.00	—		
Perf. 11					
461	2¢ pale carmine red Washington (406), type I	06/17/15	110.00	*220.00*	*1,150.00*	(6)
Privately perforated copies of #409 have been made to resemble 461.					
Issues of 1916-17, Unwmkd., Perf. 10 #462-69: Wash. (Designs of 405-06, 333-36, 407)					
462	1¢ green	09/27/16	6.25	.35	150.00	(6)
	Experimental precancel, Springfield, MA, or New Orleans, LA			10.00		
a	Booklet pane of 6	10/15/16	9.00	*1.60*		
463	2¢ carmine, type I	09/25/16	4.00	.25	130.00	(6)
	Experimental precancel, Springfield, MA			22.50		
a	Booklet pane of 6	10/08/16	90.00	*40.00*		
	Double transfer		5.75	—		
464	3¢ violet, type I	11/11/16	72.50	12.50	1,400.00	(6)
	Double transfer in "CENTS"		*87.50*	—		
465	4¢ orange brown	10/07/16	42.50	1.70	675.00	(6)
466	5¢ blue	10/17/16	72.50	1.70	950.00	(6)
	Experimental precancel, Springfield, MA			175.00		
467	5¢ carmine (error in plate of 2¢)		550.00	675.00		
468	6¢ red orange	10/10/16	90.00	7.00	1,400.00	(6)
	Experimental precancel, Springfield, MA			175.00		
469	7¢ black	10/10/16	115.00	11.00	1,400.00	(6)
	Experimental precancel, Springfield, MA			175.00		

Issues of 1916-17, Perf. 10		Un	U	PB/LP	#	FDC
#470-78: Franklin (Designs of 414-16, 434, 417-21, 423)						
470	8¢ olive green	11/13/16	55.00	5.50	575.00	(6)	
	Experimental precancel, Springfield, MA			165.00			
471	9¢ salmon red	11/16/16	55.00	14.00	775.00	(6)	
472	10¢ orange yellow	10/17/16	100.00	1.25	1,400.00	(6)	
473	11¢ dark green	11/16/16	35.00	16.00	375.00	(6)	
	Experimental precancel, Springfield, MA			575.00			
474	12¢ claret brown	10/10/16	47.50	5.00	650.00	(6)	
	Double transfer		57.50	6.00			
	Triple transfer		70.00	9.00			
475	15¢ gray	11/16/16	180.00	10.50	2,900.00	(6)	
476	20¢ light ultramarine	12/05/16	240.00	12.00	3,750.00	(6)	
476A	30¢ orange red		4,500.00	—	—	(6)	
477	50¢ light violet	03/02/17	1,000.00	60.00	40,000.00	(6)	
478	$1 violet black	12/22/16	750.00	16.00	14,000.00	(6)	
	Double transfer		800.00	20.00			
479	$2 dark blue Madison (312)	03/22/17	325.00	40.00	4,500.00	(6)	
480	$5 light green Marshall (313)	03/22/17	250.00	42.50	3,250.00	(6)	
Issues of 1916-17, Imperf.						
#481-96: Washington (Designs of 405-06, 333-35)						
481	1¢ green	11/16	1.00	.55	14.00	(6)	
	Double transfer		2.50	1.25			
482	2¢ carmine, type I	12/08/16	1.50	1.25	25.00	(6)	
482A	2¢ deep rose, type Ia			10,000.00			
483	3¢ violet, type I	10/13/17	14.00	7.50	125.00	(6)	
	Double transfer		17.50	—			
484	3¢ violet, type II		11.00	5.00	100.00	(6)	
	Double transfer		12.50	—			
485	5¢ carmine (error in plate of 2¢)	03/17	12,000.00		140.00	(6)	
Issues of 1916-22, Coil Stamps, Perf. 10 Horizontally						
486	1¢ green	01/18	.90	.25	4.75	(2)	
	Double transfer		2.25	—			
487	2¢ carmine, type II	11/15/16	14.00	3.00	110.00	(2)	
488	2¢ carmine, type III	1919	2.50	1.75	15.00	(2)	
	Cracked plate		12.00	7.50			
489	3¢ violet, type I	10/10/17	5.00	1.50	32.50	(2)	
Coil Stamps, Perf. 10 Vertically						
490	1¢ green	11/17/16	.55	.25	3.50	(2)	
	Cracked plate (horizontal)		7.50	—			
	Cracked plate (vertical) retouched		9.00	—			
	Rosette crack		50.00	—			
491	2¢ carmine, type II	11/17/16	2,000.00	525.00	9,500.00	(2)	
492	2¢ carmine, type III		9.00	.25	52.50	(2)	
493	3¢ violet, type I	07/23/17	16.00	3.00	110.00	(2)	
494	3¢ violet, type II	02/04/18	10.00	1.00	72.50	(2)	
495	4¢ orange brown	04/15/17	10.00	4.00	75.00	(2)	
	Cracked plate		25.00	—			
496	5¢ blue	01/15/19	3.50	1.00	29.00	(2)	
497	10¢ orange yellow Franklin (416)	01/31/22	20.00	10.50	140.00	(2)	4,000.00

	Issue of 1917-19		Un	U	PB	#
	Perf. 11, #498-507: Washington (Designs of 405-06, 333-36, 407)					
498	1¢ green	03/17	.40	.25	17.50	(6)
a	Vertical pair, imperf. horizontally		175.00			
b	Horizontal pair, imperf. between		100.00			
d	Double impression		175.00			
e	Booklet pane of 6	04/06/17	2.50	.50		
f	Booklet pane of 30	09/17	1,000.00			
g	Perf. 10 top or bottom		700.00	—		
	Cracked plate		7.50	—		
499	2¢ rose, type I	03/17	.40	.25	18.00	(6)
a	Vertical pair, imperf. horizontally		150.00			
b	Horizontal pair, imperf. vertically		275.00	150.00		
e	Booklet pane of 6	03/31/17	4.00	.65		
f	Booklet pane of 30	09/17	27,500.00			
g	Double impression		160.00	—		
	Double transfer		6.00	—		
500	2¢ deep rose, type Ia		240.00	180.00	1,900.00	(6)
	Pair, types I and Ia		1,000.00			
501	3¢ light violet, type I	03/17	11.00	.25	105.00	(6)
b	Booklet pane of 6	10/17/17	70.00	20.00		
d	Double impression		200.00			
502	3¢ dark violet, type II		14.00	.40	150.00	(6)
b	Booklet pane of 6	02/28/18	60.00	22.50		
c	Vertical pair, imperf. horizontally		250.00	125.00		
e	Perf. 10, top or bottom		625.00	—		
503	4¢ brown	03/17	10.00	.25	140.00	(6)
504	5¢ blue	03/17	9.00	.25	130.00	(6)
	Double transfer		11.00	—		
505	5¢ rose (error in plate of 2¢)		400.00	500.00		
506	6¢ red orange	03/17	12.50	.25	175.00	(6)
507	7¢ black	03/17	27.50	1.10	260.00	(6)
	#508-12, 514-18: Franklin (Designs of 414-16, 434, 417-21, 423)					
508	8¢ olive bister	03/17	12.00	.50	150.00	(6)
c	Perf. 10 top or bottom			725.00		
509	9¢ salmon red	03/17	14.00	1.75	150.00	(6)
510	10¢ orange yellow	03/17	17.00	.15	190.00	(6)
511	11¢ light green	05/17	9.00	2.50	130.00	(6)
	Double transfer		12.50	3.25		
512	12¢ claret brown	05/17	9.00	.35	130.00	(6)
a	12¢ brown carmine		9.50	.40		
b	Perf. 10, top or bottom		—	600.00		
513	13¢ apple green	01/10/19	11.00	6.00	130.00	(6)
	13¢ deep apple green		12.50	6.50		
514	15¢ gray	05/17	37.50	1.00	575.00	(6)
515	20¢ light ultramarine	05/17	47.50	.25	625.00	(6)
	20¢ deep ultramarine		50.00	.25		
b	Vertical pair, imperf. between		325.00			
516	30¢ orange red	05/17	37.50	1.00	600.00	(6)
a	Perf. 10 top or bottom		1,100.00	—		
517	50¢ red violet	05/17	70.00	.50	1,650.00	(6)
c	Perf. 10, top or bottom			950.00		
518	$1 violet brown	05/17	55.00	1.50	1,350.00	(6)
b	$1 deep brown		1,400.00	825.00		

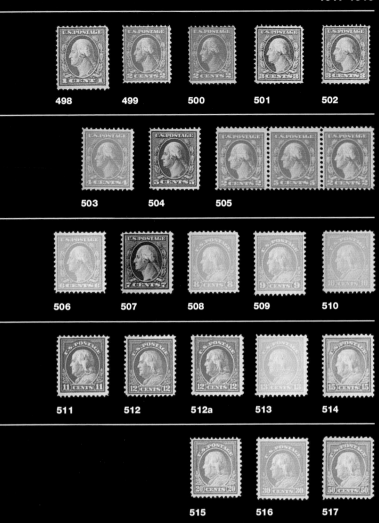

498 499 500 501 502

503 504 505

506 507 508 509 510

511 512 512a 513 514

515 516 517

We redesigned and expanded the new issues just for you! Read about the newest issues in the "1998 Issues—New U.S. Postage Stamps" section.

523

524

537

The Allied Victory sealed by Treaty of Versailles

World War I ended in 1918 with a defeat of the Central Powers (including Germany, Austria-Hungary and Turkey) by the Allies (including France, Great Britain, Russia, Italy, Japan and, from 1917, the United States). Before the armistice, President Wilson had circulated the Fourteen Points, a plan for peace presented first in an address before Congress, and Germany had accepted its terms. But the other Allies wanted compensation for damages incurred during the war and had already divided Germany's lands among themselves in secret treaties. The Paris Peace Conference convened January 18, 1919, to determine the international course of action against Germany. The conference resulted in the Treaty of Versailles, signed on June 28, 1919. The treaty provided for a 10 percent reduction of German territory and forced Germany to pay heavy reparations. Germany's resentment of these terms, which were much harsher than the Fourteen Points they had agreed to, fueled their military buildup in the 1930s—in violation of the treaty—and set the stage for World War II. (#537)

	Issue of 1917, Wmkd. (191), Perf. 11		Un	U	PB	#	FDC	Q(M̄)
519	2¢ carm. Washington (332)	10/10/17	350.00	*550.00*	2,500.00	(6)		
	Privately perforated copies of #344 have been made to resemble #519.							
520-22 Not assigned								
	Issues of 1918, Unwmkd.							
523	$2 Franklin	08/19/18	675.00	230.00	*14,000.00*	(8)		
524	$5 Franklin	08/19/18	240.00	35.00	4,000.00	(8)		
	Issues of 1918-20 #525-35: Washington (Designs of 405-06, 333)							
525	1¢ gray green	12/18	2.50	.50	25.00	(6)		
	1¢ Emerald		3.50	1.00				
a	1¢ dark green		2.75	.95				
d	Double impression		27.50	25.00				
526	2¢ carmine, type IV	03/06/20	27.50	3.50	250.00	(6)	*750.00*	
	Gash on forehead		40.00	—				
	Malformed "2" at left		37.50	6.00				
527	2¢ carmine, type V	03/20/20	20.00	1.00	175.00	(6)		
a	Double impression		60.00	10.00				
	Line through "2" and "EN"		30.00	—				
528	2¢ carmine, type Va	05/04/20	9.00	.25	85.00	(6)		
c	Double impression		27.50					
528A	2¢ carmine, type VI	06/24/20	52.50	1.50	450.00	(6)		
d	Double impression		160.00	—				
528B	2¢ carmine, type VII	11/03/20	21.00	.35	165.00	(6)		
e	Double impression		70.00					
	Retouched on cheek		400.00	—				
529	3¢ violet, type III	03/18	3.25	.25	60.00	(6)		
a	Double impression		32.50	—				
b	Printed on both sides		*450.00*					
530	3¢ purple, type IV		1.60	.20	18.50	(6)		
a	Double impression		20.00	6.00				
b	Printed on both sides		*250.00*					
	"Blister" under "U.S."		4.50	—				
	Recut under "U.S."		4.50	—				
	Imperf.							
531	1¢ green	01/19	9.00	8.00	90.00	(6)		
532	2¢ carmine rose, type IV	03/20	40.00	27.50	350.00	(6)		
533	2¢ carmine, type V	05/04/20	200.00	80.00	1,700.00	(6)		
534	2¢ carmine, type Va	05/25/20	11.00	6.50	110.00	(6)		
534A	2¢ carmine, type VI	07/26/20	40.00	22.50	350.00	(6)		
534B	2¢ carmine, type VII	12/02/20	1,400.00	800.00	*11,500.00*	(6)		
535	3¢ violet, type IV	1918	9.00	5.00	77.50	(6)		
a	Double impression		100.00	—				
	Issues of 1919, Perf. 12.5							
536	1¢ gray green Washington (405)	08/15/19	17.50	20.00	160.00	(6)		
a	Horizontal pair, imperf. vertically		*500.00*					
	Perf. 11							
537	3¢ Allied Victory	03/03/19	10.00	3.25	100.00	(6)	*750.00*	100
a	deep red violet		*450.00*	*150.00*	4,250.00	(6)		
c	red violet		40.00	12.00				
	Double transfer		—	—				

	Issues of 1919, Perf. 11 x 10		Un	U	PB	#	FDC	Q(M̄)
	#538-46: Washington (Designs of 405-06, 333; 19¹/₂–20 x 22-22¹/₄ mm)							
538	1¢ green	06/19	11.00	8.50	105.00	(4)		
a	Vertical pair, imperf. horizontally		50.00	*100.00*	900.00	(4)		
	Double transfer		17.50	—				
539	2¢ carmine rose, type II		3,000.00	*3,750.00*	18,000.00	(4)		
540	2¢ carmine rose, type III	06/14/19	12.00	8.50	100.00	(4)		
	Double transfer		20.00	—				
a	Vertical pair, imperf. horizontally		50.00	*100.00*	750.00	(4)		
b	Horizontal pair, imperf. vertically		*750.00*					
541	3¢ violet, type II	06/19	37.50	30.00	350.00	(4)		
	Issue of 1920, Perf. 10 x 11 (Design 19 x 22¹/₂–22³/₄mm)							
542	1¢ green	05/26/20	13.50	1.10	170.00	(6)	*1,250.00*	
	Issues of 1921, Perf. 10 (Design 19 x 22¹/₂mm)							
543	1¢ green	05/21	.50	.25	15.00	(4)		
a	Horizontal pair, imperf. between		*1,100.00*					
	Double transfer			—				
	Triple transfer		—	—				
	Issue of 1922, Perf. 11 (Design 19 x 22¹/₂mm)							
544	1¢ green		*13,500.00*	*3,000.00*				
	Issues of 1921 (Designs 19¹/₂–20 x 22mm)							
545	1¢ green	05/21	150.00	160.00	950.00	(4)		
546	2¢ carmine rose, type III	05/21	90.00	*150.00*	725.00	(4)		
a	Perf. 10 at left		—					
	Recut in hair		125.00	*175.00*				
	Issues of 1920, Perf. 11							
547	$2 Franklin	11/01/20	200.00	40.00	4,500.00	(8)		
	Pilgrim Tercentenary Issue							
548	1¢ The Mayflower	12/21/20	4.50	2.25	45.00	(6)	*800.00*	138
	Double transfer		—	—				
549	2¢ Landing of the Pilgrims	12/21/20	6.50	1.60	65.00	(6)	*650.00*	196
550	5¢ Signing of the Compact	12/21/20	42.50	12.50	475.00	(6)	—	11
	Issues of 1922-25, Perf. 11 (See also #581-91, 594-606, 622-23, 631-42, 658-79, 684-87, 692-701, 723)							
551	¹/₂¢ Nathan Hale	04/04/25	.15	.15	6.00	(6)	17.50 (4)	
	"Cap" on fraction bar		.45	.15				
552	1¢ Franklin	01/17/23	1.40	.15	25.00	(6)	30.00 (2)	
a	Booklet pane of 6	08/11/23	6.50	*.80*				
	Double transfer		3.50	—				
553	1¹/₂¢ Harding	03/19/25	2.60	.15	30.00	(6)	30.00 (2)	
554	2¢ Washington	01/15/23	1.40	.15	22.50	(6)	42.50	
a	Horizontal pair, imperf. vertically		200.00					
b	Vertical pair, imperf. horizontally		*500.00*					
c	Booklet pane of 6	02/10/23	7.00	*1.50*				
	Double transfer		2.50	.80				
555	3¢ Lincoln	02/12/23	19.00	1.00	160.00	(6)	35.00	
556	4¢ M. Washington	01/15/23	20.00	.25	170.00	(6)	60.00	
b	Perf. 10, top or bottom		*425.00*	—				
557	5¢ T. Roosevelt	10/27/22	20.00	.20	190.00	(6)	150.00	
a	Imperf. pair		*1,500.00*					
c	Perf. 10, top or bottom		—	*500.00*				
558	6¢ Garfield	11/20/22	37.50	.85	400.00	(6)	250.00	
	Double transfer		55.00	2.00				
	Same, recut		55.00	2.00				

547

548

549

550

551

552

553

554

555

556

557

558

559

560

561

562

563

564

565

566

567

568

569

570

571

572

573

	Issues of 1922-23, Perf. 11		Un	U	PB	#	FDC
559	7¢ McKinley	05/01/23	9.00	.55	70.00	(6)	175.00
	Double transfer		—	—			
560	8¢ Grant	05/01/23	50.00	.60	600.00	(6)	210.00
	Double transfer		—	—			
561	9¢ Jefferson	01/15/23	13.50	1.10	160.00	(6)	210.00
	Double transfer		—	—			
562	10¢ Monroe	01/15/23	19.00	.15	200.00	(6)	190.00
a	Vertical pair, imperf. horizontally		*1,250.00*				
b	Imperf. pair		*1,250.00*				
c	Perf. 10 at top or bottom			*750.00*			
563	11¢ Hayes	10/04/22	1.40	.40	30.00	(6)	600.00
564	12¢ Cleveland	03/20/23	6.25	.15	72.50	(6)	210.00
a	Horizontal pair, imperf. vertically		*1,000.00*				
565	14¢ American Indian	05/01/23	4.25	.75	50.00	(6)	450.00
	Double transfer		—	—			
566	15¢ Statue of Liberty	11/11/22	25.00	.15	250.00	(6)	600.00
567	20¢ Golden Gate	05/01/23	22.50	.15	240.00	(6)	*500.00*
a	Horizontal pair, imperf. vertically		*1,500.00*				
568	25¢ Niagara Falls	11/11/22	19.00	.45	225.00	(6)	*700.00*
b	Vertical pair, imperf. horizontally		*850.00*				
c	Perf. 10 at one side		—				
569	30¢ Buffalo	03/20/23	35.00	.35	240.00	(6)	*900.00*
	Double transfer		55.00	2.50			
570	50¢ Arlington Amphitheater	11/11/22	57.50	.15	650.00	(6)	*1,250.00*
571	$1 Lincoln Memorial	02/12/23	47.50	.45	425.00	(6)	*6,000.00*
	Double transfer		90.00	1.50			
572	$2 U.S. Capitol	03/20/23	100.00	9.00	850.00	(6)	*15,000.00*
573	$5 Head of Freedom, Capitol Dome	03/20/23	175.00	15.00	2,100.00	(8)	*25,000.00*
574	Not assigned						
	Issues of 1923-25, Imperf.						
575	1¢ green Franklin (552)	03/20/23	7.50	5.00	77.50	(6)	
576	1¹/2¢ yel. brn. Harding (553)	04/04/25	1.60	1.50	20.00	(6)	45.00
577	2¢ carmine Washington (554)		1.75	1.25	27.50	(6)	
	Issues of 1923, Perf. 11 x 10						
578	1¢ green Franklin (552)	1923	95.00	*140.00*	750.00	(4)	
579	2¢ carmine Washington (554)	1923	85.00	*125.00*	575.00	(4)	
	Recut in eye		*105.00*	*150.00*			
	Issues of 1923-26, Perf. 10 (See also #551-73, 622-23, 631-42, 658-79, 684-87, 692-701, 723)						
580	Not assigned						
581	1¢ green Franklin (552)	04/21/23	9.50	.65	105.00	(4)	*5,750.00*
582	1¹/2¢ brn. Harding (553)	03/19/25	4.50	.60	37.50	(4)	40.00
	Pair with full horiz. gutter between		*135.00*				
583	2¢ carm. Wash. (554)	04/14/24	2.50	.25	27.50	(4)	
a	Booklet pane of 6	08/27/26	85.00	27.50			*1,400.00*
584	3¢ violet Lincoln (555)	08/01/25	26.50	2.25	220.00	(4)	55.00
585	4¢ yellow brown Martha Washington (556)	03/25	16.00	.45	200.00	(4)	55.00
586	5¢ blue T. Roosevelt (557)	12/24	16.00	.25	190.00	(4)	57.50
587	6¢ red orange Garfield (558)	03/25	7.50	.35	77.50	(4)	60.00
588	7¢ black McKinley (559)	05/29/26	10.50	5.50	90.00	(4)	70.00

	Issues of 1925-26, Perf. 11 x 10		Un	U	PB/LP	#	FDC	Q(M̄)
589	8¢ olive grn. Grant (560)	05/29/26	25.00	3.50	200.00	(4)	72.50	
590	9¢ rose Jefferson (561)	05/29/26	5.00	2.25	42.50	(4)	72.50	
591	10¢ orange Monroe (562)	06/08/25	60.00	.25	500.00	(4)	95.00	
592-93	Not assigned							
	Issues of 1923, Perf. 11							
594	1¢ green Franklin (552), design 19³/₄ x 22¹/₄mm	1923	*16,000.00*	5,000.00				
595	2¢ carmine Washington (554), design 19³/₄ x 22¹/₄mm	1923	275.00	300.00	1,950.00	(4)		
596	1¢ green Franklin (552), design 19¹/₄ x 22¹/₂mm	1923		*45,000.00*				
	Issues of 1923-29, Coil Stamps, Perf. 10 Vertically							
597	1¢ green Franklin (552)	07/18/23	.35	.15	2.30	(2)	*550.00*	
	Gripper cracks or double transfer		2.60	1.00				
598	1¹/₂¢ brown Harding (553)	03/19/25	1.00	.15	4.75	(2)	50.00	
599	2¢ carmine Washington (554), type I	01/23	.40	.15	2.30	(2)	*1,500.00*	
	Double transfer		1.90	1.00				
	Gripper cracks		2.30	2.00				
599A	2¢ carmine Washington (554), type II	03/29	125.00	11.00	675.00	(2)		
600	3¢ violet Lincoln (555)	05/10/24	7.00	.15	24.00	(2)	60.00	
601	4¢ yellow brown M. Washington (556)	08/05/23	4.25	.35	27.50	(2)		
602	5¢ dark blue T. Roosevelt (557)	03/05/24	1.75	.15	10.00	(2)	82.50	
603	10¢ orange Monroe (562)	12/01/24	4.00	.15	26.00	(2)	100.00	
	Coil Stamps, Perf. 10 Horizontally							
604	1¢ yel. grn. Franklin (552)	07/19/24	.35	.15	3.75	(2)	90.00	
605	1¹/₂¢ yel. brn. Harding (553)	05/09/25	.35	.15	3.50	(2)	70.00	
606	2¢ carmine Washington (554)	12/31/23	.35	.20	2.60	(2)	100.00	
607-09	Not assigned							
	Issues of 1923, Harding Memorial Issue, Perf. 11							
610	2¢ blk. Harding	09/01/23	.65	.15	20.00	(6)	30.00	1,459
a	Horizontal pair, imperf. vertically		*1,750.00*					
	Double transfer		1.75	.50				
	Imperf.							
611	2¢ blk. Harding (610)	11/15/23	7.00	4.00	85.00	(6)	90.00	0.8
	Perf. 10							
612	2¢ blk. Harding (610)	09/12/23	16.00	1.75	275.00	(4)	100.00	100
	Perf. 11							
613	2¢ black Harding (610)	1923		*17,500.00*				
	Issues of 1924, Huguenot-Walloon Tercentary Issue, May 1							
614	1¢ Ship *Nieu Nederland*	01/05/24	3.00	3.25	35.00	(6)	42.50	51
615	2¢ Walloons' Landing at Fort Orange (Albany)	01/05/24	6.00	2.10	65.00	(6)	50.00	78
	Double transfer		12.50	3.50				
616	5¢ Huguenot Monument to Jan Ribault at Mayport, Florida	01/05/24	27.50	12.50	275.00	(6)	75.00	6

599   610

614   615   616

Details

2¢ Washington Types I-II, Series 1923-29

Detail of **#599, 634** Type I

No heavy hair lines at top center of head.

Detail of **#599A, 634A** Type II

Three heavy hair lines at top center of head.

1925-1934

617

618

619

620

621

622

623

627

628

629

630

	Issues of 1925, Perf. 11		Un	U	PB	#	FDC	Q(M̄)
	Lexington-Concord Issue							
617	1¢ Washington at Cambridge	04/04/25	2.80	2.40	40.00	(6)	35.00	16
618	2¢ "The Birth of Liberty," by Henry Sandham	04/04/25	5.50	3.90	67.50	(6)	40.00	27
619	5¢ "The Minute Man," by Daniel Chester French	04/04/25	25.00	12.50	250.00	(6)	90.00	5
	Line over head		50.00	18.50				
	Norse-American Issue							
620	2¢ Sloop *Restaurationen*	05/18/25	4.00	3.00	200.00	(8)	27.50	9
621	5¢ Viking Ship	05/18/25	16.00	10.50	650.00	(8)	42.50	2
	Issues of 1925-26 (See also #551-79, 581-91, 594-606, 631-42, 658-79, 684-87, 692-701, 723)							
622	13¢ B. Harrison	01/11/26	14.50	.45	160.00	(6)	25.00	
623	17¢ Wilson	12/28/25	16.00	.25	180.00	(6)	30.00	
624-26 Not assigned								
	Issues of 1926							
627	2¢ Independence Sesquicentennial Exposition	05/10/26	3.25	.50	37.50	(6)	10.00	308
628	5¢ John Ericsson Memorial	05/29/26	6.50	3.25	80.00	(6)	25.00	20
629	2¢ Battle of White Plains	10/18/26	2.25	1.70	35.00	(6)	6.25	41
a	Vertical pair, imperf. between		—					
	International Philatelic Exhibition Souvenir Sheet							
630	2¢ Battle of White Plains, sheet of 25 with selvage inscription (629)	10/18/26	450.00	450.00			1,500.00	0.1
	Dot over first "S" of "States"		475.00	475.00				
	Imperf. (See also #551-79, 581-91, 594-606, 622-23, 658-79, 684-87, 692-701, 723)							
631	1¹/₂¢ yellow brown Harding (553)	08/27/26	2.00	1.70	62.50	(4)	30.00	
	Issues of 1926-34, Perf. 11 x 10.5 (See also #551-73, 575-79, 581-91, 594-606, 622-23, 631-42, 684-87, 692-701, 723)							
632	1¢ green Franklin (552)	06/10/27	.15	.15	2.00	(4)	45.00	
a	Booklet pane of 6	11/02/27	5.50	1.25			3,000.00	
b	Vertical pair, imperf. between		600.00	125.00				
	Pair with full vertical gutter between		150.00	—				
	Cracked plate		—	—				
633	1¹/₂¢ yellow brown Harding (553)	05/17/27	2.00	.15	65.00	(4)	45.00	
634	2¢ carmine Washington (554), type I	12/10/26	.15	.15	1.75	(4)	47.50	
	Pair with full vertical gutter between		200.00					
b	2¢ carmine lake, type I		—	—	—	(4)		
c	Horizontal pair, imperf. between		2,000.00					
d	Booklet pane of 6	02/25/27	1.75	.75				
634A	2¢ carmine Washington (554), type II	12/28/27	350.00	13.50	1,850.00	(4)		
	Pair with full vertical or horizontal gutter between		1,000.00	—				
635	3¢ violet Lincoln (555)	02/03/27	.45	.15	7.50	(4)	47.50	
a	3¢ bright violet Lincoln	02/07/34	.25	.15	5.50	(4)	25.00	
	Gripper cracks		3.25	2.00				
636	4¢ yellow brown Martha Washington (556)	05/17/27	2.25	.15	75.00	(4)	50.00	
	Pair with full vertical gutter between		200.00					
637	5¢ dark blue Theodore Roosevelt (557)	03/24/27	2.25	.15	15.00	(4)	50.00	
	Pair with full vertical gutter between		275.00					

1927-1931

	Issues of 1927-31		Un	U	PB/LB	#	FDC	Q(M̄)
	Perf. 11 x 10.5							
638	6¢ red orange Garfield (558)	07/27/27	2.25	.15	15.00	(4)	57.50	
	Pair with full vert. gutter between		*200.00*					
639	7¢ black McKinley (559)	03/24/27	2.25	.15	15.00	(4)	57.50	
a	Vertical pair, imperf. between		275.00	85.00				
640	8¢ olive green Grant (560)	06/10/27	2.25	.15	15.00	(4)	62.50	
641	9¢ orange red Jefferson (561)	1931	2.25	.15	15.00	(4)	72.50	
642	10¢ orange Monroe (562)	02/03/27	3.75	.15	25.00	(4)	90.00	
	Double transfer		—	—				
	Perf. 11							
643	2¢ Vermont Sesquicentennial	08/03/27	1.40	.80	37.50	(6)	6.00	40
644	2¢ Burgoyne Campaign	08/03/27	3.50	2.10	35.00	(6)	12.50	26
	Issues of 1928							
645	2¢ Valley Forge	05/26/28	1.05	.40	25.00	(6)	4.00	101
	Perf. 11 x 10.5							
646	2¢ Battle of Monmouth/ Molly Pitcher	10/20/28	1.10	1.10	30.00	(4)	15.00	10
	Wide spacing, vertical pair		50.00	—				
	Hawaii Sesquicentennial Issue							
647	2¢ Washington (554)	08/13/28	5.00	4.50	110.00	(4)	15.00	6
	Wide spacing, vertical pair		100.00					
648	5¢ Theodore Roosevelt (557)	08/13/28	14.50	13.50	250.00	(4)	22.50	1
	Aeronautics Conference Issue, Perf. 11							
649	2¢ Wright Airplane	12/12/28	1.25	.80	12.50	(6)	7.00	51
650	5¢ Globe and Airplane	12/12/28	5.25	3.25	52.50	(6)	10.00	10
	Plate flaw, "prairie dog"		27.50	12.50				
	Issues of 1929							
651	2¢ George Rogers Clark	02/25/29	.65	.50	10.00	(6)	6.00	17
	Double transfer		4.25	2.25				
652	Not assigned							
	Perf. 11 x 10.5							
653	1/2¢ olive brown Nathan Hale (551)	05/25/29	.15	.15	1.50	(4)	25.00	
	Electric Light's Golden Jubilee Issue, Perf. 11							
654	2¢ Thomas Edison's First Lamp	06/05/29	.70	.70	27.50	(6)	10.00	32
	Perf. 11 x 10.5							
655	2¢ carmine rose (654)	06/11/29	.65	.15	35.00	(4)	80.00	210
	Coil Stamp, Perf. 10 Vertically							
656	2¢ carmine rose (654)	06/11/29	14.00	1.75	75.00	(2)	90.00	133
	Perf. 11							
657	2¢ Sullivan Expedition	06/17/29	.70	.60	27.50	(6)	4.00	51
	2¢ lake		175.00	—				

643   644   645

646   647   648

649   650

651

654   657

658   669

680   681

682   683

684   685

Ohio River Canalization Project finished in 1929

Steamboat traffic had increased dramatically on the Ohio River by 1835, but shallow water impeded navigation during dry periods. In the late 1870s, the U.S. Army Corps of Engineers was called upon to create a nine-foot-deep navigable channel in the river. By 1929, when the Ohio River Canalization Project was completed, a series of 53 wicket dams and locks had been installed along the 981-mile length of the river, from Pittsburgh, Pennsylvania, to Cairo, Illinois. But even before the system was finished, some of the old constructions were being replaced with more modern facilities. (#681)

	Issues of 1929		Un	U	PB/LP	#	FDC	Q(M̄)
	#658-68 overprinted "Kans.," Perf. 11 x 10.5							
	(See also #551-73, 575-79, 581-91, 594-606, 622-23, 631-42, 684-87, 692-701, 723)							
658	1¢ Franklin	05/01/29	2.50	2.00	37.50	(4)	37.50	13
a	Vertical pair, one without overprint		*325.00*					
659	1¹/₂¢ brown Harding (553)	05/01/29	4.00	2.90	52.50	(4)	37.50	8
	Wide spacing, pair		70.00					
660	2¢ carmine Washington (554)	05/01/29	4.50	1.10	50.00	(4)	37.50	87
661	3¢ violet Lincoln (555)	05/01/29	22.50	15.00	225.00	(4)	40.00	3
662	4¢ yellow brown Martha Washington (556)	05/01/29	22.50	9.00	225.00	(4)	45.00	2
663	5¢ deep blue T. Roosevelt (557)	05/01/29	14.00	9.75	155.00	(4)	45.00	3
664	6¢ red orange Garfield (558)	05/01/29	32.50	18.00	475.00	(4)	55.00	1
665	7¢ black McKinley (559)	05/01/29	30.00	27.50	525.00	(4)	55.00	1
666	8¢ olive green Grant (560)	05/01/29	110.00	75.00	850.00	(4)	105.00	2
667	9¢ light rose Jefferson (561)	05/01/29	16.00	11.25	200.00	(4)	105.00	1
668	10¢ orange yel. Monroe (562)	05/01/29	25.00	12.00	350.00	(4)	110.00	3
	#669-79 overprinted "Nebr."							
669	1¢ Franklin	05/01/29	4.00	2.25	50.00	(4)	37.50	8
a	Vertical pair, one without overprint		*300.00*					
670	1¹/₂¢ brown Harding (553)	05/01/29	3.75	2.50	55.00	(4)	37.50	9
671	2¢ carmine Washington (554)	05/01/29	3.75	1.30	45.00	(4)	37.50	73
672	3¢ violet Lincoln (555)	05/01/29	15.00	12.00	175.00	(4)	45.00	2
673	4¢ yellow brown Martha Washington (556)	05/01/29	22.50	15.00	250.00	(4)	52.50	2
	Wide spacing, pair		120.00					
674	5¢ deep blue T. Roosevelt (557)	05/01/29	20.00	15.00	275.00	(4)	52.50	2
675	6¢ red orange Garfield (558)	05/01/29	47.50	24.00	525.00	(4)	77.50	1
676	7¢ black McKinley (559)	05/01/29	27.50	18.00	325.00	(4)	82.50	0.8
677	8¢ olive green Grant (560)	05/01/29	37.50	25.00	450.00	(4)	82.50	1
678	9¢ light rose Jefferson (561)	05/01/29	42.50	27.50	550.00	(4)	95.00	0.5
679	10¢ orange yel. Monroe (562)	05/01/29	135.00	22.50	1,100.00	(4)	105.00	2
	Warning: Excellent forgeries of the Kansas and Nebraska overprints exist.							
	Perf. 11							
680	2¢ Battle of Fallen Timbers	09/14/29	.80	.80	22.50	(6)	3.50	29
681	2¢ Ohio River Canalization	10/19/29	.70	.65	17.50	(6)	3.50	33
	Issues of 1930							
682	2¢ Mass. Bay Colony	04/08/30	.60	.50	22.50	(6)	3.50	74
683	2¢ Carolina-Charleston	04/10/30	1.20	1.20	42.50	(6)	3.50	25
	Perf. 11 x 10.5							
684	1¹/₂¢ Warren G. Harding	12/01/30	.35	.15	1.75	(4)	4.50	
	Pair with full horizontal gutter between		*175.00*					
	Pair with full vertical gutter between		—					
685	4¢ William H. Taft	06/04/30	.90	.15	11.00	(4)	6.00	
	Gouge on right "4"		2.10	.60				
	Recut right "4"		2.10	.65				
	Pair with full horizontal gutter between		—					
	Coil Stamps, Perf. 10 Vertically							
686	1¹/₂¢ brn. Harding (684)	12/01/30	1.80	.15	6.50	(2)	5.00	
687	4¢ brown Taft (685)	09/18/30	3.25	.45	13.00	(2)	20.00	

	Issues of 1930, Perf. 11		Un	U	PB	#	FDC	Q(M̄)
688	2¢ Battle of Braddock's Field	07/09/30	1.00	.85	30.00	(6)	4.00	26
689	2¢ Gen. von Steuben	09/17/30	.55	.55	20.00	(6)	4.00	66
a	Imperf. pair		2,500.00		12,000.00	(6)		
	Issues of 1931							
690	2¢ General Pulaski	01/16/31	.30	.15	10.00	(6)	4.00	97
691	Not assigned							
	Perf. 11 x 10.5 (See also #551-73, 575-79, 581-91, 594-606, 622-23, 631-42, 658-79, 684-87, 723)							
692	11¢ light bl. Hayes (563)	09/04/31	2.60	.15	13.50	(4)	100.00	
	Retouched forehead		6.75	1.00				
693	12¢ brown violet Cleveland (564)	08/25/31	5.50	.15	27.50	(4)	100.00	
694	13¢ yellow green Harrison (622)	09/04/31	2.00	.15	12.50	(4)	100.00	
695	14¢ dark blue American Indian (565)	09/08/31	3.75	.25	20.00	(4)	100.00	
696	15¢ gray Statue of Liberty (566)	08/27/31	8.00	.15	40.00	(4)	125.00	
	Perf. 10.5 x 11							
697	17¢ black Wilson (623)	07/25/31	4.50	.15	25.00	(4)	2,750.00	
698	20¢ carmine rose Golden Gate (567)	09/08/31	8.75	.15	42.50	(4)	325.00	
	Double transfer		20.00	—				
699	25¢ blue green Niagara Falls (568)	07/25/31	9.00	.15	47.50	(4)	2,750.00	
700	30¢ brown Buffalo (569)	09/08/31	17.50	.15	72.50	(4)	325.00	
	Cracked plate		27.50	.85				
701	50¢ lilac Arlington Amphitheater (570)	09/04/31	40.00	.15	200.00	(4)	450.00	
	Perf. 11							
702	2¢ Red Cross	05/21/31	.25	.15	1.90	(4)	3.00	99
a	Red cross omitted		40,000.00					
703	2¢ Yorktown	10/19/31	.40	.25	2.25	(4)	3.50	25
a	2¢ lake and black		4.50	.65				
b	2¢ dark lake and black		375.00		2,000.00	(4)		
c	Pair, imperf. vertically		5,000.00					
	Issues of 1932, Washington Bicentennial Issue, Perf. 11 x 10.5							
704	¹⁄₂¢ Portrait by Charles W. Peale	01/01/32	.15	.15	4.50	(4)	5.00 (4)	88
	Broken circle		.75	.20				
705	1¢ Bust by Jean Antoine Houdon	01/01/32	.15	.15	4.25	(4)	4.00 (2)	1,266
706	1¹⁄₂¢ Portrait by Charles W. Peale	01/01/32	.45	.15	14.00	(4)	4.00 (2)	305
707	2¢ Portrait by Gilbert Stuart	01/01/32	.15	.15	1.50	(4)	4.00	4,222
	Gripper cracks		1.75	.65				
708	3¢ Portrait by Charles W. Peale	01/01/32	.60	.15	15.00	(4)	4.00	456
709	4¢ Portrait by Charles P. Polk	01/01/32	.30	.15	5.50	(4)	4.00	151
	Broken bottom frame line		1.50	.50				
710	5¢ Portrait by Charles W. Peale	01/01/32	1.80	.15	15.00	(4)	4.00	171
	Cracked plate		5.25	1.10				
711	6¢ Portrait by John Trumbull	01/01/32	3.50	.15	50.00	(4)	4.00	112
712	7¢ Portrait by John Trumbull	01/01/32	.30	.15	6.75	(4)	4.00	83
713	8¢ Portrait by Charles B.J.F. Saint Memin	01/01/32	3.00	.50	50.00	(4)	4.50	97
	Pair, full vert. gutter between		—					
714	9¢ Portrait by W. Williams	01/01/32	2.60	.15	30.00	(4)	4.50	76
715	10¢ Portrait by Gilbert Stuart	01/01/32	11.00	.15	95.00	(4)	4.50	147

688

689

690

702

703

704

705

706

707

708

709

710

711

712

713

714

715

716

717

718

719

720

724

725

726

727

728

729

730

731

732

733

734

	Issues of 1932, Perf. 11		Un	U	PB/LP	#	FDC	Q(M̄)
	Olympic Winter Games Issue							
716	2¢ Ski Jumper	01/25/32	.40	.20	10.00	(6)	6.00	51
	Recut		3.50	1.50				
	Colored "snowball"		25.00	5.00				
	Perf. 11 x 10.5							
717	2¢ Arbor Day	04/22/32	.15	.15	6.50	(4)	4.00	100
	Olympic Summer Games Issue							
718	3¢ Runner at Starting Mark	06/15/32	1.40	.15	11.50	(4)	6.00	168
	Gripper cracks		4.25	.75				
719	5¢ Myron's Discobolus	06/15/32	2.20	.20	20.00	(4)	8.00	53
	Gripper cracks		4.25	1.00				
720	3¢ Washington	06/16/32	.15	.15	1.30	(4)	7.50	
	Pair with full vertical or horizontal gutter between		200.00					
b	Booklet pane of 6	07/25/32	32.50	5.00			100.00	
c	Vertical pair, imperf. between		300.00	250.00				
	Recut lines on nose		2.00	.75				
	Coil Stamp, Perf. 10 Vertically							
721	3¢ deep violet (720)	06/24/32	2.75	.15	10.00	(2)	15.00	
	Recut lines around eyes		—	—				
	Coil Stamp, Perf. 10 Horizontally							
722	3¢ deep violet (720)	10/12/32	1.50	.35	6.25	(2)	15.00	
	Coil Stamp, Perf. 10 Vertically (See also #551-73, 575-79, 581-91, 594-606, 622-23, 631-42, 684-87, 692-701)							
723	6¢ deep orange Garfield (558)	08/18/32	11.00	.30	60.00	(2)	15.00	
	Perf. 11							
724	3¢ William Penn	10/24/32	.25	.15	8.00	(6)	3.25	49
a	Vertical pair, imperf. horizontally		—					
725	3¢ Daniel Webster	10/24/32	.30	.25	16.50	(6)	3.25	49
	Issues of 1933							
726	3¢ Georgia Settlement	02/12/33	.25	.20	10.00	(6)	3.25	61
	Perf. 10.5 x 11							
727	3¢ Peace of 1783	04/19/33	.15	.15	4.00	(4)	3.50	73
	Century of Progress Issue							
728	1¢ Restoration of Fort Dearborn	05/25/33	.15	.15	1.90	(4)	3.00 (3)	348
	Gripper cracks		2.00	—				
729	3¢ Federal Building at Chicago	05/25/33	.15	.15	2.25	(4)	3.00	480
	American Philatelic Society Issue Souvenir Sheets, Without Gum, Imperf.							
730	1¢ sheet of 25 (728)	08/25/33	27.50	27.50			100.00	0.4
a	Single stamp from sheet		.75	.45			3.25 (3)	11
731	3¢ sheet of 25 (729)	08/25/33	25.00	25.00			100.00	0.4
a	Single stamp from sheet		.65	.45			3.25	11
	Perf. 10.5 x 11							
732	3¢ NRA	08/15/33	.15	.15	1.50	(4)	3.25	1,978
	Gripper cracks		1.50	—				
	Recut at right		2.00					
	Perf. 11							
733	3¢ Byrd Antarctic Expedition II	10/09/33	.50	.50	15.00	(6)	10.00	5
	Double transfer		2.75	1.00				
734	5¢ Kosciuszko	10/13/33	.55	.25	27.50	(6)	4.50	45
a	Horizontal pair, imperf. vertically		2,000.00		25,000.00	(8)		

	Issues of 1934, Imperf.		Un	U	PB	#	FDC	Q(M̄)
	National Stamp Exhibition Issue Souvenir Sheet, Without Gum							
735	3¢ sheet of 6 (733)	02/10/34	13.00	10.00			40.00	0.8
a	Single stamp from sheet		2.10	1.65			5.00	4
	Perf. 11							
736	3¢ Maryland Tercentenary	03/23/34	.15	.15	7.50	(6)	1.60	46
	Double transfer		—	—				
	Mothers of America Issue, Perf. 11 x 10.5							
737	3¢ Portrait of his Mother, by James A. McNeill Whistler	05/02/34	.15	.15	1.00	(4)	1.60	193
	Perf. 11							
738	3¢ deep violet (737)	05/02/34	.15	.15	4.25	(6)	1.60	15
739	3¢ Wisconsin Tercentenary	07/07/34	.15	.15	3.00	(6)	1.10	64
a	Vert. pair, imperf. horiz.		250.00					
b	Horiz. pair, imperf. vert.		325.00					
	National Parks Issue, Unwmkd.							
740	1¢ El Capitan, Yosemite (California)	07/16/34	.15	.15	1.00	(6)	2.25	84
	Recut		1.50	.50				
a	Vertical pair, imperf. horizontally, with gum		450.00					
741	2¢ Grand Canyon (Ariz.)	07/24/34	.15	.15	1.25	(6)	2.25	74
a	Vertical pair, imperf. horizontally, with gum		450.00					
b	Horizontal pair, imperf. vertically, with gum		300.00					
	Double transfer		1.25	—				
742	3¢ Mirror Lake, Mt. Rainier (Washington)	08/03/34	.15	.15	1.75	(6)	2.50	95
a	Vertical pair, imperf. horizontally, with gum		350.00					
743	4¢ Cliff Palace, Mesa Verde (Colorado)	09/25/34	.40	.40	7.00	(6)	2.25	19
a	Vertical pair, imperf. horizontally, with gum		500.00					
744	5¢ Old Faithful, Yellowstone (Wyoming)	07/30/34	.75	.65	8.75	(6)	2.25	30
a	Horizontal pair, imperf. vertically, with gum		400.00					
745	6¢ Crater Lake (Oregon)	09/05/34	1.20	.85	15.00	(6)	3.00	16
746	7¢ Great Head, Acadia Park (Maine)	10/02/34	.65	.75	10.00	(6)	3.00	15
a	Horizontal pair, imperf. vertically, with gum		550.00					
747	8¢ Great White Throne, Zion Park (Utah)	09/18/34	1.70	1.50	15.00	(6)	3.25	15
748	9¢ Glacier National Park (Montana)	08/27/34	1.60	.65	15.00	(6)	3.50	17
749	10¢ Great Smoky Mountains (North Carolina)	10/08/34	3.25	1.25	25.00	(6)	6.00	18
	American Philatelic Society Issue Souvenir Sheet, Imperf.							
750	3¢ sheet of 6 (742)	08/28/34	30.00	27.50			40.00	0.5
a	Single stamp from sheet		3.50	3.25			3.25	3
	Trans-Mississippi Philatelic Exposition Issue Souvenir Sheet							
751	1¢ sheet of 6 (740)	10/10/34	12.50	12.50			35.00	0.7
a	Single stamp from sheet		1.40	1.60			3.25 (3)	4

735

736

737

739

740

741

742

743

745

744

746

747

748

749

750

751

Examples of Special Printing Position Blocks

Gutter Block 752

Centerline Block 754

Line Block 756

Arrow Block 763

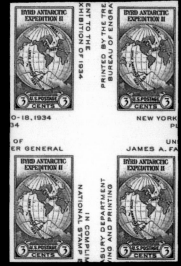

Cross-Gutter Block 768

	Issues of 1935		Un	U	PB	#	FDC	Q(M̄)
	Special Printing (#752-71), Without Gum, Perf. 10.5 x 11							
752	3¢ violet Peace of 1783 (727)	03/15/35	.15	.15	15.00	(4)	5.00	3
	Perf. 11							
753	3¢ blue Byrd Expedition II (733)	03/15/35	.50	.45	19.00	(6)	6.00	2
	Imperf.							
754	3¢ dp. vio. Whistler's Mother (737)	03/15/35	.55	.55	17.50	(6)	6.00	2
755	3¢ deep violet Wisconsin (739)	03/15/35	.55	.55	17.50	(6)	6.00	2
756	1¢ green Yosemite (740)	03/15/35	.20	.20	5.25	(6)	6.00	3
757	2¢ red Grand Canyon (741)	03/15/35	.25	.25	6.00	(6)	6.00	3
	Double transfer		—					
758	3¢ deep violet Mt. Rainier (742)	03/15/35	.50	.45	15.00	(6)	6.00	2
759	4¢ brown Mesa Verde (743)	03/15/35	.95	.95	20.00	(6)	6.50	2
760	5¢ blue Yellowstone (744)	03/15/35	1.50	1.30	25.00	(6)	6.50	2
	Double transfer		—					
761	6¢ dark blue Crater Lake (745)	03/15/35	2.40	2.10	35.00	(6)	6.50	2
762	7¢ black Acadia (746)	03/15/35	1.50	1.40	30.00	(6)	6.50	2
	Double transfer		—					
763	8¢ sage green Zion (747)	03/15/35	1.60	1.50	37.50	(6)	7.50	2
764	9¢ red orange Glacier (748)	03/15/35	1.90	1.65	42.50	(6)	7.50	2
765	10¢ gray black Smoky Mts. (749)	03/15/35	3.75	3.25	50.00	(6)	7.50	2
766	1¢ yellow grn. (728), pane of 25	03/15/35	25.00	25.00			250.00	0.1
a	Single stamp from pane		.70	.40			5.50 (3)	2
767	3¢ violet (729), pane of 25	03/15/35	23.50	23.50			250.00	0.09
a	Single stamp from pane		.60	.40			5.50	2
768	3¢ dark blue (733), pane of 6	03/15/35	20.00	15.00			250.00	0.3
a	Single stamp from pane		2.80	2.40			6.50	2
769	1¢ green (740), pane of 6	03/15/35	12.50	11.00			250.00	0.3
a	Single stamp from pane		1.85	1.80			4.00	2
770	3¢ deep violet (742), pane of 6	03/15/35	30.00	24.00			250.00	0.2
a	Single stamp from pane		3.25	3.10			5.00	1
771	16¢ dark blue Great Seal of U.S.	03/15/35	2.25	2.25	52.50	(6)	12.50	1
	For perforate variety, see #CE2.							

A number of position pieces can be collected from the panes or sheets of the 1935 Special Printing issues, including horizontal and vertical gutter (#752, 766-70) or line (#753-65, 771) blocks of four (HG/L and VG/L), arrow-and-guideline blocks of four (AGL) and crossed-gutter or centerline blocks of four (CG/L). Pairs sell for half the price of blocks of four. Arrow-and-guideline blocks for #753 are top or bottom only.

	HG/L	VG/L	AGL	CG/L		HG/L	VG/L	AGL	CG/L
752	11.00	18.00		47.50	762	8.50	7.50	8.25	14.00
753	4.50	48.00	50.00	55.00	763	7.50	9.50	11.00	17.50
754	3.50	2.80	3.00	7.25	764	10.00	9.00	10.50	22.50
755	3.50	2.80	3.00	7.25	765	18.00	21.00	24.00	30.00
756	.90	1.10	1.25	3.00	766	11.00	14.00		15.00
757	1.40	1.10	1.25	3.50	767	10.50	13.50		15.00
758	2.80	2.50	2.75	5.25	768	15.00	18.00		20.00
759	5.50	4.50	4.75	8.50	769	12.00	14.00		15.00
760	7.00	8.50	9.00	15.00	770	25.00	22.00		30.00
761	13.00	11.00	12.50	20.00	771	13.00	11.00	12.50	50.00

	Issues of 1935		Un	U	PB	#	FDC	Q(M)
	Perf. 11 x 10.5							
	Beginning with #772, unused values are for never-hinged stamps.							
772	3¢ Connecticut	04/26/35	.15	.15	1.40	(4)	9.00	71
	Defect in cent design		1.00	.25				
773	3¢ California Pacific International Expo	05/29/35	.15	.15	1.25	(4)	8.00	101
	Pair with full vertical gutter between		—					
	Perf. 11							
774	3¢ Boulder Dam	09/30/35	.15	.15	1.65	(6)	10.00	74
	Perf. 11 x 10.5							
775	3¢ Michigan Statehood	11/01/35	.15	.15	1.25	(4)	8.00	76
	Issues of 1936							
776	3¢ Republic of Texas	03/02/36	.15	.15	1.10	(4)	17.50	124
	Perf. 10.5 x 11							
777	3¢ Rhode Island	05/04/36	.15	.15	1.10	(4)	8.00	67
	Pair with full gutter between		200.00					
	Third International Philatelic Exhibition Issue Souvenir Sheet, Imperf.							
778	Sheet of 4 different stamps (#772, 773, 775 and 776)	05/09/36	1.75	1.75			13.00	3
a-d	Single stamp from sheet		.40	.30				3
779-81	Not assigned							
	Perf. 11 x 10.5							
782	3¢ Arkansas Statehood	06/15/36	.15	.15	1.10	(4)	8.00	73
783	3¢ Oregon Territory	07/14/36	.15	.15	1.10	(4)	8.50	74
	Double transfer		1.00	.50				
784	3¢ Susan B. Anthony	08/26/36	.15	.15	.75	(4)	5.00	270
	Period missing after "B"		.75	.25				

Susan B. Anthony dollars

Susan B. Anthony (1820-1906), renowned as leader of the women's suffrage movement, was given the honor not only of being on two U.S. stamps, but also of being the first woman pictured on a U.S. coin in general circulation. Minted only between 1979 and 1981, Susan B. Anthony dollars were not a hit with U.S. citizens. Since the coin is only a little larger than a quarter and has ridges along the edge like a quarter, many people had trouble distinguishing between the two coins. Ironically, the problem with Susan B. Anthony dollars could have been avoided if the coin's creators had done some research on failed coins. A twenty-cent piece, very nearly the size and weight of a quarter, had been created and then discontinued in the 1870s because the two were often confused.

(#784)

772

773

774

775

776

777

778

782

783

784

785

786

787

788

789

790

791

792

793

794

795

796

798

799

800

801

802

Issues of 1936-37		Un	U	PB	#	FDC	Q(M̄)
	Perf. 11 x 10.5, Army Issue						
785	1¢ George Washington, Nathanael Green and Mount Vernon	12/15/36	.15	.15	.85	(4)	5.00	105
	Pair with full vertical gutter between		—					
786	2¢ Andrew Jackson, Winfield Scott and The Hermitage	01/15/37	.15	.15	.85	(4)	5.00	94
787	3¢ Generals Sherman, Grant and Sheridan	02/18/37	.20	.15	1.10	(4)	5.00	88
788	4¢ Generals Robert E. Lee and "Stonewall" Jackson and Stratford Hall	03/23/37	.30	.15	8.00	(4)	5.50	36
789	5¢ U.S. Military Academy at West Point	05/26/37	.60	.15	8.50	(4)	5.50	37
	Perf. 11 x 10.5, Navy Issue						
790	1¢ John Paul Jones, John Barry, Bon Homme Richard and Lexington	12/15/36	.15	.15	.85	(4)	5.00	105
791	2¢ Stephen Decatur, Thomas Macdonough and Saratoga	01/15/37	.15	.15	.75	(4)	5.00	92
792	3¢ David G. Farragut and David D. Porter, Hartford and Powhatan	02/18/37	.15	.15	1.00	(4)	5.00	93
793	4¢ Admirals William T. Sampson, George Dewey and Winfield S. Schley	03/23/37	.30	.15	8.50	(4)	5.50	35
794	5¢ Seal of U.S. Naval Academy and Naval Cadets	05/26/37	.60	.15	8.50	(4)	5.50	37
	Issues of 1937						
795	3¢ Northwest Territory Ordinance	07/13/37	.15	.15	1.10	(4)	6.00	85
	Perf. 11						
796	5¢ Virginia Dare	08/18/37	.20	.20	6.75	(6)	7.00	25
	Society of Philatelic Americans Issue Souvenir Sheet, Imperf.						
797	10¢ blue green (749)	08/26/37	.60	.40			6.00	5
	Perf. 11 x 10.5						
798	3¢ Constitution Sesquicentennial	09/17/37	.15	.15	1.00	(4)	6.50	100
	Territorial Issues, Perf. 10.5 x 11						
799	3¢ Hawaii	10/18/37	.15	.15	1.25	(4)	7.00	78
	Perf. 11 x 10.5						
800	3¢ Alaska	11/12/37	.15	.15	1.25	(4)	7.00	77
	Pair with full gutter between		—					
801	3¢ Puerto Rico	11/25/37	.15	.15	1.25	(4)	7.00	81
802	3¢ Virgin Islands	12/15/37	.15	.15	1.25	(4)	7.00	76
	Pair with full vertical gutter between		275.00					

	Issues of 1938-39, Perf. 11 x 10.5		Un	U	PB	#	FDC
	Presidential Issue (#804b, 806b, 807a issued in 1939, 832b in 1951, 832c in 1954, rest in 1938; see also 839-51)						
803	1/2¢ Benjamin Franklin	05/19/38	.15	.15	.35	(4)	2.25
804	1¢ George Washington	04/25/38	.15	.15	.25	(4)	2.50
b	Booklet pane of 6	01/27/39	2.00	.75			15.00
	Pair with full vertical gutter between		160.00	—			
805	1 1/2¢ Martha Washington	05/05/38	.15	.15	.22	(4)	2.50
b	Horizontal pair, imperf. between		175.00	30.00			
	Pair with full horizontal gutter between		175.00				
806	2¢ John Adams	06/03/38	.15	.15	.30	(4)	2.50
b	Booklet pane of 6	01/27/39	4.75	.75			15.00
	Recut at top of head		3.00	1.50			
807	3¢ Thomas Jefferson	06/16/38	.15	.15	.25	(4)	2.50
a	Booklet pane of 6	01/27/39	8.50	1.00			18.00
b	Horizontal pair, imperf. between		900.00	—			
c	Imperf. pair		2,500.00				
808	4¢ James Madison	07/01/38	.75	.15	3.75	(4)	2.50
809	4 1/2¢ The White House	07/11/38	.15	.15	1.50	(4)	2.50
810	5¢ James Monroe	07/21/38	.20	.15	1.00	(4)	2.50
811	6¢ John Quincy Adams	07/28/38	.20	.15	1.00	(4)	2.50
812	7¢ Andrew Jackson	08/04/38	.25	.15	1.25	(4)	2.50
813	8¢ Martin Van Buren	08/11/38	.30	.15	1.40	(4)	2.50
814	9¢ William H. Harrison	08/18/38	.30	.15	1.40	(4)	3.00
	Pair with full vertical gutter between		—				
815	10¢ John Tyler	09/02/38	.25	.15	1.25	(4)	3.00
816	11¢ James K. Polk	09/08/38	.65	.15	3.00	(4)	3.00
817	12¢ Zachary Taylor	09/14/38	.90	.15	4.25	(4)	3.00
818	13¢ Millard Fillmore	09/22/38	1.25	.15	6.50	(4)	3.00
819	14¢ Franklin Pierce	10/06/38	.90	.15	4.50	(4)	3.00
820	15¢ James Buchanan	10/13/38	.40	.15	1.90	(4)	3.00
821	16¢ Abraham Lincoln	10/20/38	.90	.25	4.50	(4)	5.00
822	17¢ Andrew Johnson	10/27/38	.85	.15	4.50	(4)	5.00
823	18¢ Ulysses S. Grant	11/03/38	1.75	.15	8.75	(4)	5.00
824	19¢ Rutherford B. Hayes	11/10/38	1.25	.35	6.25	(4)	5.00
825	20¢ James A. Garfield	11/10/38	.70	.15	3.50	(4)	5.00
826	21¢ Chester A. Arthur	11/22/38	1.25	.15	7.00	(4)	5.00
827	22¢ Grover Cleveland	11/22/38	1.00	.40	9.50	(4)	5.00
828	24¢ Benjamin Harrison	12/02/38	3.50	.20	17.00	(4)	5.00
829	25¢ William McKinley	12/02/38	.60	.15	3.00	(4)	6.00
830	30¢ Theodore Roosevelt	12/08/38	4.25	.15	21.00	(4)	7.50
831	50¢ William Howard Taft	12/08/38	6.00	.15	27.50	(4)	10.00

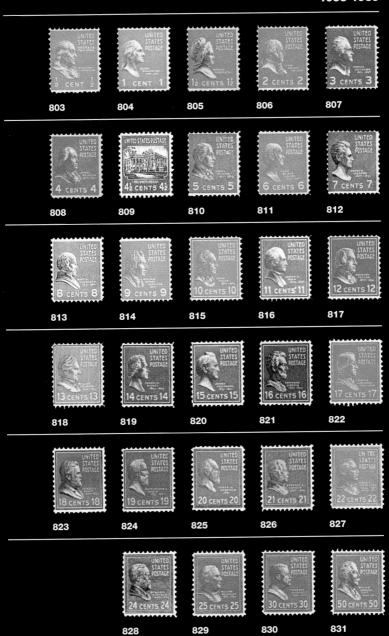

832

833

834

835

836

837

838

852

853

854

855

856

857

858

	Issues of 1938-54, Perf. 11		Un	U	PB/LP	#	FDC	Q(M̄)
832	$1 Woodrow Wilson	08/29/38	7.00	.15	35.00	(4)	50.00	
a	Vertical pair, imperf. horizontally		1,500.00					
b	Watermarked "USIR" (1951)		275.00	70.00	1,700.00	(4)		
c	$1 red violet and black	08/31/54	6.00	.15	30.00	(4)	25.00	
d	As "c," vert. pair, imperf. horiz.		1,250.00					
e	Vertical pair, imperf. between		2,750.00					
f	As "c," vert. pair, imperf. between		7,000.00					
833	$2 Warren G. Harding	09/29/38	22.50	3.75	110.00	(4)	100.00	
834	$5 Calvin Coolidge	11/17/38	105.00	3.00	475.00	(4)	150.00	
a	$5 red, brown and black		3,500.00	1,500.00				
	Issues of 1938, Perf. 11 x 10.5							
835	3¢ Constitution Ratification	06/21/38	.25	.15	3.50	(4)	6.50	73
	Perf. 11							
836	3¢ Swedish-Finnish Tercentenary	06/27/38	.15	.15	2.50	(6)	6.00	59
	Perf. 11 x 10.5							
837	3¢ Northwest Territory	07/15/38	.15	.15	7.50	(4)	6.00	66
838	3¢ Iowa Territorial Centennial	08/24/38	.15	.15	5.00	(4)	6.00	47
	Pair with full vertical gutter between		—					
	Issues of 1939, Coil Stamps, Perf. 10 Vertically							
839	1¢ green Washington (804)	01/20/39	.30	.15	1.40	(2)	5.00	
840	1¹/₂¢ bister brn. Martha Washington (805)	01/20/39	.30	.15	1.50	(2)	5.00	
841	2¢ rose carmine John Adams (806)	01/20/39	.40	.15	1.75	(2)	5.00	
842	3¢ deep violet Jefferson (807)	01/20/39	.50	.15	2.00	(2)	5.00	
	Gripper cracks		—					
	Thin, translucent paper		2.50	—				
843	4¢ red violet Madison (808)	01/20/39	8.00	.40	27.50	(2)	5.00	
844	4¹/₂¢ dark gray White House (809)	01/20/38	.70	.40	5.00	(2)	5.00	
845	5¢ bright blue Monroe (810)	01/20/39	5.00	.35	27.50	(2)	5.00	
846	6¢ red orange John Quincy Adams (811)	01/20/39	1.10	.20	7.50	(2)	7.00	
847	10¢ brown red Tyler (815)	01/20/39	11.00	.50	42.50	(2)	9.00	
	Coil Stamps, Perf. 10 Horizontally							
848	1¢ green Washington (804)	01/27/39	.85	.15	2.75	(2)	5.00	
849	1¹/₂¢ bister brn. Martha Washington (805)	01/27/39	1.25	.30	4.50	(2)	5.00	
850	2¢ rose carmine John Adams (806)	01/27/39	2.50	.40	6.50	(2)	5.00	
851	3¢ deep violet Jefferson (807)	01/27/39	2.25	.35	6.25	(2)	6.00	
	Perf. 10.5 x 11							
852	3¢ Golden Gate Exposition	02/18/39	.15	.15	1.25	(4)	6.00	114
853	3¢ New York World's Fair	04/01/39	.15	.15	1.75	(4)	12.50	102
	Perf. 11							
854	3¢ Washington's Inauguration	04/30/39	.40	.15	3.50	(6)	6.00	73
	Perf. 11 x 10.5							
855	3¢ Baseball	06/12/39	1.75	.15	7.50	(4)	35.00	81
	Perf. 11							
856	3¢ Panama Canal	08/15/39	.25	.15	3.00	(6)	6.50	68
	Perf. 10.5 x 11							
857	3¢ Printing	09/25/39	.15	.15	1.00	(4)	5.00	71
	Perf. 11 x 10.5							
858	3¢ 50th Anniversary of Statehood (Montana, North Dakota, South Dakota, Washington)	11/02/39	.15	.15	1.10	(4)	5.00	67

	Issues of 1940, Perf. 10.5 x 11		Un	U	PB	#	FDC	Q(M̄)
	Famous Americans Issue							
	Authors							
859	1¢ Washington Irving	01/29/40	.15	.15	.95	(4)	2.00	56
860	2¢ James Fenimore Cooper	01/29/40	.15	.15	.95	(4)	1.50	53
861	3¢ Ralph Waldo Emerson	02/05/40	.15	.15	1.25	(4)	1.50	53
862	5¢ Louisa May Alcott	02/05/40	.30	.20	8.25	(4)	2.25	22
863	10¢ Samuel L. Clemens (Mark Twain)	02/13/40	1.65	1.20	35.00	(4)	3.75	13
	Poets							
864	1¢ Henry W. Longfellow	02/16/40	.15	.15	1.75	(4)	1.50	52
865	2¢ John Greenleaf Whittier	02/16/40	.15	.15	1.75	(4)	1.50	52
866	3¢ James Russell Lowell	02/20/40	.15	.15	2.25	(4)	1.50	52
867	5¢ Walt Whitman	02/20/40	.35	.15	9.00	(4)	4.00	22
868	10¢ James Whitcomb Riley	02/24/40	1.75	1.25	32.50	(4)	6.00	12
	Educators							
869	1¢ Horace Mann	03/14/40	.15	.15	1.90	(4)	1.50	52
870	2¢ Mark Hopkins	03/14/40	.15	.15	1.25	(4)	1.50	52
871	3¢ Charles W. Eliot	03/28/40	.15	.15	2.25	(4)	1.50	52
872	5¢ Frances E. Willard	03/28/40	.40	.20	9.00	(4)	4.00	21
873	10¢ Booker T. Washington	04/07/40	1.25	1.10	25.00	(4)	6.50	14
	Scientists							
874	1¢ John James Audubon	04/08/40	.15	.15	.95	(4)	1.50	59
875	2¢ Dr. Crawford W. Long	04/08/40	.15	.15	.95	(4)	1.50	58
876	3¢ Luther Burbank	04/17/40	.15	.15	1.10	(4)	2.00	58
877	5¢ Dr. Walter Reed	04/17/40	.25	.15	6.25	(4)	2.50	24
878	10¢ Jane Addams	04/26/40	1.10	.85	22.50	(4)	5.00	15
	Composers							
879	1¢ Stephen Collins Foster	05/03/40	.15	.15	1.00	(4)	1.50	57
880	2¢ John Philip Sousa	05/03/40	.15	.15	1.00	(4)	1.50	58
881	3¢ Victor Herbert	05/13/40	.15	.15	1.10	(4)	1.50	56
882	5¢ Edward A. MacDowell	05/13/40	.40	.20	9.25	(4)	2.50	21
883	10¢ Ethelbert Nevin	06/10/40	3.75	1.20	32.50	(4)	5.00	13
	Artists							
884	1¢ Gilbert Charles Stuart	09/05/40	.15	.15	1.00	(4)	1.50	54
885	2¢ James A. McNeill Whistler	09/05/40	.15	.15	.95	(4)	1.50	54
886	3¢ Augustus Saint-Gaudens	09/16/40	.15	.15	1.00	(4)	1.50	55
887	5¢ Daniel Chester French	09/16/40	.50	.20	8.00	(4)	1.75	22
888	10¢ Frederic Remington	09/30/40	1.75	1.25	25.00	(4)	5.00	14
	Inventors							
889	1¢ Eli Whitney	10/07/40	.15	.15	1.90	(4)	1.50	48
890	2¢ Samuel F.B. Morse	10/07/40	.15	.15	1.10	(4)	1.50	53
891	3¢ Cyrus Hall McCormick	10/14/40	.25	.15	1.75	(4)	1.50	54
892	5¢ Elias Howe	10/14/40	1.10	.30	13.00	(4)	3.00	20
893	10¢ Alexander Graham Bell	10/28/40	11.00	2.00	70.00	(4)	7.50	14

Minimum value listed for a stamp is 15 cents; for a First Day Cover (FDC), $1.00. This minimum represents a fair-market price for having a dealer locate and provide a single stamp or cover from his or her stock. Dealers may charge less per stamp or cover for a group of such stamps or covers, or less for a single stamp or cover.

859 860 861 862 863

864 865 866 867 868

869 870 871 872 873

874 875 876 877 878

879 880 881 882 883

884 885 886 887 888

889 890 891 892 893

894

895

896

897

898

899

900

901

902

903

904

905

906

907

908

	Issues of 1940, Perf. 11 x 10.5		Un	U	PB	#	FDC	Q(M̄)
894	3¢ Pony Express	04/03/40	.25	.15	2.75	(4)	5.00	46
	Perf. 10.5 x 11							
895	3¢ Pan American Union	04/14/40	.20	.15	2.75	(4)	4.50	48
	Perf. 11 x 10.5							
896	3¢ Idaho Statehood	07/03/40	.15	.15	1.75	(4)	4.50	51
	Perf. 10.5 x 11							
897	3¢ Wyoming Statehood	07/10/40	.15	.15	1.50	(4)	4.50	50
	Perf. 11 x 10.5							
898	3¢ Coronado Expedition	09/07/40	.15	.15	1.50	(4)	4.50	61
	National Defense Issue							
899	1¢ Statue of Liberty	10/16/40	.15	.15	.45	(4)	4.25	
a	Vertical pair, imperf. between		650.00	—				
b	Horizontal pair, imperf. between		40.00	—				
	Pair with full vertical gutter between		200.00					
	Cracked plate		3.00					
	Gripper cracks		3.00					
900	2¢ 90mm Antiaircraft Gun	10/16/40	.15	.15	.45	(4)	4.25	
a	Horizontal pair, imperf. between		40.00	—				
	Pair with full vertical gutter between		275.00					
901	3¢ Torch of Enlightenment	10/16/40	.15	.15	.60	(4)	4.25	
a	Horizontal pair, imperf. between		30.00	—				
	Pair with full vertical gutter between		—					
	Perf. 10.5 x 11							
902	3¢ Thirteenth Amendment	10/20/40	.20	.15	3.00	(4)	7.50	44
	Issue of 1941, Perf. 11 x 10.5							
903	3¢ Vermont Statehood	03/04/41	.15	.15	1.75	(4)	7.00	55
	Issues of 1942							
904	3¢ Kentucky Statehood	06/01/42	.15	.15	1.10	(4)	4.00	64
905	3¢ Win the War	07/04/42	.15	.15	.40	(4)	3.75	
b	3¢ purple		—	—				
	Pair with full vertical or horizontal gutter between		175.00					
906	5¢ Chinese Resistance	07/07/42	.30	.20	8.75	(4)	6.00	21
	Issues of 1943							
907	2¢ Allied Nations	01/14/43	.15	.15	.30	(4)	3.50	1,700
	Pair with full vertical or horizontal gutter between		225.00					
908	1¢ Four Freedoms	02/12/43	.15	.15	.60	(4)	3.50	1,200

"Can We Talk?"

Comedienne Joan Rivers would have had a very short career had the answer to that question been "No!" Luckily for her and the rest of the nation, we have the right to free speech. In 1941, President Franklin D. Roosevelt (1882-1945) created the Four Freedoms in the hopes that some of our nation's freedoms could become worldwide. The Four Freedoms consist of the freedom of speech and expression, the freedom of every person to worship God in his own way, the freedom from want and the freedom from fear. The Four Freedoms proved valuable primarily as a wartime slogan since they lacked any common meaning throughout the world. **(#908)**

	Issues of 1943-44, Perf. 12		Un	U	PB	#	FDC	Q(M̄)
	Overrun Countries Issue							
909	5¢ Poland	06/22/43	.20	.15	5.00*	(4)	7.50	20
910	5¢ Czechoslovakia	07/12/43	.20	.15	3.00*	(4)	4.00	20
911	5¢ Norway	07/27/43	.15	.15	1.50*	(4)	4.00	20
912	5¢ Luxembourg	08/10/43	.15	.15	1.40*	(4)	4.00	20
913	5¢ Netherlands	08/24/43	.15	.15	1.40*	(4)	4.00	20
914	5¢ Belgium	09/14/43	.15	.15	1.25*	(4)	4.00	20
915	5¢ France	09/28/43	.15	.15	1.40*	(4)	4.00	20
916	5¢ Greece,	10/12/43	.35	.25	12.50*	(4)	4.00	15
917	5¢ Yugoslavia	10/26/43	.25	.15	5.00*	(4)	4.00	15
918	5¢ Albania	11/09/43	.20	.15	5.00*	(4)	4.00	15
919	5¢ Austria	11/23/43	.20	.15	4.00*	(4)	4.00	15
920	5¢ Denmark	12/07/43	.20	.15	5.75*	(4)	4.00	15
921	5¢ Korea	11/02/44	.15	.15	5.00*	(4)	5.00	15
	"KORPA" plate flaw		17.50	12.50				
	*Instead of plate numbers, the selvage is inscribed with the name of the country.							
	Issues of 1944, Perf. 11 x 10.5							
922	3¢ Transcontinental Railroad	05/10/44	.20	.15	1.40	(4)	6.00	61
923	3¢ Steamship	05/22/44	.15	.15	1.25	(4)	4.00	61
924	3¢ Telegraph	05/24/44	.15	.15	.90	(4)	3.50	61
925	3¢ Philippines	09/27/44	.15	.15	1.10	(4)	3.50	50
926	3¢ Motion Pictures	10/31/44	.15	.15	.90	(4)	4.00	53

Motion pictures still appeal to the masses

Since the late 19th century, no other fine art technique has created such mass appeal as the motion picture. Produced by a series of rapid projections on a screen with light and transformed by the optical phenomenon "persistence of vision," individual frames appear as images of smooth and continuous movement. Composite prints are the result of sound and picture combined. The tools required to produce a motion picture include a camera and its lenses, film, sound and lighting equipment, and a projector and screen. In 1896, Thomas Edison presented the first U.S. screening of projected motion pictures in a New York City music hall. **(#926)**

909

910

911

912

913

914

915

916

917

918

919

920

921

922

923

924

925

926

927

928

929

930

931

932

933

934

935

936

937

938

939

940

941

942

943

944

945

946

947

	Issues of 1945, Perf. 11 x 10.5		Un	U	PB	#	FDC	Q(M̄)
927	3¢ Florida Statehood	03/03/45	.15	.15	.50	(4)	4.50	62
928	5¢ United Nations Conference	04/25/45	.15	.15	.45	(4)	4.50	76
	Perf. 10.5 x 11							
929	3¢ Iwo Jima (Marines)	07/11/45	.15	.15	.40	(4)	10.00	137
	Issues of 1945-46, Franklin D. Roosevelt Issue, Perf. 11 x 10.5							
930	1¢ Roosevelt and Hyde Park Residence	07/26/45	.15	.15	.15	(4)	3.00	128
931	2¢ Roosevelt and "The Little White House" at Warm Springs, Ga.	08/24/45	.15	.15	.25	(4)	3.00	67
932	3¢ Roosevelt and White House	06/27/45	.15	.15	.30	(4)	3.00	134
933	5¢ Roosevelt, Map of Western Hemisphere and Four Freedoms	01/30/46	.15	.15	.45	(4)	3.00	76
934	3¢ Army, Sept. 28	09/28/45	.15	.15	.30	(4)	6.00	128
935	3¢ Navy	10/27/45	.15	.15	.30	(4)	6.00	136
936	3¢ Coast Guard	11/10/45	.15	.15	.30	(4)	6.00	112
937	3¢ Alfred E. Smith	11/26/45	.15	.15	.30	(4)	2.50	309
	Pair with full vertical gutter between		—					
938	3¢ Texas Statehood	12/29/45	.15	.15	.30	(4)	4.00	171
	Issues of 1946							
939	3¢ Merchant Marine	02/26/46	.15	.15	.30	(4)	5.00	136
940	3¢ Veterans of World War II	05/09/46	.15	.15	.30	(4)	4.00	260
941	3¢ Tennessee Statehood	06/01/46	.15	.15	.30	(4)	1.50	132
942	3¢ Iowa Statehood	08/03/46	.15	.15	.30	(4)	1.50	132
943	3¢ Smithsonian Institution	08/10/46	.15	.15	.30	(4)	1.50	139
944	3¢ Kearny Expedition	10/16/46	.15	.15	.30	(4)	1.50	115
	Issues of 1947, Perf. 10.5 x 11							
945	3¢ Thomas A. Edison	02/11/47	.15	.15	.30	(4)	3.00	157
	Perf. 11 x 10.5							
946	3¢ Joseph Pulitzer	04/10/47	.15	.15	.30	(4)	1.50	120
947	3¢ Postage Stamps Centenary	05/17/47	.15	.15	.30	(4)	1.50	127

Who was a major contributor to Columbia University's School of Journalism?

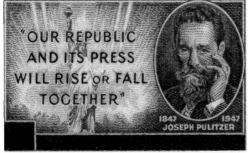

Joseph Pulitzer (1847-1911), American journalist, donated $2 million to Columbia University in New York for a school of journalism (founded in 1912) and for the establishment of the Pulitzer Prizes—awards which recognize excellence in journalism and writing. Born in Hungary, Pulitzer immigrated to the United States in 1864 and became a citizen in 1867. Known for his innovations in newspaper publishing, Pulitzer was also active in politics in St. Louis, Missouri, and was elected to the Missouri House of Representatives in 1869. **(#946)**

	Issues of 1947, Imperf.		Un	U	PB	#	FDC	Q(M̄)
	Centenary International Philatelic Exhibition Issue Souvenir Sheet							
948	Souvenir sheet of 2 stamps (#1-2)	05/19/47	.55	.45			2.00	10
a	5¢ single stamp from sheet		.20	.20				
b	10¢ single stamp from sheet		.25	.25				
	Perf. 11 x 10.5							
949	3¢ Doctors	06/09/47	.15	.15	.30	(4)	2.50	133
950	3¢ Utah Settlement	07/24/47	.15	.15	.30	(4)	1.00	132
951	3¢ U.S. Frigate *Constitution*	10/21/47	.15	.15	.30	(4)	5.00	131
	Perf. 10.5 x 11							
952	3¢ Everglades National Park	12/05/47	.15	.15	.30	(4)	1.00	122
	Issues of 1948							
953	3¢ Dr. G.W. Carver	01/05/48	.15	.15	.30	(4)	1.00	122
	Perf. 11 x 10.5							
954	3¢ California Gold	01/24/48	.15	.15	.30	(4)	1.00	131
955	3¢ Mississippi Territory	04/07/48	.15	.15	.30	(4)	1.00	123
956	3¢ Four Chaplains	05/28/48	.15	.15	.30	(4)	2.50	122
957	3¢ Wisconsin Statehood	05/29/48	.15	.15	.30	(4)	1.00	115
958	5¢ Swedish Pioneer	06/04/48	.15	.15	.45	(4)	1.00	64
959	3¢ Progress of Women	07/19/48	.15	.15	.30	(4)	1.00	118
	Perf. 10.5 x 11							
960	3¢ William Allen White	07/31/48	.15	.15	.35	(4)	1.00	78
	Perf. 11 x 10.5							
961	3¢ U.S.-Canada Friendship	08/02/48	.15	.15	.30	(4)	1.00	113
962	3¢ Francis Scott Key	08/09/48	.15	.15	.30	(4)	1.00	121
963	3¢ Salute to Youth	08/11/48	.15	.15	.30	(4)	1.00	78
964	3¢ Oregon Territory	08/14/48	.15	.15	.35	(4)	1.00	52
	Perf. 10.5 x 11							
965	3¢ Harlan F. Stone	08/25/48	.15	.15	.65	(4)	1.00	54
966	3¢ Palomar Observatory	08/30/48	.15	.15	1.00	(4)	2.00	61
a	Vertical pair, imperf. between		550.00					
	Perf. 11 x 10.5							
967	3¢ Clara Barton	09/07/48	.15	.15	.30	(4)	3.00	58

Collecting data billions of light years away

Palomar Observatory, located atop Palomar Mountain in California, is home to the 200-inch Hale Telescope and several other powerful astronomical instruments. Owned and operated by the California Institute of Technology, a private institution in Pasadena, California, the 200-inch Hale Telescope includes a 1,000-ton rotating dome and a moving structure weighing 530 tons. Although open to visitors, this amazing observatory is used exclusively by scientists to investigate other galaxies and gather information about the universe. The telescopes are so powerful that they can collect light that has been in transit to Earth for billions of years. Space telescopes orbiting Earth are also used in partnership with ground-based telescopes such as Palomar's to gather data that neither could alone. **(#966)**

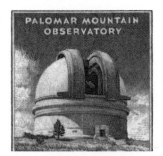

Interesting Fact: Light pollution is an increasing problem for observatories. Sky glow from rapid population growth could threaten the effectiveness of the Palomar Observatory.

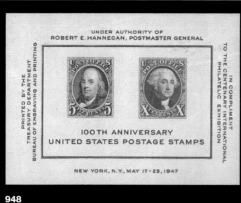

948

949

950

951

952

953

954

955

956

957

958

959

960

961

962

963

964

965

966

967

968

969

970

971

972

973

974

975

976

977

978

979

980

981

982

983

984

985

986

987

988

	Issues of 1948, Perf. 11 x 10.5		Un	U	PB	#	FDC	Q(M̄)
968	3¢ Poultry Industry	09/09/48	.15	.15	.35	(4)	1.00	53
	Perf. 10.5 x 11							
969	3¢ Gold Star Mothers	09/21/48	.15	.15	.35	(4)	1.00	77
	Perf. 11 x 10.5							
970	3¢ Fort Kearny	09/22/48	.15	.15	.35	(4)	1.00	58
971	3¢ Volunteer Firemen	10/04/48	.15	.15	.35	(4)	5.00	56
972	3¢ Indian Centennial	10/15/48	.15	.15	.35	(4)	1.00	58
973	3¢ Rough Riders	10/27/48	.15	.15	.40	(4)	1.00	54
974	3¢ Juliette Gordon Low	10/29/48	.15	.15	.30	(4)	1.50	64
	Perf. 10.5 x 11							
975	3¢ Will Rogers	11/04/48	.15	.15	.40	(4)	1.00	67
976	3¢ Fort Bliss	11/05/48	.15	.15	1.10	(4)	2.00	65
	Perf. 11 x 10.5							
977	3¢ Moina Michael	11/09/48	.15	.15	.35	(4)	1.00	64
978	3¢ Gettysburg Address	11/19/48	.15	.15	.35	(4)	1.00	63
	Perf. 10.5 x 11							
979	3¢ American Turners	11/20/48	.15	.15	.30	(4)	1.00	62
980	3¢ Joel Chandler Harris	12/09/48	.15	.15	.55	(4)	1.00	57
	Issues of 1949, Perf. 11 x 10.5							
981	3¢ Minnesota Territory	03/03/49	.15	.15	.30	(4)	1.00	99
982	3¢ Washington and Lee University	04/12/49	.15	.15	.30	(4)	1.00	105
983	3¢ Puerto Rico Election	04/27/49	.15	.15	.30	(4)	1.00	109
984	3¢ Annapolis Tercentenary	05/23/49	.15	.15	.30	(4)	1.00	107
985	3¢ Grand Army of the Republic	08/29/49	.15	.15	.30	(4)	1.00	117
	Perf. 10.5 x 11							
986	3¢ Edgar Allan Poe	10/07/49	.15	.15	.45	(4)	1.00	123
	Thin outer frame line at top, inner frame line missing		6.00					
	Issues of 1950, Perf. 11 x 10.5							
987	3¢ American Bankers	01/03/50	.15	.15	.30	(4)	2.00	131
	Perf. 10.5 x 11							
988	3¢ Samuel Gompers	01/27/50	.15	.15	.30	(4)	1.00	128

Muscogee or Creek?

The Five Civilized Tribes celebrated on the Indian Centennial stamp of 1948 are commonly identified as Cherokee, Chickasaw, Choctaw, Creek and Seminole. Why, then, is Muscogee listed on the stamp in place of Creek? The name Muscogee is an English form of the name "Mvskoke" which the Indians from this southeast region called themselves. "Mvskoke" or "Muscogee" is the language spoken by this group of people. However, in the early 1700s, the English began referring to the inhabitants on the Ochese Creek near the Okmulgee River as just "Creek," but the tribe's name for itself remained Muscogee, the name that appears on the stamp. **(#972)**

	Issues of 1950		Un	U	PB	#	FDC	Q(M̄)
	National Capital Sesquicentennial Issue, Perf. 10.5 x 11, 11 x 10.5							
989	3¢ Statue of Freedom on Capitol Dome	04/20/50	.15	.15	.30	(4)	1.00	132
990	3¢ Executive Mansion	06/12/50	.15	.15	.40	(4)	1.00	130
991	3¢ Supreme Court	08/02/50	.15	.15	.30	(4)	1.00	131
992	3¢ U.S. Capitol	11/22/50	.15	.15	.40	(4)	1.00	130
	Gripper cracks		1.00	.50				
	Perf. 11 x 10.5							
993	3¢ Railroad Engineers	04/29/50	.15	.15	.30	(4)	1.00	122
994	3¢ Kansas City, MO	06/03/50	.15	.15	.30	(4)	1.00	122
995	3¢ Boy Scouts	06/30/50	.15	.15	.30	(4)	5.00	132
996	3¢ Indiana Territory	07/04/50	.15	.15	.30	(4)	1.00	122
997	3¢ California Statehood	09/09/50	.15	.15	.30	(4)	1.00	121
	Issues of 1951							
998	3¢ United Confederate Veterans	05/30/51	.15	.15	.30	(4)	1.00	119
999	3¢ Nevada Settlement	07/14/51	.15	.15	.30	(4)	1.00	112
1000	3¢ Landing of Cadillac	07/24/51	.15	.15	.30	(4)	1.00	114
1001	3¢ Colorado Statehood	08/01/51	.15	.15	.30	(4)	1.00	114
1002	3¢ American Chemical Society	09/04/51	.15	.15	.30	(4)	2.00	117
1003	3¢ Battle of Brooklyn	12/10/51	.15	.15	.30	(4)	1.00	116
	Issues of 1952							
1004	3¢ Betsy Ross	01/02/52	.15	.15	.35	(4)	1.00	116
1005	3¢ 4-H Club	01/15/52	.15	.15	.30	(4)	1.00	116
1006	3¢ B&O Railroad	02/28/52	.15	.15	.35	(4)	1.25	113
1007	3¢ American Automobile Association	03/04/52	.15	.15	.30	(4)	1.00	117

Railroad engineer and hero

"Casey Jones, he pushed on the throttler,
Casey Jones was a brave engineer,
Come on, Casey, and blow the whistler,
Blow the whistler so they all can hear!"

That's exactly what John Luther "Casey" Jones (1864-1900) did! Engine wiper Wallace Saunders wrote these ballad lyrics about his good friend Casey, arguably the most famous in a long line of railroad engineer heroes to have died at his post. With one hand on the whistle cord and the other on the airbrake lever, Casey perished at the throttle of his speeding engine when it crashed into another freight train stalled in its path. Sim Webb, the fireman on Casey's doomed train, survived the crash because his boss ordered him to jump. "I remember," Webb said later, "that as I jumped, Casey held down the whistle in

a long, piercing scream. I think he must have had in mind to warn the freight conductor in the caboose so he could jump." Thanks to the courageous actions of Casey Jones, everyone else on the trains escaped with only minor injuries. **(#993)**

989

990

991

992

993

994

995

996

997

998

999

1000

1001

1002

1003

1004

1005

1006

1007

1008　　**1009**　　**1010**

1011

1012　　**1013**　　**1014**

1015　　**1016**　　**1017**

1018　　**1019**　　**1020**

1021　　**1022**　　**1023**

1024　　**1025**　　**1026**

1027　　**1028**　　**1029**

	Issues of 1952, Perf. 11 x 10.5		Un	U	PB	#	FDC	Q(M̄)
1008	3¢ NATO	04/04/52	.15	.15	.30	(4)	1.00	2,900
1009	3¢ Grand Coulee Dam	05/15/52	.15	.15	.30	(4)	1.00	115
1010	3¢ Arrival of Lafayette	06/13/52	.15	.15	.30	(4)	1.00	113
	Perf. 10.5 x 11							
1011	3¢ Mt. Rushmore Memorial	08/11/52	.15	.15	.35	(4)	1.00	116
	Perf. 11 x 10.5							
1012	3¢ Engineering	09/06/52	.15	.15	.30	(4)	1.00	114
1013	3¢ Service Women	09/11/52	.15	.15	.30	(4)	1.00	124
1014	3¢ Gutenberg Bible	09/30/52	.15	.15	.30	(4)	1.00	116
1015	3¢ Newspaper Boys	10/04/52	.15	.15	.30	(4)	1.00	115
1016	3¢ International Red Cross	11/21/52	.15	.15	.30	(4)	1.00	136
	Issues of 1953							
1017	3¢ National Guard	02/23/53	.15	.15	.30	(4)	1.00	115
1018	3¢ Ohio Statehood	03/02/53	.15	.15	.35	(4)	1.00	119
1019	3¢ Washington Territory	03/02/53	.15	.15	.30	(4)	1.00	114
1020	3¢ Louisiana Purchase	04/30/53	.15	.15	.30	(4)	1.00	114
1021	5¢ Opening of Japan	07/14/53	.15	.15	.75	(4)	1.00	89
1022	3¢ American Bar Association	08/24/53	.15	.15	.30	(4)	3.00	115
1023	3¢ Sagamore Hill	09/14/53	.15	.15	.30	(4)	1.00	116
1024	3¢ Future Farmers	10/13/53	.15	.15	.30	(4)	1.00	115
1025	3¢ Trucking Industry	10/27/53	.15	.15	.30	(4)	1.00	124
1026	3¢ General George S. Patton	11/11/53	.15	.15	.40	(4)	4.00	115
1027	3¢ New York City	11/20/53	.15	.15	.35	(4)	1.00	116
1028	3¢ Gadsden Purchase	12/30/53	.15	.15	.30	(4)	1.00	116
	Issue of 1954							
1029	3¢ Columbia University	01/04/54	.15	.15	.30	(4)	1.00	119

The first books printed from movable type

When German metalsmith Johannes Gutenberg created a new movable type in 1455, he invented the gateway for mass production of the written word. The 200 Bibles printed with his movable-type method became known as the Gutenberg Bibles. His Western movable-type system, using a press with a precisely calibrated type-mold and smudge-resistant ink, worked so well that it remained virtually unchanged for 350 years. His method spread rapidly and, by 1500, an estimated half a million printed books were in circulation. **(#1014)**

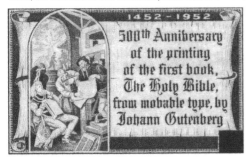

Interesting Fact: In 1997, LIFE *magazine named Gutenberg's printing of the Bibles as the most important technological event of the second millennium.*

	Issues of 1954-67, Perf. 11 x 10.5, 10.5 x 11		Un	U	PB	#	FDC
	Liberty Issue						
1030	¹/₂¢ Franklin	10/20/55	.15	.15	.25	(4)	1.00
1031	1¢ Washington	03/56	.15	.15	.20	(4)	
	Pair with full vertical or horizontal gutter between		150.00				
b	Wet printing		.15	.15	.20	(4)	1.00
	Perf. 10.5 x 11						
1031A	1¹/₄¢ Palace of the Governors	06/17/60	.15	.15	.45	(4)	1.00
1032	1¹/₂¢ Mt. Vernon	02/22/56	.15	.15	2.00	(4)	1.00
	Perf. 11 x 10.5						
1033	2¢ Jefferson	09/15/54	.15	.15	.22	(4)	1.00
	Pair with full vertical or horizontal gutter between		—				
1034	2¹/₂¢ Bunker Hill	06/17/59	.15	.15	.50	(4)	1.00
1035	3¢ Statue of Liberty	06/24/54	.15	.15	.25	(4)	
a	Booklet pane of 6	06/30/54	4.00	.90			5.00
b	Tagged	07/06/66	.25	.25	5.00	(4)	15.00
c	Imperf. pair		2,250.00				
d	Horizontal pair, imperf. between		—				
e	Wet printing	06/24/54	.15	.15	.30		1.00
f	As "a," untagged		5.00	.60			
1036	4¢ Lincoln	11/19/54	.15	.15	.35	(4)	
a	Booklet pane of 6	07/31/58	2.75	.80			4.00
b	Tagged	11/02/63	.50	.40	6.50	(4)	50.00
	Perf. 10.5 x 11						
1037	4¹/₂¢ The Hermitage	03/16/59	.15	.15	.65	(4)	1.00
	Perf. 11 x 10.5						
1038	5¢ James Monroe	12/02/54	.15	.15	.45	(4)	1.00
	Pair with full vertical gutter between		200.00				
1039	6¢ T. Roosevelt	11/18/55	.25	.15	1.10	(4)	
a	Wet printing	11/18/55	.40	.15	1.65	(4)	1.00
1040	7¢ Wilson	01/10/56	.20	.15	1.00	(4)	1.00
	Perf. 11						
1041	8¢ Statue of Liberty	04/09/54	.25	.15	2.25	(4)	1.00
a	Carmine double impression		650.00				
1042	8¢ Statue of Liberty, redrawn	03/22/58	.20	.15	.90	(4)	1.00
	Perf. 11 x 10.5						
1042A	8¢ Gen. John J. Pershing	11/17/61	.20	.15	.95	(4)	1.00
	Perf. 10.5 x 11						
1043	9¢ The Alamo	06/14/56	.30	.15	1.30	(4)	1.50
1044	10¢ Independence Hall	07/04/56	.25	.15	1.10	(4)	1.00
b	Tagged	07/06/66	2.00	1.00	20.00	(4)	15.00
	Perf. 11						
1044A	11¢ Statue of Liberty	06/15/61	.30	.15	1.25	(4)	1.00
c	Tagged	01/11/67	2.00	1.60	35.00	(4)	22.50

1031A

1030 **1031**

1032

1033 **1034**

1037

1035 **1036**

1038 **1039** **1040**

1041 **1042** **1042A**

1043 **1044**

1044A

1045　　　**1046**

1047

1048　　　**1049**

1050　　　**1051**

1052　　　**1053**

"One if by land, and two if by sea"

Paul Revere was a popular figure from the American Revolution who was immortalized in Henry Wadsworth Longfellow's poem, "Paul Revere's Ride." On the night of April 18-19, 1775, Revere and William Dawes left Boston on horseback to ride through the Massachusetts countryside warning residents that the British were on the march. Previously, Revere had also arranged for a signal to identify the route of the British: "One if by land, and two if by sea." Two lamps appeared in the bell tower of Boston's Christ Church, and the late-night warnings from the riders ensured that minutemen were ready the next morning on the village green in Lexington, where the fateful battle started the War of Independence. (#1048)

Issues of 1954-67, Perf. 11 x 10.5		Un	U	PB/LP	#	FDC
1045	12¢ Benjamin Harrison	06/06/59	.35	.15	1.50	(4)	1.00
a	Tagged	1968	.35	.15	4.00	(4)	25.00
1046	15¢ John Jay	12/12/58	.60	.15	3.00	(4)	1.00
a	Tagged	07/06/66	1.10	.35	7.50	(4)	20.00
	Perf. 10.5 x 11						
1047	20¢ Monticello	04/13/56	.40	.15	1.75	(4)	1.20
	Perf. 11 x 10.5						
1048	25¢ Paul Revere	04/18/58	1.10	.15	4.75	(4)	1.30
1049	30¢ Robert E. Lee	09/21/55	.70	.15	3.50	(4)	
a	Wet printing	09/21/55	1.10	.15	5.00	(4)	1.50
1050	40¢ John Marshall	04/58	1.50	.15	7.50	(4)	
a	Wet printing	09/24/55	2.25	.25	12.50	(4)	1.75
1051	50¢ Susan B. Anthony	04/58	1.50	.15	6.75	(4)	
a	Wet printing	08/25/55	1.75	.15	10.00	(4)	6.00
1052	$1 Patrick Henry	10/58	5.00	.15	22.50	(4)	
a	Wet printing	10/07/55	5.00	.15	22.50	(4)	10.00
	Perf. 11						
1053	$5 Alexander Hamilton	03/19/56	80.00	6.75	350.00	(4)	65.00
	Issues of 1954-73, Coil Stamps, Perf. 10 Vertically						
1054	1¢ dark green Washington (1031)	08/57	.20	.15	.90	(2)	
b	Imperf. pair		2,500.00	—			
c	Wet printing	10/08/54	.35	.20	1.75	(2)	1.00
	Coil Stamp, Perf. 10 Horizontally						
1054A	1¹/4¢ turquoise Palace of the Governors (1031A)	06/17/60	.15	.15	2.25	(2)	1.00
	Coil Stamps, Perf. 10 Vertically						
1055	2¢ rose carmine Jefferson (1033)	05/57	.15	.15	.75	(2)	
a	Tagged	05/06/68	.15	.15	.75	(2)	11.00
b	Imperf. pair (Bureau precanceled)			550.00			
c	As "a," imperf. pair		550.00				
d	Wet printing	10/22/54	.40	.15	3.50	(2)	1.00
1056	2¹/2¢ gray blue Bunker Hill (1034)	09/09/59	.25	.25	3.50	(2)	2.00
1057	3¢ deep violet Statue of Liberty (1035)	10/56	.15	.15	.55	(2)	
a	Imperf. pair		1,750.00	—	2,750.00	(2)	
b	Tagged	06/26/67	1.00	.50	20.00	(2)	
c	Wet printing	07/20/54	.30	.15	2.00	(2)	1.00
1058	4¢ red violet Lincoln (1036)	07/31/58	.15	.15	2.00	(2)	1.00
a	Imperf. pair		110.00	70.00	200.00	(2)	
b	Wet printing (Bureau precanceled)		27.50	.50	375.00	(2)	
	Coil Stamp, Perf. 10 Horizontally						
1059	4¹/2¢ blue green The Hermitage (1037)	05/01/59	1.50	1.20	14.00	(2)	1.75
	Coil Stamp, Perf. 10 Vertically						
1059A	25¢ green Revere (1048)	02/25/65	.50	.30	2.00	(2)	1.25
b	Tagged	04/03/73	.65	.20	3.00	(2)	14.00
	Dull finish gum	1980	.65		3.00	(2)	
c	Imperf. pair		50.00		85.00	(2)	

	Issues of 1954, Perf. 11 x 10.5		Un	U	PB	#	FDC	Q(M)
1060	3¢ Nebraska Territory	05/07/54	.15	.15	.30	(4)	1.00	116
1061	3¢ Kansas Territory	05/31/54	.15	.15	.30	(4)	1.00	114
	Perf. 10.5 x 11							
1062	3¢ George Eastman	07/12/54	.15	.15	.30	(4)	1.00	128
	Perf. 11 x 10.5							
1063	3¢ Lewis and Clark Expedition	07/28/54	.15	.15	.30	(4)	1.00	116
	Issues of 1955, Perf. 10.5 x 11							
1064	3¢ Pennsylvania Academy of the Fine Arts	01/15/55	.15	.15	.30	(4)	1.00	116
	Perf. 11 x 10.5							
1065	3¢ Land-Grant Colleges	02/12/55	.15	.15	.30	(4)	1.00	120
1066	8¢ Rotary International	02/23/55	.20	.15	.95	(4)	3.00	54
1067	3¢ Armed Forces Reserve	05/21/55	.15	.15	.30	(4)	1.00	176
	Perf. 10.5 x 11							
1068	3¢ New Hampshire	06/21/55	.15	.15	.35	(4)	1.00	126
	Perf. 11 x 10.5							
1069	3¢ Soo Locks	06/28/55	.15	.15	.30	(4)	1.00	122
1070	3¢ Atoms for Peace	07/28/55	.15	.15	.35	(4)	1.00	134
1071	3¢ Fort Ticonderoga	09/18/55	.15	.15	.30	(4)	1.00	119
1072	3¢ Andrew W. Mellon	12/20/55	.15	.15	.30	(4)	1.00	112

Kansas and Nebraska Territories born during political turmoil

On May 26, 1854, Congress approved the Kansas-Nebraska Act, organizing these two western territories and repealing the Missouri Compromise of 1820, which had outlawed slavery north of latitude 36° 30" in the Louisiana Purchase lands. The Act also included the principle of popular sovereignty, giving residents of the new territories the right to determine the issue of slavery for themselves. Because the expansion of slavery was a major conflict between the northern and southern states, the Act was highly controversial. To oppose the spread of slavery, the Republican Party was formed soon after the Act was signed. Bloody conflict ensued in the Kansas Territory over the question of whether Kansas would be admitted to the Union as a free or slave state. **(#1060)**

1060

1061

1062

1063

1064

1065

1066

1067

1068

1069

1070

1071

1072

1956

1074

1073

1076

1075

1077

1078

1079

1081

1080

1082

1083

1085

1084

	Issues of 1956, Perf. 10.5 x 11		Un	U	PB	#	FDC	Q(M̄)
1073	3¢ Benjamin Franklin	01/17/56	.15	.15	.30	(4)	1.00	129
	Perf. 11 x 10.5							
1074	3¢ Booker T. Washington	04/05/56	.15	.15	.30	(4)	1.25	121
	Fifth International Philatelic Exhibition Issues Souvenir Sheet, Imperf.							
1075	Sheet of 2 stamps (1035, 1041)	04/28/56	2.25	2.00			5.00	3
a	3¢ (1035), single stamp from sheet		.90	.80				
b	8¢ (1041), single stamp from sheet		1.25	1.00				
	Perf. 11 x 10.5							
1076	3¢ New York Coliseum and Columbus Monument	04/30/56	.15	.15	.30	(4)	1.00	120
	Wildlife Conservation Issue							
1077	3¢ Wild Turkey	05/05/56	.15	.15	.35	(4)	1.10	123
1078	3¢ Pronghorn Antelope	06/22/56	.15	.15	.35	(4)	1.10	123
1079	3¢ King Salmon	11/09/56	.15	.15	.35	(4)	1.10	109
	Perf. 10.5 x 11							
1080	3¢ Pure Food and Drug Laws	06/27/56	.15	.15	.30	(4)	1.00	113
	Perf. 11 x 10.5							
1081	3¢ Wheatland	08/05/56	.15	.15	.30	(4)	1.00	125
	Perf. 10.5 x 11							
1082	3¢ Labor Day	09/03/56	.15	.15	.30	(4)	1.00	118
	Perf. 11 x 10.5							
1083	3¢ Nassau Hall	09/22/56	.15	.15	.30	(4)	1.00	122
	Perf. 10.5 x 11							
1084	3¢ Devils Tower	09/24/56	.15	.15	.30	(4)	1.00	118
	Pair with full horizontal gutter between		—					
	Perf. 11 x 10.5							
1085	3¢ Children's Stamp	12/15/56	.15	.15	.30	(4)	1.00	101

Which animal sheds its horns annually?

Found only in North America, the pronghorn can reach a top speed of more than 60 miles per hour and has acute vision. The male pronghorn grows horns that are more than 12 inches long. The horns are composed of a bony core and a black outer sheath. The antelope shed the outer sheaths of the horns each fall and grow them back by the next summer. The pronghorn is the only animal known to shed its horns annually. **(#1078)**

	Issues of 1957, Perf. 11 x 10.5		Un	U	PB	#	FDC	Q(M̄)
1086	3¢ Alexander Hamilton	01/11/57	.15	.15	.30	(4)	1.00	115
	Perf. 10.5 x 11							
1087	3¢ Polio	01/15/57	.15	.15	.30	(4)	1.00	187
	Perf. 11 x 10.5							
1088	3¢ Coast and Geodetic Survey	02/11/57	.15	.15	.30	(4)	1.00	115
1089	3¢ American Institute of Architects	02/23/57	.15	.15	.30	(4)	1.00	107
	Perf. 10.5 x 11							
1090	3¢ Steel Industry	05/22/57	.15	.15	.30	(4)	1.00	112
	Perf. 11 x 10.5							
1091	3¢ International Naval Review-Jamestown Festival	06/10/57	.15	.15	.30	(4)	1.00	118
1092	3¢ Oklahoma Statehood	06/14/57	.15	.15	.35	(4)	1.00	102
1093	3¢ School Teachers	07/01/57	.15	.15	.30	(4)	2.00	102
	Perf. 11							
1094	4¢ Flag	07/04/57	.15	.15	.35	(4)	1.00	84
	Perf. 10.5 x 11							
1095	3¢ Shipbuilding	08/15/57	.15	.15	.30	(4)	1.00	126
	Champion of Liberty Issue, Ramon Magsaysay, Perf. 11							
1096	8¢ Bust of Magsaysay on Medal	08/31/57	.20	.15	.85	(4)	1.00	39
	Plate block of 4, ultramarine # omitted		—					
	Perf. 10.5 x 11							
1097	3¢ Lafayette	09/06/57	.15	.15	.30	(4)	1.00	123
	Perf. 11							
1098	3¢ Wildlife Conservation	11/22/57	.15	.15	.35	(4)	1.00	174
	Perf. 10.5 x 11							
1099	3¢ Religious Freedom	12/27/57	.15	.15	.30	(4)	1.00	114
	Issues of 1958							
1100	3¢ Gardening-Horticulture	03/15/58	.15	.15	.30	(4)	1.00	123
1101-03	Not assigned							
	Perf. 11 x 10.5							
1104	3¢ Brussels Universal and International Exhibition	04/17/58	.15	.15	.30	(4)	1.00	114
1105	3¢ James Monroe	04/28/58	.15	.15	.30	(4)	1.00	120
1106	3¢ Minnesota Statehood	05/11/58	.15	.15	.30	(4)	1.00	121
	Perf. 11							
1107	3¢ International Geophysical Year	05/31/58	.15	.15	.35	(4)	1.00	126
	Perf. 11 x 10.5							
1108	3¢ Gunston Hall	06/12/58	.15	.15	.30	(4)	1.00	108

Minimum value listed for a stamp is 15 cents; for a First Day Cover (FDC), $1.00. This minimum represents a fair-market price for having a dealer locate and provide a single stamp or cover from his or her stock. Dealers may charge less per stamp or cover for a group of such stamps or covers, or less for a single stamp or cover.

1086

1087

1088

1089

1090

1091

1092

1093

1094

1095

1096

1097

1098

1099

1100

1104

1105

1106

1107

1108

163

1110

1111

1112

1109

1115

1116

1113

1114

1120

1117

1118

1119

1123

1124

1121

1122

1125

1126

1127

1128

1129

1130

1131

	Issues of 1958, Perf. 10.5 x 11		Un	U	PB	#	FDC	Q(M̄)
1109	3¢ Mackinac Bridge	06/25/58	.15	.15	.30	(4)	1.00	107
	Champion of Liberty Issue, Simon Bolivar							
1110	4¢ Bust of Bolivar on Medal	07/24/58	.15	.15	.35	(4)	1.00	115
	Perf. 11							
1111	8¢ Bust of Bolivar on Medal	07/24/58	.20	.15	1.40	(4)	1.00	39
	Plate block of four, ocher # only		—					
	Perf. 11 x 10.5							
1112	4¢ Atlantic Cable	08/15/58	.15	.15	.35	(4)	1.00	114
	Issues of 1958-59, Lincoln Sesquicentennial Issue, Perf. 10.5 x 11							
1113	1¢ Portrait by George Healy	02/12/59	.15	.15	.20	(4)	1.00	120
1114	3¢ Sculptured Head by Gutzon Borglum	02/27/59	.15	.15	.30	(4)	1.00	91
	Perf. 11 x 10.5							
1115	4¢ Lincoln and Stephen Douglas Debating, by Joseph Boggs Beale	08/27/58	.15	.15	.35	(4)	1.00	114
1116	4¢ Statue in Lincoln Memorial by Daniel Chester French	05/30/59	.15	.15	.40	(4)	1.00	126
	Champion of Liberty Issue, Lajos Kossuth, Perf. 10.5 x 11							
1117	4¢ Bust of Kossuth on Medal	09/19/58	.15	.15	.30	(4)	1.00	120
	Perf. 11							
1118	8¢ Bust of Kossuth on Medal	09/19/58	.20	.15	1.10	(4)	1.00	44
	Perf. 10.5 x 11							
1119	4¢ Freedom of the Press	09/22/58	.15	.15	.30	(4)	1.00	118
	Perf. 11 x 10.5							
1120	4¢ Overland Mail	10/10/58	.15	.15	.30	(4)	1.00	125
	Perf. 10.5 x 11							
1121	4¢ Noah Webster	10/16/58	.15	.15	.30	(4)	1.00	114
	Perf. 11							
1122	4¢ Forest Conservation	10/27/58	.15	.15	.30	(4)	1.00	156
	Perf. 11 x 10.5							
1123	4¢ Fort Duquesne	11/25/58	.15	.15	.30	(4)	1.00	124
	Issues of 1959							
1124	4¢ Oregon Statehood	02/14/59	.15	.15	.30	(4)	1.00	120
	Champion of Liberty Issue, José de San Martin, Perf. 10.5 x 11							
1125	4¢ Bust of San Martin on Medal	02/25/59	.15	.15	.30	(4)	1.00	133
a	Horizontal pair, imperf. between		1,500.00					
	Perf. 11							
1126	8¢ Bust of San Martin on Medal	02/25/59	.20	.15	.85	(4)	1.00	45
	Perf. 10.5 x 11							
1127	4¢ NATO	04/01/59	.15	.15	.30	(4)	1.00	122
	Perf. 11 x 10.5							
1128	4¢ Arctic Explorations	04/06/59	.15	.15	.40	(4)	1.00	131
1129	8¢ World Peace Through World Trade	04/20/59	.20	.15	.85	(4)	1.00	47
1130	4¢ Silver Centennial	06/08/59	.15	.15	.30	(4)	1.00	123
	Perf. 11							
1131	4¢ St. Lawrence Seaway	06/26/59	.15	.15	.30	(4)	1.00	126
	Pair with full horizontal gutter between		—					

	Issues of 1959, Perf. 11		Un	U	PB	#	FDC	Q(M̄)
1132	4¢ 49-Star Flag	07/04/59	.15	.15	.40	(4)	1.00	209
1133	4¢ Soil Conservation	08/26/59	.15	.15	.35	(4)	1.00	121
	Perf. 10.5 x 11							
1134	4¢ Petroleum Industry	08/27/59	.15	.15	.30	(4)	1.00	116
	Perf. 11 x 10.5							
1135	4¢ Dental Health	09/14/59	.15	.15	.40	(4)	2.00	118
	Champion of Liberty Issue, Ernst Reuter, Perf. 10.5 x 11							
1136	4¢ Bust of Reuter on Medal	09/29/59	.15	.15	.30	(4)	1.00	112
	Perf. 11							
1137	8¢ Bust of Reuter on Medal	09/29/59	.20	.15	.85	(4)	1.00	43
	Perf. 10.5 x 11							
1138	4¢ Dr. Ephraim McDowell	12/03/59	.15	.15	.40	(4)	1.00	115
a	Vertical pair, imperf. between		450.00					
b	Vertical pair, imperf. horizontally		350.00					
	Issues of 1960-61, American Credo Issue, Perf. 11							
1139	4¢ Quotation from Washington's Farewell Address	01/20/60	.15	.15	.40	(4)	1.25	126
1140	4¢ Benjamin Franklin Quotation	03/31/60	.15	.15	.40	(4)	1.25	125
1141	4¢ Thomas Jefferson Quotation	05/18/60	.15	.15	.45	(4)	1.25	115
1142	4¢ Francis Scott Key Quotation	09/14/60	.15	.15	.45	(4)	1.25	122
1143	4¢ Abraham Lincoln Quotation	11/19/60	.15	.15	.50	(4)	1.25	121
	Pair with full horizontal gutter between		—					
1144	4¢ Patrick Henry Quotation	01/11/61	.15	.15	.50	(4)	1.25	113
	Issues of 1960							
1145	4¢ Boy Scouts	02/08/60	.15	.15	.40	(4)	3.50	139
	Olympic Winter Games Issue, Perf. 10.5 x 11							
1146	4¢ Olympic Rings and Snowflake	02/18/60	.15	.15	.40	(4)	1.00	124
	Champion of Liberty Issue, Thomas G. Masaryk							
1147	4¢ Bust of Masaryk on Medal	03/07/60	.15	.15	.30	(4)	1.00	114
a	Vertical pair, imperf. between		3,250.00					
	Perf. 11							
1148	8¢ Bust of Masaryk on Medal	03/07/60	.20	.15	.95	(4)	1.00	44
a	Horizontal pair, imperf. between		—					
	Perf. 11 x 10.5							
1149	4¢ World Refugee Year	04/07/60	.15	.15	.30	(4)	1.00	113
	Perf. 11							
1150	4¢ Water Conservation	04/18/60	.15	.15	.35	(4)	1.00	122
	Perf. 10.5 x 11							
1151	4¢ SEATO	05/31/60	.15	.15	.35	(4)	1.00	115
a	Vertical pair, imperf. between		175.00					

1132

1133

1134

1135

1136

1137

1138

1139

1140

1141

1142

1143

1144

1145

1146

1147

1148

1149

1150

1151

1152

1153

1154

1155

1156

1157

1158

1159

1160

1161

1162

1163

1164

1165

1166

1167

1168

1169

1170

1171

1172

1173

	Issues of 1960, Perf. 11 x 10.5		Un	U	PB	#	FDC	Q(M̄)
1152	4¢ American Woman	06/02/60	.15	.15	.30	(4)	1.00	111
	Perf. 11							
1153	4¢ 50-Star Flag	07/04/60	.15	.15	.30	(4)	1.00	153
	Perf. 11 x 10.5							
1154	4¢ Pony Express	07/19/60	.15	.15	.40	(4)	1.00	120
	Perf. 10.5 x 11							
1155	4¢ Employ the Handicapped	08/28/60	.15	.15	.30	(4)	1.00	118
1156	4¢ 5th World Forestry Congress	08/29/60	.15	.15	.30	(4)	1.00	118
	Perf. 11							
1157	4¢ Mexican Independence	09/16/60	.15	.15	.30	(4)	1.00	112
1158	4¢ U.S.-Japan Treaty	09/28/60	.15	.15	.30	(4)	1.00	125
	Champion of Liberty Issue, Ignacy Jan Paderewski, Perf. 10.5 x 11							
1159	4¢ Bust of Paderewski on Medal	10/08/60	.15	.15	.30	(4)	1.00	120
	Perf. 11							
1160	8¢ Bust of Paderewski on Medal	10/08/60	.20	.15	.90	(4)	1.00	43
	Perf. 10.5 x 11							
1161	4¢ Sen. Robert A. Taft Memorial	10/10/60	.15	.15	.35	(4)	1.00	107
	Perf. 11 x 10.5							
1162	4¢ Wheels of Freedom	10/15/60	.15	.15	.30	(4)	1.00	110
	Perf. 11							
1163	4¢ Boys' Clubs of America	10/18/60	.15	.15	.30	(4)	1.00	124
1164	4¢ First Automated Post Office	10/20/60	.15	.15	.30	(4)	1.00	124
	Champion of Liberty Issue, Gustaf Mannerheim, Perf. 10.5 x 11							
1165	4¢ Bust of Mannerheim on Medal	10/26/60	.15	.15	.30	(4)	1.00	125
	Perf. 11							
1166	8¢ Bust of Mannerheim on Medal	10/26/60	.20	.15	.80	(4)	1.00	42
1167	4¢ Camp Fire Girls	11/01/60	.15	.15	.30	(4)	1.00	116
	Champion of Liberty Issue, Giusseppe Garibaldi, Perf. 10.5 x 11							
1168	4¢ Bust of Garibaldi on Medal	11/02/60	.15	.15	.30	(4)	1.00	126
	Perf. 11							
1169	8¢ Bust of Garibaldi on Medal	11/02/60	.20	.15	.85	(4)	1.00	43
	Perf. 10.5 x 11							
1170	4¢ Sen. Walter F. George Memorial	11/05/60	.15	.15	.35	(4)	1.00	124
1171	4¢ Andrew Carnegie	11/25/60	.15	.15	.35	(4)	1.00	120
1172	4¢ John Foster Dulles Memorial	12/06/60	.15	.15	.35	(4)	1.00	117
	Perf. 11 x 10.5							
1173	4¢ Echo I-Communications for Peace	12/15/60	.15	.15	.75	(4)	2.00	124

	Issues of 1961, Perf. 10.5 x 11		Un	U	PB	#	FDC	Q(M̄)
	Champion of Liberty Issue, Mahatma Gandhi							
1174	4¢ Bust of Gandhi on Medal	01/26/61	.15	.15	.30	(4)	1.00	113
	Perf. 11							
1175	8¢ Bust of Gandhi on Medal	01/26/61	.20	.15	1.00	(4)	1.00	42
1176	4¢ Range Conservation	02/02/61	.15	.15	.40	(4)	1.00	111
	Perf. 10.5 x 11							
1177	4¢ Horace Greeley	02/03/61	.15	.15	.30	(4)	1.00	99
	Issues of 1961-65, Civil War Centennial Issue, Perf. 11 x 10.5							
1178	4¢ Fort Sumter	04/12/61	.15	.15	.65	(4)	2.00	101
1179	4¢ Shiloh	04/07/62	.15	.15	.50	(4)	2.00	125
	Perf. 11							
1180	5¢ Gettysburg	07/01/63	.15	.15	.60	(4)	2.00	80
1181	5¢ The Wilderness	05/05/64	.15	.15	.60	(4)	2.00	125
1182	5¢ Appomattox	04/09/65	.30	.15	1.15	(4)	2.00	113
a	Horizontal pair, imperf. vertically		4,500.00					
1183	4¢ Kansas Statehood	05/10/61	.15	.15	.35	(4)	1.00	106
	Perf. 11 x 10.5							
1184	4¢ Sen. George W. Norris	07/11/61	.15	.15	.35	(4)	1.00	111
1185	4¢ Naval Aviation	08/20/61	.15	.15	.35	(4)	1.00	117
	Pair with full vertical gutter between		150.00					
	Perf. 10.5 x 11							
1186	4¢ Workmen's Compensation	09/04/61	.15	.15	.35	(4)	1.00	121
	With plate # inverted				.60	(4)		
	Perf. 11							
1187	4¢ Frederic Remington	10/04/61	.15	.15	.40	(4)	1.00	112
	Perf. 10.5 x 11							
1188	4¢ Republic of China	10/10/61	.15	.15	.35	(4)	1.50	111
1189	4¢ Naismith-Basketball	11/06/61	.15	.15	.45	(4)	6.00	109
	Perf. 11							
1190	4¢ Nursing	12/28/61	.15	.15	.40	(4)	4.00	145
	Issues of 1962							
1191	4¢ New Mexico Statehood	01/06/62	.15	.15	.30	(4)	1.00	113
1192	4¢ Arizona Statehood	02/14/62	.15	.15	.30	(4)	1.00	122
1193	4¢ Project Mercury	02/20/62	.15	.15	.35	(4)	3.00	289
1194	4¢ Malaria Eradication	03/30/62	.15	.15	.30	(4)	1.00	120
	Perf. 10.5 x 11							
1195	4¢ Charles Evans Hughes	04/11/62	.15	.15	.30	(4)	1.00	125

Project Mercury sent the first U.S. astronauts into space

Initiated in 1958 and conducted from 1961 into 1963, Project Mercury was the first series of U.S. manned space flights. On May 5, 1961, three weeks after Soviet cosmonaut Yuri Gagarin became the first human in space, astronaut Alan B. Shepard Jr. piloted a Mercury space capsule, dubbed Freedom 7, on a suborbital 302-mile flight for 15 minutes. The first U.S. manned flight was launched into orbit on February 20, 1962. Commanded by astronaut John H. Glenn, it completed three orbits before landing in the Atlantic Ocean near the Bahamas. The final Mercury flight, on May 15, 1963, carried L. Gordon Cooper Jr. and finished 22 orbits in 34 hours and 20 minutes. **(#1193)**

1174

1175

1176

1177

1178

1179

1180

1181

1182

1183

1184

1185

1186

1187

1188

1189

1190

1191

1192

1193

1194

1195

1962-1963

1196

1197

1198

1199

1200

1201

1202

1203

1204

1205

1206

1207

1208

1209

1213

1230

1231

	Issues of 1962, Perf. 11		Un	U	PB/LP	#	FDC	Q(M̄)
1196	4¢ Seattle World's Fair	04/25/62	.15	.15	.30	(4)	1.00	147
1197	4¢ Louisiana Statehood	04/30/62	.15	.15	.30	(4)	1.00	119
	Perf. 11 x 10.5							
1198	4¢ Homestead Act	05/20/62	.15	.15	.30	(4)	1.00	123
1199	4¢ Girl Scout Jubilee	07/24/62	.15	.15	.30	(4)	4.00	127
	Pair with full vertical gutter between		250.00					
1200	4¢ Sen. Brien McMahon	07/28/62	.15	.15	.30	(4)	1.00	131
1201	4¢ Apprenticeship	08/31/62	.15	.15	.30	(4)	1.00	120
	Perf. 11							
1202	4¢ Sam Rayburn	09/16/62	.15	.15	.30	(4)	1.00	121
1203	4¢ Dag Hammarskjold	10/23/62	.15	.15	.30	(4)	1.00	121
1204	4¢ black, brown and yellow (yellow inverted), Dag Hammarskjold, special printing	11/16/62	.15	.15	1.25	(4)	6.00	40
	Christmas Issue							
1205	4¢ Wreath and Candles	11/01/62	.15	.15	.30	(4)	1.00	862
1206	4¢ Higher Education	11/14/62	.15	.15	.35	(4)	1.50	120
1207	4¢ Winslow Homer	12/15/62	.15	.15	.45	(4)	1.00	118
a	Horizontal pair, imperf. between		6,750.00					
	Issue of 1963-66							
1208	5¢ Flag over White House	01/09/63	.15	.15	.40	(4)	1.00	
a	Tagged	08/25/66	.20	.15	1.40	(4)	11.50	
b	Horizontal pair, imperf. between		1,500.00					
	Pair with full horizontal gutter between		—					
	Issues of 1962-66, Perf. 11 x 10.5							
1209	1¢ Andrew Jackson	03/22/63	.15	.15	.20	(4)	1.00	
a	Tagged	07/06/66	.15	.15	.30	(4)	5.75	
	Horizontal pair, imperf. between, tagged		—					
1210-12 Not assigned								
1213	5¢ George Washington	11/23/62	.15	.15	.40	(4)	1.00	
a	Booklet pane of 5 + label		3.00	1.75			4.00	
b	Tagged	10/28/63	.50	.20	4.50	(4)	5.75	
c	As "a," tagged	10/28/63	1.75	1.50			125.00	
1214-24 Not assigned								
	Coil Stamps, Perf. 10 Vertically							
1225	1¢ green Jackson (1209)	05/31/63	.15	.15	2.25	(2)	1.00	
a	Tagged	07/06/66	.15	.15	.75	(2)	5.00	
1226-28 Not assigned								
1229	5¢ dark blue gray Washington (1213)	11/23/62	1.25	.15	4.00	(2)	1.00	
a	Tagged	10/28/63	1.25	.15	4.00	(2)	20.00	
b	Imperf. pair		400.00		1,250.00	(2)		
	Issues of 1963, Perf. 11							
1230	5¢ Carolina Charter	04/06/63	.15	.15	.40	(4)	1.00	130
1231	5¢ Food for Peace-Freedom from Hunger	06/04/63	.15	.15	.40	(4)	1.00	136
1232	5¢ West Virginia Statehood	06/20/63	.15	.15	.40	(4)	1.00	138
1233	5¢ Emancipation Proclamation	08/16/63	.15	.15	.40	(4)	1.00	132
1234	5¢ Alliance for Progress	08/17/63	.15	.15	.40	(4)	1.00	136

Issues of 1963, Perf. 10.5 x 11		Un	U	PB	#	FDC	Q(M̄)
1235	5¢ Cordell Hull 10/05/63	.15	.15	.40	(4)	1.00	131
	Perf. 11 x 10.5						
1236	5¢ Eleanor Roosevelt 10/11/63	.15	.15	.40	(4)	1.00	133
	Perf. 11						
1237	5¢ The Sciences 10/14/63	.15	.15	.40	(4)	1.00	130
1238	5¢ City Mail Delivery 10/26/63	.15	.15	.50	(4)	1.00	128
1239	5¢ International Red Cross 10/29/63	.15	.15	.40	(4)	1.00	119
	Christmas Issue						
1240	5¢ National Christmas Tree and White House 11/01/63	.15	.15	.40	(4)	1.00	1,300
a	Tagged 11/02/63	.65	.40	4.00	(4)	60.00	
	Pair with full horizontal gutter between	—					
1241	5¢ John James Audubon, (See also #C71) 12/07/63	.15	.15	.40	(4)	1.00	175
	Issues of 1964, Perf. 10.5 x 11						
1242	5¢ Sam Houston 01/10/64	.15	.15	.45	(4)	1.00	126
	Perf. 11						
1243	5¢ Charles M. Russell 03/19/64	.15	.15	.40	(4)	1.00	128
	Perf. 11 x 10.5						
1244	5¢ New York World's Fair 04/22/64	.15	.15	.40	(4)	2.00	146
	Perf. 11						
1245	5¢ John Muir 04/29/64	.15	.15	.40	(4)	1.00	120
	Perf. 11 x 10.5						
1246	5¢ President John Fitzgerald Kennedy Memorial 05/29/64	.15	.15	.55	(4)	3.50	512
	Perf. 10.5 x 11						
1247	5¢ New Jersey Settlement 06/15/64	.15	.15	.40	(4)	1.00	124
	Perf. 11						
1248	5¢ Nevada Statehood 07/22/64	.15	.15	.40	(4)	1.00	123
1249	5¢ Register and Vote 08/01/64	.15	.15	.45	(4)	1.00	453
	Perf. 10.5 x 11						
1250	5¢ Shakespeare 08/14/64	.15	.15	.40	(4)	1.00	123
1251	5¢ Doctors William and Charles Mayo 09/11/64	.15	.15	.50	(4)	1.50	123
	Perf. 11						
1252	5¢ American Music 10/15/64	.15	.15	.40	(4)	1.00	127
a	Blue omitted	1,000.00					
1253	5¢ Homemakers 10/26/64	.15	.15	.40	(4)	1.00	121

All matters, great and small

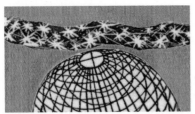

Covering everything from astronomy to microbiology, the National Academy of Sciences (NAS) serves as an official adviser to the government in all matters of science and technology. The NAS was created by congressional charter in 1863. Recognition of distinguished and continuing achievements in original research is the basis for membership in the Academy, and election to the NAS is considered one of the highest honors bestowed upon scientists and engineers. **(#1237)**

Interesting Fact: About 7% of the Academy's 1,800 members have won Nobel Prizes.

1236

1237

1235

1239

1240

1238

1241

1243

1244

1242

1245

1246

1247

1248

1249

1252

1253

1250

1251

1254   1255

1256   1257   1257b

1258

1259

1260

1261

1262

1263

1264

1265

1266

1267

1268

1269

1270

1271

1272

1273

1274

1275

1276

	Issues of 1964, Perf. 11		Un	U	PB	#	FDC	Q(M̄)
	Christmas Issue							
1254	5¢ Holly	11/09/64	.25	.15			1.00	352
1255	5¢ Mistletoe	11/09/64	.25	.15			1.00	352
1256	5¢ Poinsettia	11/09/64	.25	.15			1.00	352
1257	5¢ Sprig of Conifer	11/09/64	.25	.15			1.00	352
b	Block of four, #1254-57		1.10	1.00	1.40	(4)	3.00	
c	As "b," tagged		2.50	2.00			57.50	
	Perf. 10.5 x 11							
1258	5¢ Verrazano-Narrows Bridge	11/21/64	.15	.15	.40	(4)	1.00	120
	Perf. 11							
1259	5¢ Fine Arts	12/02/64	.15	.15	.40	(4)	1.00	126
	Perf. 10.5 x 11							
1260	5¢ Amateur Radio	12/15/64	.15	.15	.40	(4)	1.00	122
	Issues of 1965, Perf. 11							
1261	5¢ Battle of New Orleans	01/08/65	.15	.15	.40	(4)	1.00	116
1262	5¢ Physical Fitness-Sokol	02/15/65	.15	.15	.50	(4)	1.00	115
1263	5¢ Crusade Against Cancer	04/01/65	.15	.15	.40	(4)	1.00	120
	Perf. 10.5 x 11							
1264	5¢ Winston Churchill Memorial	05/13/65	.15	.15	.40	(4)	1.50	125
	Perf. 11							
1265	5¢ Magna Carta	06/15/65	.15	.15	.40	(4)	1.00	120
	Corner block of four, black PB# omitted		—					
1266	5¢ International Cooperation Year—United Nations	06/26/65	.15	.15	.40	(4)	1.00	115
1267	5¢ Salvation Army	07/02/65	.15	.15	.40	(4)	2.50	116
	Perf. 10.5 x 11							
1268	5¢ Dante Alighieri	07/17/65	.15	.15	.40	(4)	1.00	115
1269	5¢ President Herbert Hoover Memorial	08/10/65	.15	.15	.45	(4)	1.00	115
	Perf. 11							
1270	5¢ Robert Fulton	08/19/65	.15	.15	.40	(4)	1.00	116
1271	5¢ Florida Settlement	08/28/65	.15	.15	.45	(4)	1.00	117
a	Yellow omitted		425.00					
1272	5¢ Traffic Safety	09/03/65	.15	.15	.45	(4)	1.00	114
1273	5¢ John Singleton Copley	09/17/65	.15	.15	.50	(4)	1.00	115
1274	11¢ International Telecommunication Union	10/06/65	.35	.20	5.75	(4)	1.00	27
1275	5¢ Adlai E. Stevenson Memorial	10/23/65	.15	.15	.40	(4)	1.00	128
	Christmas Issue							
1276	5¢ Angel with Trumpet (1840 Weather Vane)	11/02/65	.15	.15	.40	(4)	1.00	1,140
a	Tagged	11/15/65	.75	.25	5.00	(4)	42.50	
1277	Not assigned							

The stamp listings contain a number of "a," "b," "c," etc. additions which include recognized varieties and errors. These listings are as complete as space permits.

	Issues of 1965-78		Un	U	PB	#	FDC
	Prominent Americans Issue, Perf. 11 x 10.5, 10.5 x 11 (See also #1299, 1303-05C)						
1278	1¢ Jefferson	01/12/68	.15	.15	.20	(4)	1.00
a	Booklet pane of 8	01/12/68	1.00	.50			2.50
b	Bklt. pane of 4 + 2 labels	05/10/71	.80	.30			12.50
c	Untagged (Bureau precanceled)			.15			
1279	1¼¢ Albert Gallatin	01/30/67	.15	.15	7.50	(4)	1.00
1280	2¢ Frank Lloyd Wright	06/08/66	.15	.15	.25	(4)	1.00
a	Booklet pane of 5 + label	01/08/68	1.25	.60			4.00
b	Untagged (Bureau precanceled)			.15			
c	Booklet pane of 6	05/07/71	1.00	.50			15.00
	Pair with full vertical gutter between		—				
1281	3¢ Francis Parkman	09/16/67	.15	.15	.25	(4)	1.00
a	Untagged (Bureau precanceled)			.15			
1282	4¢ Lincoln	11/19/65	.15	.15	.40	(4)	1.00
a	Tagged	12/01/65	.15	.15	.55	(4)	20.00
	Pair with full horizontal gutter between		—				
1283	5¢ Washington	02/22/66	.15	.15	.50	(4)	1.00
a	Tagged	02/23/66	.15	.15	.60	(4)	22.50
1283B	5¢ redrawn	11/17/67	.15	.15	.50	(4)	1.00
	Dull finish gum		.20		1.40	(4)	
d	Untagged (Bureau precanceled)			.15			
1284	6¢ Roosevelt	01/29/66	.15	.15	.60	(4)	1.00
a	Tagged	12/29/66	.15	.15	.80	(4)	20.00
b	Booklet pane of 8	12/28/67	1.50	.75			3.00
c	Booklet pane of 5 + label	01/09/68	1.50	.75			100.00
1285	8¢ Albert Einstein	03/14/66	.20	.15	.85	(4)	3.00
a	Tagged	07/06/66	.20	.15	.85	(4)	14.00
1286	10¢ Jackson	03/15/67	.20	.15	1.00	(4)	1.00
b	Untagged (Bureau precanceled)			.20			
1286A	12¢ Henry Ford	07/30/68	.25	.15	1.00	(4)	1.00
c	Untagged (Bureau precanceled)			.25			
1287	13¢ John F. Kennedy	05/29/67	.30	.15	1.25	(4)	2.50
a	Untagged (Bureau precanceled)			.35			
1288	15¢ Oliver Wendell Holmes	03/08/68	.30	.15	1.25	(4)	1.00
a	Untagged (Bureau precanceled)			.30			
	Booklet Stamp, Perf. 10						
1288B	15¢ dark rose claret Holmes (1288), Single from booklet		.30	.15			1.00
c	Booklet pane of 8	06/14/78	2.50	1.75			3.00
e	As "c," vert. imperf. between		—				
	Perf. 11 x 10.5, 10.5 x 11						
1289	20¢ George C. Marshall	10/24/67	.45	.15	1.75	(4)	1.00
a	Tagged	04/03/73	.40	.15	1.75	(4)	12.50
1290	25¢ Frederick Douglass	02/14/67	.55	.15	2.25	(4)	1.25
a	Tagged	04/03/73	.45	.15	2.00	(4)	14.00
1291	30¢ John Dewey	10/21/68	.60	.15	2.50	(4)	1.25
a	Tagged	04/03/73	.50	.15	2.25	(4)	14.00
1292	40¢ Thomas Paine	01/29/68	.85	.15	3.25	(4)	2.00
a	Tagged	04/03/73	.65	.15	2.75	(4)	15.00
1293	50¢ Lucy Stone	08/13/68	1.00	.15	4.00	(4)	3.25
a	Tagged	04/03/73	.85	.15	3.50	(4)	20.00
1294	$1 Eugene O'Neill	10/16/67	2.25	.15	10.00	(4)	7.50
a	Tagged	04/03/73	1.65	.15	6.75	(4)	22.50

1278   1279

1281

1280

1282   1283   1283B

1284

1285   1286

1286A

1287   1288

1291

1289   1290

1292   1293   1294

1295   1305

1306   1307

1310

1308   1309

1311

1314

1312   1313

	Issues of 1965-78		Un	U	PB/LP	#	FDC	Q(M)
	Perf. 11 x 10.5, 10.5 x 11							
1295	$5 John Bassett Moore	12/03/66	10.00	2.25	40.00	(4)	40.00	
a	Tagged	04/03/73	8.00	2.00	32.50	(4)	65.00	
1296	Not assigned							
	Issues of 1967-75, Coil Stamps, Perf. 10 Horizontally							
1297	3¢ violet Parkman (1281)	11/04/75	.15	.15	.45	(2)	1.00	
a	Imperf. pair		30.00		50.00	(2)		
b	Untagged (Bureau precanceled)			.15				
c	As "b," imperf. pair			6.00	25.00	(2)		
1298	6¢ Roosevelt (1284)	12/28/67	.15	.15	1.25	(2)	1.00	
a	Imperf. pair		2,000.00					
	Issues of 1966-81, Coil Stamps, Perf. 10 Vertically (See also #1279-96)							
1299	1¢ green Jefferson (1278)	01/12/68	.15	.15	.25	(2)	1.00	
a	Untagged (Bureau precanceled)			.15				
b	Imperf. pair		30.00	—	60.00	(2)		
1300-02	Not assigned							
1303	4¢ blk. Lincoln (1282)	05/28/66	.15	.15	.75	(2)	1.00	
a	Untagged (Bureau precanceled)			.15				
b	Imperf. pair		900.00		2,000.00	(2)		
1304	5¢ bl. Washington (1283)	09/08/66	.15	.15	.40	(2)	1.00	
a	Untagged (Bureau precanceled)			.15				
b	Imperf. pair		175.00		400.00	(2)		
e	As "a," imperf. pair			450.00	900.00	(2)		
1304C	5¢ redrawn (1283B)	1981	.15	.15	1.25	(2)		
d	Imperf. pair		1,000.00					
1305	6¢ gray brown Roosevelt	02/28/68	.15	.15	.55	(2)	1.00	
a	Imperf. pair		75.00		130.00	(2)		
b	Untagged (Bureau precanceled)			.20				
1305E	15¢ rose claret Holmes (1288)	06/14/78	.25	.15	1.25	(2)	1.00	
	Dull finish gum		.60		2.00	(2)		
f	Untagged (Bureau precanceled)			.30				
g	Imperf. pair		30.00		75.00	(2)		
h	Pair, imperf. between		225.00		600.00	(2)		
1305C	$1 dull purple Eugene O'Neill (1294)	01/12/73	1.75	.20	5.00	(2)	5.00	
d	Imperf. pair		2,250.00		4,000.00	(2)		
	Issues of 1966, Perf. 11							
1306	5¢ Migratory Bird Treaty	03/16/66	.15	.15	.40	(4)	1.00	117
1307	5¢ Humane Treatment of Animals	04/09/66	.15	.15	.40	(4)	1.00	117
1308	5¢ Indiana Statehood	04/16/66	.15	.15	.40	(4)	1.00	124
1309	5¢ American Circus	05/02/66	.15	.15	.50	(4)	4.00	131
	Sixth International Philatelic Exhibition Issue							
1310	5¢ Stamped Cover	05/21/66	.15	.15	.40	(4)	1.00	122
	Souvenir Sheet, Imperf.							
1311	5¢ Stamped Cover (1310) and Washington, D.C., Scene	05/23/66	.15	.15			1.00	15
	Perf. 11							
1312	5¢ The Bill of Rights	07/01/66	.15	.15	.45	(4)	1.00	114
	Perf. 10.5 x 11							
1313	5¢ Poland's Millennium	07/30/66	.15	.15	.45	(4)	1.00	128
	Perf. 11							
1314	5¢ National Park Service	08/25/66	.15	.15	.45	(4)	1.00	120
a	Tagged	08/26/66	.30	.25	2.00	(4)	20.00	

1966-1967

	Issues of 1966, Perf. 11		Un	U	PB	#	FDC	Q(M̄)
1315	5¢ Marine Corps Reserve	08/29/66	.15	.15	.45	(4)	2.00	125
a	Tagged		.30	.20	2.00	(4)	25.00	
b	Black and bister omitted		16,000.00					
1316	5¢ Women's Clubs	09/12/66	.15	.15	.45	(4)	1.00	115
a	Tagged	09/13/66	.30	.20	2.00	(4)	22.50	
	American Folklore Issue, Johnny Appleseed							
1317	5¢ Johnny Appleseed and Apple	09/24/66	.15	.15	.45	(4)	1.00	124
a	Tagged	09/26/66	.30	.20	2.00	(4)	22.50	
1318	5¢ Beautification of America	10/05/66	.15	.15	.45	(4)	1.00	128
a	Tagged		.30	.20	2.00	(4)	20.00	
1319	5¢ Great River Road	10/21/66	.15	.15	.45	(4)	1.00	128
a	Tagged	10/22/66	.30	.20	2.00	(4)	22.50	
1320	5¢ Savings Bond-Servicemen	10/26/66	.15	.15	.45	(4)	1.00	116
a	Tagged	10/27/66	.30	.20	2.00	(4)	22.50	
b	Red, dark bl. and blk. omitted		5,000.00					
c	Dark blue omitted		8,000.00					
	Christmas Issue							
1321	5¢ Madonna and Child, by Hans Memling	11/01/66	.15	.15	.40	(4)	1.00	1,174
a	Tagged	11/02/66	.30	.20	1.75	(4)	9.50	
1322	5¢ Mary Cassatt	11/17/66	.15	.15	.60	(4)	1.00	114
a	Tagged		.30	.25	2.00	(4)	20.00	
	Issues of 1967							
1323	5¢ National Grange	04/17/67	.15	.15	.40	(4)	1.00	121
a	Tagging omitted		3.50	—				
1324	5¢ Canada	05/25/67	.15	.15	.40	(4)	1.00	132
1325	5¢ Erie Canal	07/04/67	.15	.15	.40	(4)	1.00	119
1326	5¢ Search for Peace	07/05/67	.15	.15	.40	(4)	1.00	122
1327	5¢ Henry David Thoreau	07/12/67	.15	.15	.40	(4)	1.00	112
1328	5¢ Nebraska Statehood	07/29/67	.15	.15	.40	(4)	1.00	117
a	Tagging omitted		5.00	—				
1329	5¢ Voice of America	08/01/67	.15	.15	.40	(4)	1.00	112
	American Folklore Issue, Davy Crockett							
1330	5¢ Davy Crockett	08/17/67	.15	.15	.40	(4)	1.00	114
a	Vertical pair, imperf. between		6,000.00					
b	Green omitted		—					
c	Black and green omitted		—					
d	Yellow and green omitted		—					
	Accomplishments in Space Issue							
1331	5¢ Space-Walking Astronaut	09/29/67	.55	.15			3.00	60
a	Attached pair, #1331-32		1.30	1.20			8.00	
1332	5¢ Gemini 4 Capsule and Earth	09/29/67	.55	.15	3.00	(4)	3.00	60
1333	5¢ Urban Planning	10/02/67	.15	.15	.50	(4)	1.00	111
1334	5¢ Finland Independence	10/06/67	.15	.15	.50	(4)	1.00	111

Minimum value listed for a stamp is 15 cents; for a First Day Cover (FDC), $1.00. This minimum represents a fair-market price for having a dealer locate and provide a single stamp or cover from his or her stock. Dealers may charge less per stamp or cover for a group of such stamps or covers, or less for a single stamp or cover.

1315

1316

1317

1318

1319

1320

1321

1322

1323

1324

1325

1326

1327

1328

1329

1330

1331   1332   1331a

1333   1334

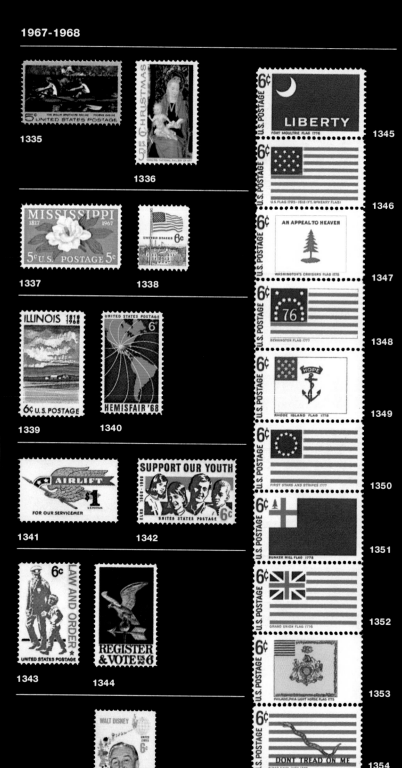

1335

1336

1337

1338

1339

1340

1341

1342

1343

1344

1345

1346

1347

1348

1349

1350

1351

1352

1353

1354

1354a

1355

	Issues of 1967, Perf. 12		Un	U	PB	#	FDC	Q(M̄)
1335	5¢ Thomas Eakins	11/02/67	.15	.15	.50	(4)	1.00	114
	Christmas Issue, Perf. 11							
1336	5¢ Madonna and Child, by Hans Memling	11/06/67	.15	.15	.40	(4)	1.00	1,209
1337	5¢ Mississippi Statehood	12/11/67	.15	.15	.50	(4)	1.00	113
	Issues of 1968-1971							
1338	6¢ Flag over White House (design 19 x 22mm)	01/24/68	.15	.15	.45	(4)	1.00	
k	Vertical pair, imperf. between		550.00					
	Coil Stamp, Perf. 10 Vertically							
1338A	6¢ dk bl, rd and grn (1338)	05/30/69	.15	.15	.30	(2)	1.00	
b	Imperf. pair		500.00					
	Perf. 11 x 10.5							
1338D	6¢ dark blue, red and green (1338, design 18¼ x 21mm)	08/07/70	.15	.15	2.60	(20)	1.00	
e	Horizontal pair, imperf. between		175.00					
1338F	8¢ dk bl, rd and slt grn (1338)	05/10/71	.15	.15	3.00	(20)	1.00	
i	Imperf., vertical pair		50.00					
j	Horizontal pair, imperf. between		60.00					
	Coil Stamp, Perf. 10 Vertically							
1338G	8¢ dk bl, rd and slt grn (1338)	05/10/71	.20	.15	.40	(2)	1.00	
h	Imperf. pair		55.00					
	Issues of 1968, Perf. 11							
1339	6¢ Illinois Statehood	02/12/68	.15	.15	.50	(4)	1.00	141
1340	6¢ HemisFair '68	03/30/68	.15	.15	.50	(4)	1.00	144
a	White omitted		1,500.00					
1341	$1 Airlift	04/04/68	2.25	1.25	12.50	(4)	6.50	
	Pair with full horizontal gutter between			—				
1342	6¢ Support Our Youth-Elks	05/01/68	.15	.15	.50	(4)	1.00	147
1343	6¢ Law and Order	05/17/68	.15	.15	.50	(4)	1.50	130
1344	6¢ Register and Vote	06/27/68	.15	.15	.50	(4)	1.00	159
	Historic Flag Issue							
1345	6¢ Ft. Moultrie Flag, 1776	07/04/68	.40	.25			3.00	23
1346	6¢ Ft. McHenry (U.S.) Flag, 1795-1818	07/04/68	.30	.25			3.00	23
1347	6¢ Washington's Cruisers Flag, 1775	07/04/68	.25	.25			3.00	23
1348	6¢ Bennington Flag, 1777	07/04/68	.25	.25			3.00	23
1349	6¢ Rhode Island Flag, 1775	07/04/68	.25	.25			3.00	23
1350	6¢ First Stars and Stripes, 1777	07/04/68	.25	.25			3.00	23
1351	6¢ Bunker Hill Flag, 1775	07/04/68	.25	.25			3.00	23
1352	6¢ Grand Union Flag, 1776	07/04/68	.25	.25			3.00	23
1353	6¢ Philadelphia Light Horse Flag, 1775	07/04/68	.25	.25			3.00	23
1354	6¢ First Navy Jack, 1775	07/04/68	.25	.25			3.00	23
a	Strip of 10, #1345-54		2.75	3.25	6.50	(20)	15.00	
	Perf. 12							
1355	6¢ Walt Disney	09/11/68	.15	.15	.70	(4)	10.00	153
a	Ocher omitted		850.00	—				
b	Vertical pair, imperf. horizontally		750.00					
c	Imperf. pair		675.00					
d	Black omitted		2,000.00					
e	Horizontal pair, imperf. between		4,750.00					
f	Blue omitted		2,250.00					

	Issues of 1968, Perf. 11		Un	U	PB	#	FDC	Q(M̄)
1356	6¢ Father Marquette	09/20/68	.15	.15	.50	(4)	1.00	133
	American Folklore Issue, Daniel Boone							
1357	6¢ Pennsylvania Rifle, Powder Horn, Tomahawk, Pipe and Knife	09/26/68	.15	.15	.50	(4)	1.00	130
a	Tagging omitted		—					
1358	6¢ Arkansas River Navigation	10/01/68	.15	.15	.50	(4)	1.00	132
1359	6¢ Leif Erikson	10/09/68	.15	.15	.50	(4)	1.00	129
	Perf. 11 x 10.5							
1360	6¢ Cherokee Strip	10/15/68	.15	.15	.60	(4)	1.00	125
a	Tagging omitted		5.00	—				
	Perf. 11							
1361	6¢ John Trumbull	10/18/68	.15	.15	.60	(4)	1.00	128
1362	6¢ Waterfowl Conservation	10/24/68	.15	.15	.65	(4)	2.00	142
a	Vertical pair, imperf. between		550.00					
b	Red and dark blue omitted		1,200.00					
	Christmas Issue							
1363	6¢ Angel Gabriel, from "The Annunciation," by Jan Van Eyck	11/01/68	.15	.15	2.00	(10)	1.00	1,411
a	Untagged	11/02/68	.15	.15	2.00	(10)	6.50	
b	Imperf. pair tagged		250.00					
c	Light yellow omitted		85.00					
d	Imperf. pair (untagged)		325.00					
1364	6¢ American Indian	11/04/68	.15	.15	.70	(4)	1.00	125
	Issues of 1969, Beautification of America Issue							
1365	6¢ Capitol, Azaleas and Tulips	01/16/69	.35	.15			1.00	48
1366	6¢ Washington Monument, Potomac River and Daffodils	01/16/69	.35	.15			1.00	48
1367	6¢ Poppies and Lupines along Highway	01/16/69	.35	.15			1.00	48
1368	6¢ Blooming Crabapple Trees Lining Avenue	01/16/69	.35	.15			1.00	48
a	Block of 4, #1365-68		1.50	1.75	2.25	(4)	4.00	
b	As "a," tagging omitted		—					
1369	6¢ American Legion	03/15/69	.15	.15	.45	(4)	1.00	149
	American Folklore Issue, Grandma Moses							
1370	6¢ "July Fourth," by Grandma Moses	05/01/69	.15	.15	.50	(4)	1.00	139
a	Horizontal pair, imperf. between		250.00					
b	Black and Prussian blue omitted		900.00					
1371	6¢ Apollo 8	05/05/69	.15	.15	.65	(4)	3.00	187
a	Imperf. pair		—					
1372	6¢ W.C. Handy	05/17/69	.15	.15	.45	(4)	1.00	126
a	Tagging omitted		6.00	—				
1373	6¢ California Settlement	07/16/69	.15	.15	.45	(4)	1.00	144
1374	6¢ John Wesley Powell	08/01/69	.15	.15	.45	(4)	1.00	136
1375	6¢ Alabama Statehood	08/02/69	.15	.15	.45	(4)	1.00	151

1356

1357

1358

1359

1360

1361

1362

1363

1364

1365   **1366**

1367   **1368**   **1368a**

1369

1370

1371

1372

1373

1374

1375

1376   **1377**

1378   **1379**   **1379a**

1380

1381

1382

1383

1384

1384 Precancel

1385

1386

1387   **1388**

AMERICAN BALD EAGLE   AFRICAN ELEPHANT HERD

HAIDA CEREMONIAL CANOE   THE AGE OF REPTILES

1389   **1390**   **1390a**

1391

1392

	Issues of 1969, Perf. 11		Un	U	PB	#	FDC	Q(M)
	Botanical Congress Issue							
1376	6¢ Douglas Fir (Northwest)	08/23/69	.45	.15			1.50	40
1377	6¢ Lady's Slipper (Northeast)	08/23/69	.45	.15			1.50	40
1378	6¢ Ocotillo (Southwest)	08/23/69	.45	.15			1.50	40
1379	6¢ Franklinia (Southeast)	08/23/69	.45	.15			1.50	40
a	Block of 4, #1376-79		2.00	2.25	3.00	(4)	5.00	
	Perf. 10.5 x 11							
1380	6¢ Dartmouth College Case	09/22/69	.15	.15	.50	(4)	1.00	130
	Perf. 11							
1381	6¢ Professional Baseball	09/24/69	.65	.15	3.00	(4)	10.00	131
a	Black omitted		1,100.00					
1382	6¢ College Football	09/26/69	.15	.15	.85	(4)	6.00	139
1383	6¢ Dwight D. Eisenhower	10/14/69	.15	.15	.50	(4)	1.00	151
	Christmas Issue, Perf. 11 x 10.5							
1384	6¢ Winter Sunday in Norway, Maine	11/03/69	.15	.15	1.40	(10)	1.00	1,710
	Precanceled		.50	.15				
b	Imperf. pair		1,100.00					
c	Light green omitted		25.00					
d	Light green and yellow omitted		1,000.00	—				
e	Yellow omitted		—					
f	Tagging omitted		4.00	—				

Precanceled versions issued on an experimental basis in four cities whose names appear on the stamps: Atlanta, GA; Baltimore, MD; Memphis, TN; and New Haven, CT.

	Perf. 11							
1385	6¢ Hope for the Crippled	11/20/69	.15	.15	.50	(4)	1.00	128
1386	6¢ William M. Harnett	12/03/69	.15	.15	.55	(4)	1.00	146
	Issues of 1970, Natural History Issue							
1387	6¢ American Bald Eagle	05/06/70	.15	.15			1.50	50
1388	6¢ African Elephant Herd	05/06/70	.15	.15			1.50	50
1389	6¢ Tlingit Chief in Haida Ceremonial Canoe	05/06/70	.15	.15			1.50	50
1390	6¢ Brontosaurus, Stegosaurus and Allosaurus from Jurassic Period	05/06/70	.15	.15			1.50	50
a	Block of 4, #1387-90		.50	.60	.65	(4)	4.00	
1391	6¢ Maine Statehood	07/09/70	.15	.15	.50	(4)	1.25	172
	Perf. 11 x 10.5							
1392	6¢ Wildlife Conservation	07/20/70	.15	.15	.50	(4)	1.00	142

This case helped protect business from government regulation

In 1818, the board of trustees of Dartmouth College prevailed upon a graduate to represent them before the Supreme Court of the United States. Two years earlier the New Hampshire state legislature revised the 1769 charter that had been granted to the college's founders by the King of Great Britain. The legislature stripped the board of their governing power, established a board of overseers and renamed the college Dartmouth University. The 1819 Supreme Court decision ruled that the original charter was a contract protected by the Constitution and, consequently, could not be altered by the state. This ruling helped make contracts difficult to break, thus lending substantial protection to business charters. **(#1380)**

	Issues of 1970-74, Perf. 11 x 10.5		Un	U	PB/LP	#	FDC	Q(M)
1393	6¢ Eisenhower	08/06/70	.15	.15	.50	(4)	1.00	
a	Booklet pane of 8		1.50	.65			3.00	
b	Booklet pane of 5 + label		1.50	.65			1.50	
c	Untagged (Bureau precanceled)			.15				
	Perf. 10.5 x 11							
1393D	7¢ Franklin	10/20/72	.15	.15	.60	(4)	1.00	
e	Untagged (Bureau precanceled)			.15				
	Perf. 11							
1394	8¢ Eisenhower	05/10/71	.15	.15	.60	(4)	1.00	
	Pair with full vertical gutter between		—					
	Perf. 11 x 10.5							
1395	8¢ deep claret Eisenhower (1394), Single from booklet		.20	.15			1.00	
a	Booklet pane of 8	05/10/71	1.80	1.25			3.00	
b	Booklet pane of 6	05/10/71	1.25	.90			3.00	
c	Booklet pane of 4 + 2 labels	01/28/72	1.65	.80			2.25	
d	Booklet pane of 7 + label	01/28/72	1.90	1.00			2.00	
1396	8¢ U.S. Postal Service	07/01/71	.15	.15	2.00	(12)	1.00	
1397	14¢ Fiorello H. LaGuardia	04/24/72	.25	.15	1.15	(4)	1.00	
a	Untagged (Bureau precanceled)			.25				
1398	16¢ Ernie Pyle	05/07/71	.30	.15	1.25	(4)	1.00	
a	Untagged (Bureau precanceled)			.35				
1399	18¢ Dr. Elizabeth Blackwell	01/23/74	.35	.15	1.50	(4)	1.25	
1400	21¢ Amadeo P. Giannini	06/27/73	.40	.15	1.65	(4)	1.00	
	Coil Stamps, Perf. 10 Vertically							
1401	6¢ dark blue gray Eisenhower (1393)	08/06/70	.15	.15	.50	(2)	1.00	
a	Untagged (Bureau precanceled)			.15				
b	Imperf. pair		2,000.00		—	(2)		
1402	8¢ deep claret Eisenhower (1394)	05/10/71	.15	.15	.55	(2)	1.00	
a	Imperf. pair		45.00		70.00	(2)		
b	Untagged (Bureau precanceled)			.15				
c	Pair, imperf. between		6,250.00					
1403-04	Not assigned							
	Issues of 1970, Perf. 11							
1405	6¢ Edgar Lee Masters	08/22/70	.15	.15	.50	(4)	1.00	138
a	Tagging omitted		7.50	—				
1406	6¢ Woman Suffrage	08/26/70	.15	.15	.50	(4)	1.00	135
1407	6¢ South Carolina Settlement	09/12/70	.15	.15	.50	(4)	1.00	136
1408	6¢ Stone Mountain Memorial	09/19/70	.15	.15	.50	(4)	1.00	133
1409	6¢ Ft. Snelling	10/17/70	.15	.15	.50	(4)	1.00	135
	Anti-Pollution Issue, Perf. 11 x 10.5							
1410	6¢ Save Our Soil— Globe and Wheat Field	10/28/70	.20	.15			1.25	40
1411	6¢ Save Our Cities— Globe and City Playground	10/28/70	.20	.15			1.25	40
1412	6¢ Save Our Water— Globe and Bluegill Fish	10/28/70	.20	.15			1.25	40
1413	6¢ Save Our Air— Globe and Seagull	10/28/70	.20	.15			1.25	40
a	Block of 4, #1410-13		1.00	1.25	2.50	(10)	3.00	

1393　　　**1393D**　　　**1394**　　　**1396**

1397　　　**1398**　　　**1399**　　　**1400**

1406　　　**1407**

1405

1408　　　**1409**

1410　　　**1411**

1412　　　**1413**　　　**1413a**

1414

1414a

1415 **1416**

1417 **1418** **1418b**

1419

1420 **1421** **1422** **1421a**

1423 **1424**

1425

1426

1427 **1428**

1429 **1430** **1430a**

Issues of 1970, Perf. 10.5 x 11		Un	U	PB	#	FDC	Q(M)
	Christmas Issue						
1414	6¢ Nativity, by Lorenzo Lotto 11/05/70	.15	.15	1.10	(8)	1.40	639*
a	Precanceled	.15	.15	1.90	(8)	10.00	358
b	Black omitted	650.00					
c	As "a," blue omitted	1,500.00					
	#1414a-18a were furnished to 68 cities. Unused prices are for copies with gum and used prices are for copies with or without gum but with an additional cancellation. *Includes #1414a.						
	Perf. 11 x 10.5						
1415	6¢ Tin and Cast-iron Locomotive 11/05/70	.30	.15			1.40	122
a	Precanceled	.75	.15				110
b	Black omitted	2,500.00					
1416	6¢ Toy Horse on Wheels 11/05/70	.30	.15			1.40	122
a	Precanceled	.75	.15				110
b	Black omitted	2,500.00					
c	Imperf. pair		4,000.00				
1417	6¢ Mechanical Tricycle 11/05/70	.30	.15			1.40	122
a	Precanceled	.75	.15				110
b	Black omitted	2,500.00					
1418	6¢ Doll Carriage 11/05/70	.30	.15			1.40	122
a	Precanceled	.75	.15				110
b	Block of 4, #1415-18	1.25	1.50	3.75	(8)	3.50	
c	Block of 4, #1415a-18a	3.25	3.25	7.50	(8)	6.00	
d	Black omitted	2,500.00					
	Perf. 11						
1419	6¢ United Nations 11/20/70	.15	.15	.50	(4)	1.00	128
	Pair with full horizontal gutter between	—					
1420	6¢ Landing of the Pilgrims 11/21/70	.15	.15	.50	(4)	1.00	130
a	Orange and yellow omitted	1,000.00					
	Disabled American Veterans and Servicemen Issue						
1421	6¢ Disabled American Veterans Emblem 11/24/70	.15	.15			1.25	67
a	Attached pair, #1421-22	.25	.30	1.00	(4)	1.50	
1422	6¢ U.S. Servicemen 11/24/70	.15	.15			1.25	67
	Issues of 1971						
1423	6¢ American Wool Industry 01/19/71	.15	.15	.50	(4)	1.00	136
a	Tagging omitted	—					
1424	6¢ Gen. Douglas MacArthur 01/26/71	.15	.15	.50	(4)	1.00	135
1425	6¢ Blood Donor 03/12/71	.15	.15	.50	(4)	1.00	131
a	Tagging omitted	5.00	—				
	Perf. 11 x 10.5						
1426	8¢ Missouri Statehood 05/08/71	.15	.15	2.00	(12)	1.00	161*
	Wildlife Conservation Issue, Perf. 11						
1427	8¢ Trout 06/12/71	.15	.15			1.25	44
1428	8¢ Alligator 06/12/71	.15	.15			1.25	44
1429	8¢ Polar Bear 06/12/71	.15	.15			1.25	44
1430	8¢ California Condor 06/12/71	.15	.15			1.25	44
a	Block of 4, #1427-30	.80	.90	.90	(4)	3.00	
b	As "a," light green and dark green omitted from #1427-28	3,500.00					
c	As "a," red omitted from #1427, 1429-30	9,000.00					

	Issues of 1971, Perf. 11		Un	U	PB	#	FDC	Q(M̄)
1431	8¢ Antarctic Treaty	06/23/71	.15	.15	.65	(4)	1.00	139
a	Tagging omitted		5.00					
	American Revolution Bicentennial Issue							
1432	8¢ Bicentennial Commission Emblem	07/04/71	.20	.15	.85	(4)	1.00	138
a	Gray and black omitted		*750.00*					
b	Gray omitted		*1,250.00*					
1433	8¢ John Sloan	08/02/71	.15	.15	.70	(4)	1.00	152
a	Tagging omitted		—					
	Space Achievement Decade Issue							
1434	8¢ Earth, Sun and Landing Craft on Moon	08/02/71	.15	.15				88
a	Attached pair, #1434-35		.40	.45	.65	(4)	2.50	
b	As "a," blue and red omitted		*1,500.00*					
1435	8¢ Lunar Rover and Astronauts	08/02/71	.15	.15				88
a	Tagging omitted		6.00					
1436	8¢ Emily Dickinson	08/28/71	.15	.15	.65	(4)	1.00	143
a	Black and olive omitted		*950.00*					
b	Pale rose omitted		*7,500.00*					
1437	8¢ San Juan, Puerto Rico	09/12/71	.15	.15	.65	(4)	1.00	149
a	Tagging omitted		6.50					
	Perf. 10.5 x 11							
1438	8¢ Prevent Drug Abuse	10/04/71	.15	.15	1.00	(6)	1.00	139
1439	8¢ CARE	10/27/71	.15	.15	1.25	(8)	1.00	131
a	Black omitted		*4,750.00*					
b	Tagging omitted		4.00					
	Historic Preservation Issue, Perf. 11							
1440	8¢ Decatur House, Washington, D.C.	10/29/71	.15	.15			1.25	43
1441	8¢ Whaling Ship *Charles W. Morgan*, Mystic, Connecticut	10/29/71	.15	.15			1.25	43
1442	8¢ Cable Car, San Francisco	10/29/71	.15	.15			1.25	43
1443	8¢ San Xavier del Bac Mission, Tucson, Arizona	10/29/71	.15	.15			1.25	43
a	Block of 4, #1440-43		.75	.85	.85	(4)	3.00	
b	As "a," black brown omitted		*2,750.00*					
c	As "a," ocher omitted		—					
	Christmas Issue, Perf. 10.5 x 11							
1444	8¢ Adoration of the Shepherds, by Giorgione	11/10/71	.15	.15	1.75	(12)	1.00	1,074
a	Gold omitted		*600.00*					
1445	8¢ Partridge in a Pear Tree	11/10/71	.15	.15	1.75	(12)	1.00	980

The stamp listings contain a number of "a," "b," "c," etc. additions which include recognized varieties and errors. These listings are as complete as space permits.

1431

1432

1433

1434   **1435**   **1434a**

1436   **1437**   **1438**   **1439**

1440   **1441**

1442   **1443**   **1443a**

1444   **1445**

1446   1447

1448   1449

1452

1450   1451 1451a   1453

1454

1456   1457

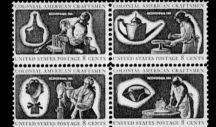

1455

1458   1459   1459a

1460   1461   1462

1463

	Issues of 1972, Perf. 11		Un	U	PB	#	FDC	Q(M)
1446	8¢ Sidney Lanier	02/03/72	.15	.15	.65	(4)	1.00	137
	Perf. 10.5 x 11							
1447	8¢ Peace Corps	02/11/72	.15	.15	1.00	(6)	1.00	150
	National Parks Centennial Issue, Cape Hatteras, (See also #C84)							
1448	2¢ Ship at Sea	04/05/72	.15	.15				43
1449	2¢ Cape Hatteras Lighthouse	04/05/72	.15	.15				43
1450	2¢ Laughing Gulls on Driftwood	04/05/72	.15	.15				43
1451	2¢ Laughing Gulls and Dune	04/05/72	.15	.15				43
a	Block of 4, #1448-51		.25	.25	.50	(4)	2.00	
b	As "a," black omitted		2,750.00					
	Wolf Trap Farm							
1452	6¢ Performance at Shouse Pavilion	06/26/72	.15	.15	.55	(4)	1.00	104
1453	8¢ Old Faithful, Yellowstone	03/01/72	.15	.15	.70	(4)	1.00	164
a	Tagging omitted		14.00					
	Mount McKinley							
1454	15¢ View of Mount McKinley in Alaska	07/28/72	.30	.20	1.30	(4)	1.00	54

Note: Beginning with this National Parks Centennial issue, the USPS began to offer stamp collectors first day c ancellations affixed to 8" x 10$^1/_2$" souvenir pages. The pages are similar to the stamp announcements that have appeared on Post Office bulletin boards beginning with Scott #1132. See "Souvenir Pages" listed in the back of this book (see Table of Contents).

1455	8¢ Family Planning	03/18/72	.15	.15	.65	(4)	1.00	153
a	Yellow omitted		1,650.00					
b	Dark brown and olive omitted		—					
	American Bicentennial Issue, Colonial American Craftsmen, Perf. 11 x 10.5							
1456	8¢ Glassblower	07/04/72	.15	.15			1.00	50
1457	8¢ Silversmith	07/04/72	.15	.15			1.00	50
1458	8¢ Wigmaker	07/04/72	.15	.15			1.00	50
1459	8¢ Hatter	07/04/72	.15	.15			1.00	50
a	Block of 4, #1456-59		.65	.75	.75	(4)	2.50	
	Olympic Games Issue, (See also #C85)							
1460	6¢ Bicycling and Olympic Rings	08/17/72	.15	.15	1.25	(10)	1.00	67
	Plate flaw (broken red ring)		7.50					
1461	8¢ Bobsledding and Olympic Rings	08/17/72	.15	.15	1.60	(10)	1.00	180
1462	15¢ Running and Olympic Rings	08/17/72	.30	.20	3.00	(10)	1.00	46
1463	8¢ Parent Teachers Association	09/15/72	.15	.15	.65	(4)	1.00	180

The toughest job you'll ever love

In October 1960, while campaigning for the presidency, John F. Kennedy gave a 2:00 a.m. speech to students at the University of Michigan. In it, he challenged the students to devote two years of their lives to helping children in developing countries. Less than six months later, his idea was realized when, as President, he issued an Executive Order creating the Peace Corps. Within a year of the original idea, the first group of volunteers departed for service. **(#1447)**

Interesting Fact: Currently, approximately 6,500 volunteers serve in 83 countries throughout the world.

	Issues of 1972, Perf. 11 x 10.5		Un	U	PB	#	FDC	Q(M)
	Wildlife Conservation Issue, Perf. 11							
1464	8¢ Fur Seals	09/20/72	.15	.15			1.50	50
1465	8¢ Cardinal	09/20/72	.15	.15			1.50	50
1466	8¢ Brown Pelican	09/20/72	.15	.15			1.50	50
1467	8¢ Bighorn Sheep	09/20/72	.15	.15			1.50	50
a	Block of 4, #1464-67		.65	.75	.75	(4)	3.00	
b	As "a," brown omitted		4,000.00					
c	As "a," green and blue omitted		4,750.00					

Note: With this Wildlife Conservation issue the USPS introduced the "American Commemorative Series" Stamp Panels. Each panel contains a block of four or more mint stamps with text and background illustrations. See pages 444-449 for a complete listing.

1468	8¢ Mail Order Business	09/27/72	.15	.15	1.75	(12)	1.00	185
	Perf. 10.5 x 11							
1469	8¢ Osteopathic Medicine	10/09/72	.15	.15	1.00	(6)	1.00	162
	American Folklore Issue, Tom Sawyer, Perf. 11							
1470	8¢ Tom Sawyer Whitewashing a Fence, by Norman Rockwell	10/13/72	.15	.15	.65	(4)	1.00	163
a	Horizontal pair, imperf. between		4,500.00					
b	Red and black omitted		2,250.00					
c	Yellow and tan omitted		2,400.00					
	Christmas Issue, Perf. 10.5 x 11							
1471	8¢ Angels from "Mary, Queen of Heaven," by the Master of the St. Lucy Legend	11/09/72	.15	.15	1.75	(12)	1.00	1,003
a	Pink omitted		200.00					
b	Black omitted		4,000.00					
1472	8¢ Santa Claus	11/09/72	.15	.15	1.75	(12)	1.00	1,017
	Perf. 11							
1473	8¢ Pharmacy	11/10/72	.15	.15	.65	(4)	4.50	166
a	Blue and orange omitted		1,000.00					
b	Blue omitted		2,250.00					
c	Orange omitted		2,250.00					
1474	8¢ Stamp Collecting	11/17/72	.15	.15	.65	(4)	1.00	167
a	Black omitted		1,000.00					
	Issues of 1973, Perf. 11 x 10.5							
1475	8¢ Love	01/26/73	.15	.15	1.00	(6)	2.50	320
	American Bicentennial Issue, Communications in Colonial Times, Perf. 11							
1476	8¢ Printer and Patriots Examining Pamphlet	02/16/73	.15	.15	.65	(4)	1.00	166
1477	8¢ Posting a Broadside	04/13/73	.15	.15	.65	(4)	1.00	163
	Pair with full horizontal gutter between		—					
1478	8¢ Postrider	06/22/73	.15	.15	.65	(4)	1.00	159
1479	8¢ Drummer	09/28/73	.15	.15	.65	(4)	1.00	147
	Boston Tea Party							
1480	8¢ British Merchantman	07/04/73	.15	.15			1.00	49
1481	8¢ British Three-Master	07/04/73	.15	.15			1.00	49
1482	8¢ Boats and Ship's Hull	07/04/73	.15	.15			1.00	49
1483	8¢ Boat and Dock	07/04/73	.15	.15			1.00	49
a	Block of 4, #1480-83		.65	.75	.75	(4)	3.00	
b	As "a," blk. (engraved) omitted		1,500.00					
c	As "a," blk. (lithographed) omitted		1,500.00					

1464 **1465**

1468

1466 **1467** **1467a**

1469 **1470**

1473

1474

1471 **1472**

1475

1476 **1477**

1478 **1479**

1480 **1481**

1482 **1483** **1483a**

1973

1484 GEORGE GERSHWIN

1485 ROBINSON JEFFERS

1486

1487 WILLA CATHER

Copernicus
1473 - 1973

8 cts

1488

U.S. POSTAL SERVICE 8¢   U.S. POSTAL SERVICE 8¢   U.S. POSTAL SERVICE 8¢   U.S. POSTAL SERVICE 8¢   U.S. POSTAL SERVICE 8¢

1489   **1490**   **1491**   **1492**   **1493**

Nearly 27 billion U.S. stamps are sold yearly to carry your letters to every corner of the world.	Mail is picked up from nearly a third of a million local collection boxes, as well as your mailbox.	More than 87 billion letters and packages are handled yearly—almost 300 million every delivery day.	The People in your Postal Service handle and deliver more than 500 million packages yearly.	Thousands of machines, buildings, and vehicles must be operated and maintained to keep your mail moving.
People Serving You	People Serving You	People Serving You	People Serving You	People Serving You

U.S. POSTAL SERVICE 8¢   U.S. POSTAL SERVICE 8¢   U.S. POSTAL SERVICE 8¢   U.S. POSTAL SERVICE 8¢   U.S. POSTAL SERVICE 8¢

1494   **1495**   **1496**   **1497**   **1498**

The skill of sorting mail manually is still vital to delivery of your mail.	Employees use modern, high-speed equipment to sort and process huge volumes of mail in central locations.	Thirteen billion pounds of mail are handled yearly by postal employees as they speed your letters and packages.	Our customers include 54 million urban and 12 million rural families, plus 9 million businesses.	Employees cover 4 million miles each delivery day to bring mail to your home or business.
People Serving You	People Serving You	People Serving You	People Serving You	People Serving You

Issues of 1973, Perf. 11		Un	U	PB	#	FDC	Q(M)
	American Arts Issue						
1484	8¢ George Gershwin and Scene from "Porgy and Bess" 02/28/73	.15	.15	1.75	(12)	1.00	139
a	Vertical pair, imperf. horizontally	250.00					
1485	8¢ Robinson Jeffers, Man and Children of Carmel with Burro 08/13/73	.15	.15	1.75	(12)	1.00	128
a	Vertical pair, imperf. horizontally	250.00					
1486	8¢ Henry Ossawa Tanner, Palette and Rainbow 09/10/73	.15	.15	1.75	(12)	1.00	146
1487	8¢ Willa Cather, Pioneer Family and Covered Wagon 09/20/73	.15	.15	1.75	(12)	1.00	140
a	Vertical pair, imperf. horizontally	275.00					
1488	8¢ Nicolaus Copernicus 04/23/73	.15	.15	.65	(4)	1.50	159
a	Orange omitted	1,000.00					
b	Black omitted	1,500.00					
	Postal Service Employees Issue, Perf. 10.5 x 11						
1489	8¢ Stamp Counter 04/30/73	.15	.15			1.00	49
1490	8¢ Mail Collection 04/30/73	.15	.15			1.00	49
1491	8¢ Letter Facing on Conveyor 04/30/73	.15	.15			1.00	49
1492	8¢ Parcel Post Sorting 04/30/73	.15	.15			1.00	49
1493	8¢ Mail Canceling 04/30/73	.15	.15			1.00	49
1494	8¢ Manual Letter Routing 04/30/73	.15	.15			1.00	49
1495	8¢ Electronic Letter Routing 04/30/73	.15	.15			1.00	49
1496	8¢ Loading Mail on Truck 04/30/73	.15	.15			1.00	49
1497	8¢ Carrier Delivering Mail 04/30/73	.15	.15			1.00	49
1498	8¢ Rural Mail Delivery	.15	.15			1.00	49
a	Strip of 10, #1489-98	1.50	1.75	3.00	(20)	5.00	

#1489-98 were the first United States postage stamps to have printing on the back. (See also 1559-62.)

#1498a plate block (above). As shown on the bottom row, when these stamps are turned over, the inscriptions appear in the reverse order from the designs (each appearing on the back of the appropriate image).

	Issues of 1973, Perf. 11		Un	U	PB	#	FDC	Q(M̄)
1499	8¢ Harry S. Truman	05/08/73	.15	.15	.65	(4)	1.00	157
	Progress in Electronics Issue, (See also #C86)							
1500	6¢ Marconi's Spark Coil and Gap	07/10/73	.15	.15	.55	(4)	1.00	53
1501	8¢ Transistors and Printed Circuit Board	07/10/73	.15	.15	.70	(4)	1.00	160
a	Black omitted		800.00					
b	Tan and lilac omitted		1,500.00					
1502	15¢ Microphone, Speaker, Vacuum Tube, TV Camera Tube	07/10/73	.30	.15	1.30	(4)	1.00	39
a	Black omitted		1,500.00					
1503	8¢ Lyndon B. Johnson	08/27/73	.15	.15	1.90	(12)	1.00	153
a	Horizontal pair, imperf. vertically		350.00					
	Issues of 1973-74, Rural America Issue							
1504	8¢ Angus and Longhorn Cattle, by F.C. Murphy	10/05/73	.15	.15	.65	(4)	1.00	146
a	Green and red brown omitted		1,000.00					
b	Vertical pair, imperf. between		—					
1505	10¢ Chautauqua Tent and Buggies	08/06/74	.20	.15	.85	(4)	1.00	151
1506	10¢ Wheat Fields and Train	08/16/74	.20	.15	.85	(4)	1.00	141
a	Black and blue omitted		900.00					
	Issues of 1973, Christmas Issue, Perf. 10.5 x 11							
1507	8¢ Small Cowper Madonna, by Raphael	11/07/73	.15	.15	1.75	(12)	1.00	885
	Pair with full vertical gutter between		—					
1508	8¢ Christmas Tree in Needlepoint	11/07/73	.15	.15	1.75	(12)	1.00	940
a	Vertical pair, imperf. between		350.00					
	Pair with full horizontal gutter between		—					
	Issues of 1973-74, Perf. 11 x 10.5							
1509	10¢ 50-Star and 13-Star Flags	12/08/73	.20	.15	4.25	(20)	1.00	
a	Horizontal pair, imperf. between		60.00	—				
b	Blue omitted		175.00					
c	Imperf. pair		1,150.00					
1510	10¢ Jefferson Memorial	12/14/73	.20	.15	.85	(4)	1.00	
a	Untagged (Bureau precanceled)			.20				
b	Booklet pane of 5 + label		1.65	.55			2.25	
c	Booklet pane of 8		1.65	.70			2.50	
d	Booklet pane of 6	08/05/74	5.25	1.00			3.00	
e	Vertical pair, imperf. horizontally		525.00					
f	Vertical pair, imperf. between		—					

1499

1500

1501

1502

1503

1504

1505

1506

1507

1508

1509

1510

1511

1518

1525

1526

1527

1528

1529

1530   **1531**   **1532**   **1533**

1534   **1535**   **1536**   **1537**   **1537a**

	Issues of 1973-74, Perf. 11 x 10.5		Un	U	PB/LP	#	FDC	Q(M)
1511	10¢ ZIP Code	01/04/74	.20	.15	1.75	(8)	1.00	
a	Yellow omitted		65.00					
	Pair with full horizontal gutter between		—					
1512-17	Not assigned							
	Coil Stamps, Perf. 10 Vertically							
1518	6.3¢ Liberty Bell	10/01/74	.15	.15	.80	(2)	1.00	
a	Untagged (Bureau precanceled)			.15	.80	(2)		
b	Imperf. pair		225.00		600.00	(2)		
c	As "a," imperf. pair			110.00	250.00	(2)		
1519	10¢ red and blue Flags (1509)	12/08/73	.20	.15			1.00	
a	Imperf. pair		37.50					
1520	10¢ blue Jefferson Memorial (1510)	12/14/73	.25	.15	.75	(2)	1.00	
a	Untagged (Bureau precanceled)			.25				
b	Imperf. pair		42.50		70.00	(2)		
1521-24	Not assigned							
	Issues of 1974, Perf. 11							
1525	10¢ Veterans of Foreign Wars	03/11/74	.20	.15	.85	(4)	2.00	149
	Perf. 10.5 x 11							
1526	10¢ Robert Frost	03/26/74	.20	.15	.85	(4)	1.00	145
	Perf. 11							
1527	10¢ Expo '74 World's Fair	04/18/74	.20	.15	2.50	(12)	1.00	135
	Perf. 11 x 10.5							
1528	10¢ Horse Racing	05/04/74	.20	.15	2.50	(12)	2.00	156
a	Blue omitted		1,000.00					
b	Red omitted		—					
	Perf. 11							
1529	10¢ Skylab	05/14/74	.20	.15	.85	(4)	1.50	164
a	Vertical pair, imperf. between		—					
	Universal Postal Union Issue							
1530	10¢ Michelangelo, from "School of Athens," by Raphael	06/06/74	.20	.15			1.00	24
1531	10¢ "Five Feminine Virtues," by Hokusai	06/06/74	.20	.15			1.00	24
1532	10¢ "Old Scraps," by John Fredrick Peto	06/06/74	.20	.15			1.00	24
1533	10¢ "The Lovely Reader," by Jean Etienne Liotard	06/06/74	.20	.15			1.00	24
1534	10¢ "Lady Writing Letter," by Gerard Terborch	06/06/74	.20	.15			1.00	24
1535	10¢ Inkwell and Quill, from "Boy with a Top," by Jean-Baptiste Simeon Chardin	06/06/74	.20	.15			1.00	24
1536	10¢ Mrs. John Douglas, by Thomas Gainsborough	06/06/74	.20	.15			1.00	24
1537	10¢ Don Antonio Noriega, by Francisco de Goya	06/06/74	.20	.15			1.00	24
a	Block of 8, #1530-37		1.60	1.60	3.50	(16)	4.00	
b	As "a," imperf. vertically		7,500.00					

	Issues of 1974, Perf. 11		Un	U	PB	#	FDC	Q(M̄)
	Mineral Heritage Issue							
1538	10¢ Petrified Wood	06/13/74	.20	.15			1.00	42
a	Light blue and yellow omitted		—					
1539	10¢ Tourmaline	06/13/74	.20	.15			1.00	42
a	Light blue omitted		—					
b	Black and purple omitted		—					
1540	10¢ Amethyst	06/13/74	.20	.15			1.00	42
a	Light blue and yellow omitted		—					
1541	10¢ Rhodochrosite	06/13/74	.20	.15			1.00	42
a	Block of 4, #1538-41		.80	.90	.90	(4)	2.50	
b	As "a," light blue and yellow omitted		2,000.00					
c	Light blue omitted		—					
d	Black and red omitted		—					
1542	10¢ First Kentucky Settlement-Ft. Harrod	06/15/74	.20	.15	.85	(4)	1.00	156
a	Dull black omitted		900.00					
b	Green, black and blue omitted		3,750.00					
c	Green omitted		—					
d	Green and black omitted		—					
	American Bicentennial Issue, First Continental Congress							
1543	10¢ Carpenters' Hall	07/04/74	.20	.15			1.00	49
1544	10¢ "We Ask but for Peace, Liberty and Safety"	07/04/74	.20	.15			1.00	49
1545	10¢ "Deriving Their Just Powers from the Consent of the Governed"	07/04/74	.20	.15			1.00	49
1546	10¢ Independence Hall	07/04/74	.20	.15			1.00	49
a	Block of 4, #1543-46		.80	.90	.90	(4)	2.75	
1547	10¢ Energy Conservation	09/23/74	.20	.15	.85	(4)	1.00	149
a	Blue and orange omitted		900.00					
b	Orange and green omitted		750.00					
c	Green omitted		900.00					
	American Folklore Issue, The Legend of Sleepy Hollow							
1548	10¢ Headless Horseman and Ichabod Crane	10/10/74	.20	.15	.85	(4)	1.50	157
1549	10¢ Retarded Children	10/12/74	.20	.15	.85	(4)	1.00	150
	Christmas Issue, Perf. 10.5 x 11							
1550	10¢ Angel from Perussis Altarpiece	10/23/74	.20	.15	2.10	(10)	1.00	835
	Perf. 11 x 10.5							
1551	10¢ "The Road-Winter," by Currier and Ives	10/23/74	.20	.15	2.50	(12)	1.00	883
	Precanceled Self-Adhesive, Imperf.							
1552	10¢ Dove Weather Vane atop Mount Vernon	11/15/74	.20	.15	4.25	(20)	1.00	213
	Issues of 1975, American Arts Issue, Perf. 10.5 x 11							
1553	10¢ Benjamin West, Self-Portrait	02/10/75	.20	.15	2.10	(10)	1.00	157
	Perf. 11							
1554	10¢ Paul Laurence Dunbar and Lamp	05/01/75	.20	.15	2.10	(10)	1.00	146
a	Imperf. pair		1,300.00					
1555	10¢ D.W. Griffith and Motion-Picture Camera	05/27/75	.20	.15	.85	(4)	1.00	149
a	Brown omitted		750.00					

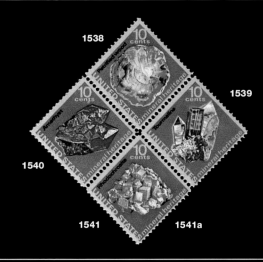

1538

1539

1540

1541　　1541a

1542

1543　　1544

1545　　1546　　1546a

1547

1548

1549

1550

1551

1552

1553

1554

1555

1556

1557

1558

1559

1560

1561

YOUTHFUL HEROINE
On the dark night of April 26, 1777, 16-year-old Sybil Ludington rode her horse "Star" alone through the Connecticut countryside rallying her father's militia to repel a raid by the British on Danbury.

GALLANT SOLDIER
The conspicuously courageous actions of black foot soldier Salem Poor at the Battle of Bunker Hill on June 17, 1775, earned him citations for his bravery and leadership ability.

FINANCIAL HERO
Businessman and broker Haym Salomon was responsible for raising most of the money needed to finance the American Revolution and later to save the new nation from collapse.

1562

US Bicentennial 10cents

1563

US Bicentennial 10c

1564

FIGHTER EXTRAORDINARY
Peter Francisco's strength and bravery made him a legend around campfires. He fought with distinction at Brandywine, Yorktown and Guilford Court House.

1565   **1566**   **1569**

1570   **1569a**

	Issues of 1975, Perf. 11		Un	U	PB	#	FDC	Q(M)
	Space Issues							
1556	10¢ Pioneer 10 Passing Jupiter	02/28/75	.20	.15	.85	(4)	2.00	174
a	Red and yellow omitted		1,500.00					
b	Blue omitted		950.00					
1557	10¢ Mariner 10, Venus and Mercury	04/04/75	.20	.15	.85	(4)	2.00	159
a	Red omitted		700.00					
b	Ultramarine and bister omitted		2,000.00					
1558	10¢ Collective Bargaining	03/13/75	.20	.15	1.75	(8)	1.00	153
	Imperfs. of #1558 exist from printer's waste.							
	American Bicentennial Issue, Contributors to the Cause, Perf. 11 x 10.5							
1559	8¢ Sybil Ludington Riding Horse	03/25/75	.15	.15	1.50	(10)	1.00	63
a	Back inscription omitted		275.00					
1560	10¢ Salem Poor Carrying Musket	03/25/75	.20	.15	2.10	(10)	1.00	158
a	Back inscription omitted		225.00					
1561	10¢ Haym Salomon Figuring Accounts	03/25/75	.20	.15	2.10	(10)	1.00	167
a	Back inscription omitted		250.00					
b	Red omitted		250.00					
1562	18¢ Peter Francisco Shouldering Cannon	03/25/75	.35	.20	3.60	(10)	1.00	45
	Battle of Lexington & Concord, Perf. 11							
1563	10¢ "Birth of Liberty," by Henry Sandham	04/19/75	.20	.15	2.50	(12)	1.00	144
a	Vertical pair, imperf. horizontally		425.00					
	Battle of Bunker Hill							
1564	10¢ "Battle of Bunker Hill," by John Trumbull	06/17/75	.20	.15	2.50	(12)	1.00	140
	Military Uniforms							
1565	10¢ Soldier with Flintlock Musket, Uniform Button	07/04/75	.20	.15			1.00	45
1566	10¢ Sailor with Grappling Hook, First Navy Jack, 1775	07/04/75	.20	.15			1.00	45
1567	10¢ Marine with Musket, Full-Rigged Ship	07/04/75	.20	.15			1.00	45
1568	10¢ Militiaman with Musket, Powder Horn	07/04/75	.20	.15			1.00	45
a	Block of 4, #1565-68		.85	.90	2.50	(12)	2.50	
	Apollo Soyuz Space Issue							
1569	10¢ Apollo and Soyuz after Docking and Earth	07/15/75	.20	.15			3.00	81
a	Attached pair, #1569-70		.45	.40	2.50	(12)	5.00	
b	As "a," vertical pair, imperf. horizontally		2,000.00					
	Pair with full horizontal gutter between		—					
1570	10¢ Spacecraft before Docking, Earth and Project Emblem	07/15/75	.20	.15			3.00	81

	Issues of 1975, Perf. 11 x 10.5		Un	U	PB	#	FDC	Q(M̄)
1571	10¢ International Women's Year	08/26/75	.20	.15	1.30	(6)	1.00	146
	Postal Service Bicentennial Issue							
1572	10¢ Stagecoach and Trailer Truck	09/03/75	.20	.15			1.00	42
1573	10¢ Old and New Locomotives	09/03/75	.20	.15			1.00	42
1574	10¢ Early Mail Plane and Jet	09/03/75	.20	.15			1.00	42
1575	10¢ Satellite for Mailgrams	09/03/75	.20	.15			1.00	42
a	Block of 4, #1572-75		.85	.90	2.50	(12)	1.25	
b	As "a," red "10¢" omitted		9,500.00					
	Perf. 11							
1576	10¢ World Peace Through Law	09/29/75	.20	.15	.85	(4)	1.25	147
	Banking and Commerce Issue							
1577	10¢ Engine Turning, Indian Head Penny and Morgan Silver Dollar	10/06/75	.20	.15			1.00	73
a	Attached pair, #1577-78		.40	.40	.85	(4)	1.25	
b	Brown and blue omitted		2,250.00					
c	As "a," brn., blue and yel. omitted		2,750.00					
1578	10¢ Seated Liberty Quarter, $20 Gold Piece and Engine Turning	10/06/75	.20	.15			1.00	73
	Christmas Issue							
1579	(10¢) Madonna and Child, by Domenico Ghirlandaio	10/14/75	.20	.15	2.50	(12)	1.00	739
a	Imperf. pair		110.00					
	Plate flaw ("d" damaged)		5.00	—				
1580	(10¢) Christmas Card, by Louis Prang, 1878	10/14/75	.20	.15	2.50	(12)	1.00	879
a	Imperf. pair		120.00					
b	Perf. 10.5 x 11		.60	.15	15.00	(12)		
	Issues of 1975-81, Americana Issue, Perf. 11 x 10.5 (Designs 18 1/2 x 22 1/2mm; #1590-90a, 17 1/2 x 20mm; see also 1606, 1608, 1610-19, 1622-23, 1625, 1811, 1813, 1816)							
1581	1¢ Inkwell & Quill	12/08/77	.15	.15	.25	(4)	1.00	
a	Untagged (Bureau precanceled)			.15				
1582	2¢ Speaker's Stand	12/08/77	.15	.15	.25	(4)	1.00	
a	Untagged (Bureau precanceled)			.15				
1583	Not assigned							
1584	3¢ Early Ballot Box	12/08/77	.15	.15	.30	(4)	1.00	
a	Untagged (Bureau precanceled)			.15				
1585	4¢ Books, Eyeglasses	12/08/77	.15	.15	.40	(4)	1.00	
a	Untagged (Bureau precanceled)			1.25				
1586-89	Not assigned							
	Booklet Stamp							
1590	9¢ Capitol Dome (1591), single from booklet (1623a)	03/11/77	.50	.20			1.00	
	Booklet Stamp, Perf. 10							
a	Single (1591) from booklet (1623c)		20.00	12.50				
	#1590 is on white paper; #1591 is on gray paper.							
	Perf. 11 x 10.5							
1591	9¢ Capitol Dome	11/24/75	.20	.15	.85	(4)	1.00	
a	Untagged (Bureau precanceled)			.20				
1592	10¢ Contemplation of Justice	11/17/77	.20	.15	.90	(4)	1.00	
a	Untagged (Bureau precanceled)			.25				
1593	11¢ Printing Press	11/13/75	.20	.15	.90	(4)	1.00	
1594	12¢ Torch	04/08/81	.25	.15	1.25	(4)	1.00	

1571

1572 **1573**

1574 **1575** **1575a**

1576

1577 **1578** **1577a**

1579 **1580**

1581 **1582**

1584 **1585**

1591 **1592**

1593 **1594**

1605   **1606**

1608   **1610**

1611   **1612**

1613   **1614**   **1615**   **1615C**

	Issues of 1975-79, Perf. 11 x 10.5		Un	U	PB/LP	#	FDC
	Americana Issue (continued) (See also #1581-82, 1584-85, 1590-99, 1603-08, 1610-19, 1622-23, 1625, 1811, 1813, 1816)						
1595	13¢ Liberty Bell, single from booklet		.25	.15			1.00
a	Booklet pane of 6	10/31/75	2.00	.75			2.00
b	Booklet pane of 7 + label		1.75	.75			2.75
c	Booklet pane of 8		2.00	1.00			2.50
d	Booklet pane of 5 + label	04/02/76	1.50	.75			2.25
	Perf. 11						
1596	13¢ Eagle and Shield	12/01/75	.25	.15	3.25	(12)	1.00
a	Imperf. pair		50.00	—			
b	Yellow omitted		225.00				
1597	15¢ Ft. McHenry Flag	06/30/78	.30	.15	1.90	(6)	1.00
a	Imperf. pair		20.00				
b	Gray omitted		700.00				
	Booklet Stamp, Perf. 11 x 10.5						
1598	15¢ Ft. McHenry Flag (1597), single from booklet		.35	.15			1.00
a	Booklet pane of 8	06/30/78	3.50	.80			2.50
1599	16¢ Head of Liberty	03/31/78	.35	.15	1.90	(4)	1.00
1600-02	Not assigned						
1603	24¢ Old North Church	11/14/75	.45	.15	1.90	(4)	1.00
1604	28¢ Ft. Nisqually	08/11/78	.55	.15	2.30	(4)	1.25
	Dull finish gum		1.10		10.00	(4)	
1605	29¢ Sandy Hook Lighthouse	04/14/78	.55	.15	2.75	(4)	1.25
	Dull finish gum		2.00		15.00	(4)	
1606	30¢ One-Rm. Schoolhouse	08/27/79	.55	.15	2.30	(4)	1.25
1607	Not assigned						
	Perf. 11						
1608	50¢ Whale Oil Lamp	09/11/79	.85	.15	3.75	(4)	1.50
a	Black omitted		300.00				
b	Vertical pair, imperf. horizontally		1,750.00				
1609	Not assigned						
1610	$1 Candle and Rushlight Holder	07/02/79	1.75	.20	7.50	(4)	3.00
a	Brown omitted		300.00				
b	Tan, orange and yellow omitted		350.00				
c	Brown inverted		16,000.00				
1611	$2 Kerosene Table Lamp	11/16/78	3.25	.75	14.00	(4)	5.00
1612	$5 Railroad Lantern	08/23/79	7.75	1.75	31.00	(4)	12.50
	Coil Stamps, Perf. 10 Vertically						
1613	3.1¢ Guitar	10/25/79	.15	.15	1.50	(2)	1.00
a	Untagged (Bureau precanceled)			.50			
b	Imperf. pair		1,400.00		3,600.00	(2)	
1614	7.7¢ Saxhorns	11/20/76	.20	.15	1.00	(2)	1.00
a	Untagged (Bureau precanceled)			.35			
b	As "a," imperf. pair		1,400.00		4,400.00	(2)	
1615	7.9¢ Drum	04/23/76	.20	.15	.75	(2)	1.00
a	Untagged (Bureau precanceled)			.20			
b	Imperf. pair		600.00				
1615C	8.4¢ Piano	07/13/78	.20	.15	3.25	(2)	1.00
d	Untagged (Bureau precanceled)			.30			
e	As "d," pair, imperf. between			70.00	130.00	(2)	
f	As "d," imperf. pair			15.00	30.00	(2)	

	Issues of 1975-81, Perf. 10 Vertically		Un	U	PB/LP	#	FDC
	Americana Issue (continued) (See also #1581-82, 1584-85, 1590-99, 1603-05, 1811, 1813, 1816)						
1616	9¢ slate green Capitol Dome (1591)	03/05/76	.20	.15	1.00	(2)	1.00
a	Imperf. pair		175.00		400.00	(2)	
b	Untagged (Bureau precanceled)			.35			
c	As "b," imperf. pair			700.00	—	(2)	
1617	10¢ purple Contemplation of Justice (1592)	11/04/77	.20	.15	1.10	(2)	1.00
a	Untagged (Bureau precanceled)			.25			
b	Imperf. pair		70.00		125.00	(2)	
	Dull finish gum		.30		2.75	(2)	
1618	13¢ brown Liberty Bell (1595)	11/25/75	.25	.15	.70	(2)	1.00
a	Untagged (Bureau precanceled)			.45			
b	Imperf. pair		25.00		65.00	(2)	
g	Pair, imperf. between		—				
1618C	15¢ Ft. McHenry Flag (1597)	06/30/78	.40	.15			1.00
d	Imperf. pair		25.00				
e	Pair, imperf. between		150.00				
f	Gray omitted		40.00				
1619	16¢ blue Head of Liberty (1599)	03/31/78	.35	.15	1.50	(2)	1.00
a	Huck Press printing (white background with a bluish tinge, fraction of a millimeter smaller)		.50	.15	2.00	(2)	
1620-21	Not assigned						
	Perf. 11 x 10.5						
1622	13¢ Flag over Independence Hall	11/15/75	.25	.15	5.75	(20)	1.00
a	Horizontal pair, imperf. between		55.00				
b	Imperf. pair		1,100.00				
c	Perf. 11	1981	.65	.15	62.50	(20)	
d	As "c," vertical pair, imperf.		150.00				
e	Horizontal pair, imperf. vertically		—				
	Booklet Stamps						
1623	13¢ Flag over Capitol, single from booklet (1623a)		.25	.15			1.00
a	Booklet pane of 8, (1 #1590 and 7 #1623)	03/11/77	2.25	1.10			25.00
	Booklet Stamps, Perf. 10						
b	13¢ Single from booklet		1.00	1.00			
c	Booklet pane of 8, (1 #1590a and 7 #1623b)		30.00	—			12.50
	#1623, 1623b issued only in booklets. All stamps are imperf. at one side or imperf. at one side and bottom.						
	Booklet Stamps, Perf. 11 x 10.5						
d	Attached pair, #1590 and 1623		.75	.75			
	Booklet Stamps, Perf. 10						
e	Attached pair, #1590a and 1623b		22.50	20.00			
1624	Not assigned						
	Coil Stamp, Perf. 10 Vertically						
1625	13¢ Flag over Independence Hall (1622)	11/15/75	.25	.15			1.00
a	Imperf. pair		25.00				

1622

1623a

A symbol of our nation

The U.S. Capitol stands on Capitol Hill in Washington, D.C., and is a powerful symbol of the U.S. government and its people. Begun in 1793, the Capitol was built in the neoclassical style of the 19th century. On August 24, 1814, the building was not yet complete when British troops set fire to it during the War of 1812. The Capitol was not completely destroyed, and repairs and restoration were begun in 1815. Amid miscellaneous improvement and modernization projects, the U.S. House of Representatives and Senate have been making legislative decisions in the Capitol for nearly 200 years. (#1623)

1632

1629   1630   1631'   1631a

1633   1634   1635

1636   1637

1638   1639   1640

1641   1642

1643   1644   1645

1646   1647

Issues of 1976, Perf. 11			Un	U	PB	#	FDC	Q(M̄)
American Bicentennial Issue, The Spirit of '76								
1629	13¢ Drummer Boy	01/01/76	.20	.15			1.25	73
1630	13¢ Old Drummer	01/01/76	.20	.15			1.25	73
1631	13¢ Fife Player	01/01/76	.20	.15			1.25	73
a	Strip of 3, #1629-31		.60	.65	2.50	(12)	2.00	
b	As "a," imperf.		1,300.00					
c	Imperf. pair, #1631		800.00					
1632	13¢ Interphil 76	01/17/76	.20	.15	1.00	(4)	1.00	158
State Flags								
1633	13¢ Delaware	02/23/76	.25	.20			1.25	9
1634	13¢ Pennsylvania	02/23/76	.25	.20			1.25	9
1635	13¢ New Jersey	02/23/76	.25	.20			1.25	9
1636	13¢ Georgia	02/23/76	.25	.20			1.25	9
1637	13¢ Connecticut	02/23/76	.25	.20			1.25	9
1638	13¢ Massachusetts	02/23/76	.25	.20			1.25	9
1639	13¢ Maryland	02/23/76	.25	.20			1.25	9
1640	13¢ South Carolina	02/23/76	.25	.20			1.25	9
1641	13¢ New Hampshire	02/23/76	.25	.20			1.25	9
1642	13¢ Virginia	02/23/76	.25	.20			1.25	9
1643	13¢ New York	02/23/76	.25	.20			1.25	9
1644	13¢ North Carolina	02/23/76	.25	.20			1.25	9
1645	13¢ Rhode Island	02/23/76	.25	.20			1.25	9
1646	13¢ Vermont	02/23/76	.25	.20			1.25	9
1647	13¢ Kentucky	02/23/76	.25	.20			1.25	9

We are the world

Held in conjunction with the U.S. Bicentennial, the Interphil 76 International Philatelic Exhibition convened from May 29 to June 6, 1976, in Philadelphia, Pennsylvania, and attracted large numbers of collectors and exhibitors. Collecting stamps from around the world provides a foundation for social studies, which includes foreign languages, culture, geography and history. When people learn about other countries, their perspectives change from "me" to "we" in a global sense, opening the door to better acceptance of new ideas and people. **(#1632)**

Issues of 1976, Perf. 11		Un	U	FDC	Q(M̄)
American Bicentennial Issue (continued), State Flags					
1648	13¢ Tennessee	02/23/76	.25	.20	1.25	9
1649	13¢ Ohio	02/23/76	.25	.20	1.25	9
1650	13¢ Louisiana	02/23/76	.25	.20	1.25	9
1651	13¢ Indiana	02/23/76	.25	.20	1.25	9
1652	13¢ Mississippi	02/23/76	.25	.20	1.25	9
1653	13¢ Illinois	02/23/76	.25	.20	1.25	9
1654	13¢ Alabama	02/23/76	.25	.20	1.25	9
1655	13¢ Maine	02/23/76	.25	.20	1.25	9
1656	13¢ Missouri	02/23/76	.25	.20	1.25	9
1657	13¢ Arkansas	02/23/76	.25	.20	1.25	9
1658	13¢ Michigan	02/23/76	.25	.20	1.25	9
1659	13¢ Florida	02/23/76	.25	.20	1.25	9
1660	13¢ Texas	02/23/76	.25	.20	1.25	9
1661	13¢ Iowa	02/23/76	.25	.20	1.25	9
1662	13¢ Wisconsin	02/23/76	.25	.20	1.25	9
1663	13¢ California	02/23/76	.25	.20	1.25	9
1664	13¢ Minnesota	02/23/76	.25	.20	1.25	9
1665	13¢ Oregon	02/23/76	.25	.20	1.25	9
1666	13¢ Kansas	02/23/76	.25	.20	1.25	9
1667	13¢ West Virginia	02/23/76	.25	.20	1.25	9

Home to our 42nd President

The election of Bill Clinton to the office of the President of the United States in 1992 and his re-election in 1996 brought national attention to his home state of Arkansas. This state, whose name comes from a Native American tribe, is known as the "Natural State." The state's varying terrain—mountains to the west and north, and lowlands to the east and south—explains the diversity in Arkansas' natural resources and crops. The state ranks number one in this country's rice production, but soybeans actually occupy the most acreage in the state. Numerous state parks, caverns and natural springs draw thousands of visitors each year, making tourism an important industry in Arkansas. **(#1657)**

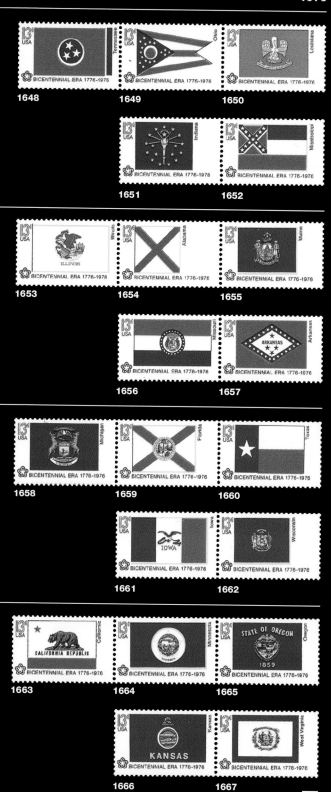

1648 1649 1650

1651 1652

1653 1654 1655

1656 1657

1658 1659 1660

1661 1662

1663 1664 1665

1666 1667

1976

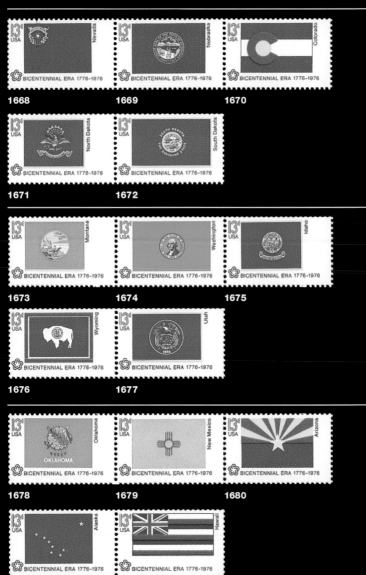

1668 1669 1670

1671 1672

1673 1674 1675

1676 1677

1678 1679 1680

1681 1682

	Issues of 1976, Perf. 11		Un	U	FDC	Q(M̄)
	American Bicentennial Issue (continued), State Flags					
1668	13¢ Nevada	02/23/76	.25	.20	1.25	9
1669	13¢ Nebraska	02/23/76	.25	.20	1.25	9
1670	13¢ Colorado	02/23/76	.25	.20	1.25	9
1671	13¢ North Dakota	02/23/76	.25	.20	1.25	9
1672	13¢ South Dakota	02/23/76	.25	.20	1.25	9
1673	13¢ Montana	02/23/76	.25	.20	1.25	9
1674	13¢ Washington	02/23/76	.25	.20	1.25	9
1675	13¢ Idaho	02/23/76	.25	.20	1.25	9
1676	13¢ Wyoming	02/23/76	.25	.20	1.25	9
1677	13¢ Utah	02/23/76	.25	.20	1.25	9
1678	13¢ Oklahoma	02/23/76	.25	.20	1.25	9
1679	13¢ New Mexico	02/23/76	.25	.20	1.25	9
1680	13¢ Arizona	02/23/76	.25	.20	1.25	9
1681	13¢ Alaska	02/23/76	.25	.20	1.25	9
1682	13¢ Hawaii	02/23/76	.25	.20	1.25	9
a	Pane of 50, #1633-82		13.00	—	27.50	

Example of 1682a

	Issues of 1976, Perf. 11		Un	U	PB	#	FDC	Q(M̄)
1683	13¢ Telephone Centennial	03/10/76	.25	.15	1.10	(4)	1.00	158
1684	13¢ Commercial Aviation	03/19/76	.25	.15	2.75	(10)	1.00	156
1685	13¢ Chemistry	04/06/76	.25	.15	3.25	(12)	2.00	158
	Pair with full vertical gutter between		—					

American Bicentennial Issue Souvenir Sheets, 5 stamps each

			Un	U			FDC	Q(M̄)
1686	13¢ The Surrender of Lord Cornwallis at Yorktown, by John Trumbull	05/29/76	3.25	—			6.00	2
a	13¢ Two American Officers		.45	.40				2
b	13¢ Gen. Benjamin Lincoln		.45	.40				2
c	13¢ George Washington		.45	.40				2
d	13¢ John Trumbull, Col. David Cobb, General Friedrich von Steuben, Marquis de Lafayette and Thomas Nelson		.45	.40				2
e	13¢ Alexander Hamilton, John Laurens and Walter Stewart		.45	.40				2
f	"USA/13¢" omitted on "b," "c" and "d," imperf.		—	2,250.00				
g	"USA/13¢" omitted on "a" and "e"		450.00	—				
h	Imperf. (untagged)			2,250.00				
i	"USA/13¢" omitted on "b," "c" and "d"		450.00					
j	"USA/13¢" double on "b"		—					
k	"USA/13¢" omitted on "c" and "d"		800.00					
l	"USA/13¢" omitted on "e"		500.00					
m	"USA/13¢" omitted, imperf. (untagged)		—	—				
1687	18¢ The Declaration of Independence, 4 July 1776 at Philadelphia, by John Trumbull	05/29/76	4.25	—			7.50	2
a	18¢ John Adams, Roger Sherman and Robert R. Livingston		.55	.55				2
b	18¢ Thomas Jefferson and Benjamin Franklin		.55	.55				2
c	18¢ Thomas Nelson, Jr., Francis Lewis, John Witherspoon and Samuel Huntington		.55	.55				2
d	18¢ John Hancock and Charles Thomson		.55	.55				2
e	18¢ George Read, John Dickinson and Edward Rutledge		.55	.55				2
f	Design and marginal inscriptions omitted		3,000.00					
g	"USA/18¢" omitted on "a" and "c"		800.00					
h	"USA/18¢" omitted on "b," "d" and "e"		500.00					
i	"USA/18¢" omitted on "d"		550.00	500.00				
j	Black omitted in design		2,000.00					
k	"USA/18¢" omitted, imperf. (untagged)		3,000.00					
m	"USA/18¢" omitted on "b" and "e"		500.00					

1683

1684

1685

The Surrender of Lord Cornwallis at Yorktown
From a Painting by John Trumbull

1686

The Declaration of Independence, 4 July 1776 at Philadelphia
From a Painting by John Trumbull

Washington Crossing the Delaware
From a Painting by Emanuel Leutze / Eastman Johnson

1688

Washington Reviewing His Ragged Army at Valley Forge
From a Painting by William T. Trego

1689

	Issues of 1976, Perf. 11		Un	U		FDC	Q(M̄)
	American Bicentennial Issue (continued) Souvenir Sheets, 5 stamps each						
1688	24¢ Washington Crossing the Delaware, by Emanuel Leutze/ Eastman Johnson	05/29/76	5.25	—		8.50	2
a	24¢ Boatmen		.70	.70			2
b	24¢ George Washington		.70	.70			2
c	24¢ Flagbearer		.70	.70			2
d	24¢ Men in Boat		.70	.70			2
e	24¢ Steersman and Men on Shore		.70	.70			2
f	"USA/24¢" omitted, imperf.		3,500.00				
g	"USA/24¢" omitted on "d" and "e"		450.00	450.00			
h	Design and marginal inscriptions omitted		3,250.00				
i	"USA/24¢" omitted on "a," "b" and "c"		500.00	—			
j	Imperf. (untagged)		3,000.00				
k	"USA/24¢" inverted on "d" and "e"		—				
1689	31¢ Washington Reviewing His Ragged Army at Valley Forge, by William T. Trego	05/29/76	6.25	—		9.50	2
a	31¢ Two Officers		.85	.85			2
b	31¢ George Washington		.85	.85			2
c	31¢ Officer and Brown Horse		.85	.85			2
d	31¢ White Horse and Officer		.85	.85			2
e	31¢ Three Soldiers		.85	.85			2
f	"USA/31¢" omitted, imperf.		2,750.00				
g	"USA/31¢" omitted on "a" and "c"		450.00				
h	"USA/31¢" omitted on "b," "d" and "e"		450.00	—			
i	"USA/31¢" omitted on "e"		500.00				
j	Black omitted in design		2,000.00				
k	Imperf. (untagged)			2,250.00			
l	"USA/31¢" omitted on "b" and "d"		—				
m	"USA/31¢" omitted on "a," "c" and "e"		—				
n	As "m," imperf. (untagged)		—				
p	As "h," imperf. (untagged)			2,500.00			
q	As "g," imperf. (untagged)		2,750.00				

	Issues of 1976, Perf.11		Un	U	PB	#	FDC	Q(M̄)
	American Bicentennial Issue, Benjamin Franklin							
1690	13¢ Bust of Franklin, Map of North America, 1776	06/01/76	.25	.15	1.10	(4)	1.00	165
a	Light blue omitted		300.00					
	Declaration of Independence, by John Trumbull							
1691	13¢ Delegates	07/04/76	.25	.15			1.00	41
1692	13¢ Delegates and John Adams	07/04/76	.25	.15			1.00	41
1693	13¢ Roger Sherman, Robert R. Livingston, Thomas Jefferson and Benjamin Franklin	07/04/76	.25	.15			1.00	41
1694	13¢ John Hancock, Charles Thomson, George Read, John Dickinson and Edward Rutledge	07/04/76	.25	.15			1.00	41
a	Strip of 4, #1691-94		1.10	1.10	5.50	(20)	2.00	
	Olympic Games Issue							
1695	13¢ Diver and Olympic Rings	07/16/76	.25	.15			1.00	46
1696	13¢ Skier and Olympic Rings	07/16/76	.25	.15			1.00	46
1697	13¢ Runner and Olympic Rings	07/16/76	.25	.15			1.00	46
1698	13¢ Skater and Olympic Rings	07/16/76	.25	.15			1.00	46
a	Block of 4, #1695-98		1.10	1.10	3.75	(12)	2.00	
b	As "a," imperf.		750.00					
1699	13¢ Clara Maass	08/18/76	.25	.15	3.25	(12)	2.00	131
a	Horizontal pair, imperf. vertically		475.00					
1700	13¢ Adolph S. Ochs	09/18/76	.25	.15	1.10	(4)	1.00	158
	Christmas Issue							
1701	13¢ Nativity, by John Singleton Copley	10/27/76	.25	.15	3.25	(12)	1.00	810
a	Imperf. pair		100.00					
1702	13¢ "Winter Pastime," by Nathaniel Currier	10/27/76	.25	.15	2.75	(10)	1.00	482*
a	Imperf. pair		100.00					
	*Includes #1703 printing							
1703	13¢ as #1702	10/27/76	.25	.15	6.00	(20)	1.00	
a	Imperf. pair		110.00					
b	Vertical pair, imperf. between		—					

#1702 has overall tagging. Lettering at base is black and usually $1/2$mm below design. As a rule, no "snowflaking" in sky or pond. Pane of 50 has margins on 4 sides with slogans. #1703 has block tagging the size of the printed area. Lettering at base is gray-black and usually $3/4$mm below design. "Snowflaking" generally in sky and pond. Pane of 50 has margin only at right or left and no slogans.

	Issues of 1977, American Bicentennial Issue, Washington at Princeton							
1704	13¢ Washington, Nassau Hall, Cannon and 13-star Flag, by Charles Willson Peale	01/03/77	.25	.15	2.75	(10)	1.00	150
a	Horizontal pair, imperf. vertically		550.00					
1705	13¢ Sound Recording	03/23/77	.25	.15	1.10	(4)	1.00	177

1690

1691 1692 1693 1694 1694a

1695 1696

1699

1700

1697 1698 1698a

1701

1702

1703

1704

1705

1706 **1707**

1710

1711

1708 **1709** **1709a**

1712 **1713**

1716

1714 **1715** **1715a**

1717 **1718**

1721

1719 **1720** **1720a**

Issues of 1977, Perf. 11		Un	U	PB	#	FDC	Q(M)
American Folk Art Issue, Pueblo Pottery							
1706 13¢ Zia Pot	04/13/77	.25	.15			1.00	49
1707 13¢ San Ildefonso Pot	04/13/77	.25	.15			1.00	49
1708 13¢ Hopi Pot	04/13/77	.25	.15			1.00	49
1709 13¢ Acoma Pot	04/13/77	.25	.15			1.00	49
a Block of 4, #1706-09		1.00	1.00	2.75	(10)	2.00	
b As "a," imperf. vertically		2,500.00					
1710 13¢ Solo Transatlantic Flight	05/20/77	.25	.15	3.25	(12)	3.00	209
a Imperf. pair		1,250.00					
1711 13¢ Colorado Statehood	05/21/77	.25	.15	3.25	(12)	1.00	192
a Horizontal pair, imperf. between		600.00					
b Horizontal pair, imperf. vertically		900.00					
c Perf. 11.2		.35	.25				
Butterfly Issue							
1712 13¢ Swallowtail	06/06/77	.25	.15			1.00	55
1713 13¢ Checkerspot	06/06/77	.25	.15			1.00	55
1714 13¢ Dogface	06/06/77	.25	.15			1.00	55
1715 13¢ Orange-Tip	06/06/77	.25	.15			1.00	55
a Block of 4, #1712-15		1.00	1.00	3.25	(12)	2.00	
b As "a," imperf. horizontally		15,000.00					
American Bicentennial Issue, Lafayette's Landing in South Carolina							
1716 13¢ Marquis de Lafayette	06/13/77	.25	.15	1.10	(4)	1.00	160
Skilled Hands for Independence							
1717 13¢ Seamstress	07/04/77	.25	.15			1.00	47
1718 13¢ Blacksmith	07/04/77	.25	.15			1.00	47
1719 13¢ Wheelwright	07/04/77	.25	.15			1.00	47
1720 13¢ Leatherworker	07/04/77	.25	.15			1.00	47
a Block of 4, #1717-20		1.00	1.00	3.25	(12)	1.75	
Perf. 11 x 10.5							
1721 13¢ Peace Bridge	08/04/77	.25	.15	1.10	(4)	1.00	164

A French hero of the American Revolution

Marie-Joseph-Paul-Yves-Roch-Gilbert du Motier, the Marquis de Lafayette (1757-1834), earned his place on U.S. postage stamps based on his exploits in the American War for Independence. In France in 1775, Lafayette heard about the war, and in December 1776, he decided to help the struggling colonies.

Spending part of his fortune, he bought a ship and headed for America with several French officers. Soon after arriving in June 1777, Lafayette was appointed mayor general by the Continental Congress but refused payment for his service. He later solicited funds, soldiers and ships from the King of France to help in the revolution. **(#1716)**

Interesting Fact: Although Lafayette proudly retained his French citizenship, he appears on four U.S. postage stamps.

1977-1978

Issues of 1977, Perf. 11		Un	U	PB	#	FDC	Q(M̄)
American Bicentennial Issue, Battle of Oriskany							
1722	13¢ Herkimer at Oriskany, by Frederick Yohn	08/06/77	.25	.15	2.75 (10)		1.00	156
Energy Issue							
1723	13¢ Energy Conservation	10/20/77	.25	.15			1.25	79
a	Attached pair, #1723-24		.50	.50	3.25 (12)		1.25	
1724	13¢ Energy Development	10/20/77	.25	.15			1.25	79
1725	13¢ First Civil Settlement—Alta, California	09/09/77	.25	.15	1.10 (4)		1.00	154
American Bicentennial Issue, Articles of Confederation							
1726	13¢ Members of Continental Congress in Conference	09/30/77	.25	.15	1.10 (4)		1.00	168
1727	13¢ Talking Pictures	10/06/77	.25	.15	1.10 (4)		1.25	157
American Bicentennial Issue, Surrender at Saratoga							
1728	13¢ Surrender of Burgoyne, by John Trumbull	10/07/77	.25	.15	2.75 (10)		1.00	154
Christmas Issue							
1729	13¢ Washington at Valley Forge, by J.C. Leyendecker	10/21/77	.25	.15	5.75 (20)		1.00	882
a	Imperf. pair		75.00					
1730	13¢ Rural Mailbox	10/21/77	.25	.15	2.75 (10)		1.00	922
a	Imperf. pair		300.00					
Issues of 1978							
1731	13¢ Carl Sandburg	01/06/78	.25	.15	1.10 (4)		1.00	157
Captain Cook Issue							
1732	13¢ Capt. James Cook–Alaska, by Nathaniel Dance	01/20/78	.25	.15			2.00	101
a	Attached pair, #1732-33		.50	.50	1.10 (4)		3.00	
b	As "a," imperf. between		4,500.00					
1733	13¢ Resolution and Discovery–Hawaii, by John Webber	01/20/78	.25	.15			2.00	101
a	Vertical pair, imperf. horizontally		—					
1734	13¢ Indian Head Penny	01/11/78	.25	.15	1.25 (4)		1.00	
	Pair with full horizontal gutter between		—					
a	Horizontal pair, imperf. vertically		300.00					
1735	(15¢) "A" Stamp	05/22/78	.25	.15	1.25 (4)		1.00	
a	Imperf. pair		110.00					
b	Vertical pair, imperf. horizontally		750.00					
Booklet Stamp, Perf. 11 x 10.5							
1736	(15¢) "A" orange Eagle (1735), single from booklet	05/22/78	.25	.15			1.00	
a	Booklet pane of 8	05/22/78	2.25	.90			2.50	
Roses Booklet Issue, Perf. 10							
1737	15¢ Roses, single from booklet	07/11/78	.25	.15			1.00	
a	Booklet pane of 8	07/11/78	2.25	.90			2.50	
b	As "a," imperf.		—					

#1736-37 issued only in booklets. All stamps are imperf. on one side or on one side and bottom.

US Bicentennial 13 cents

1722

1723

1724 **1723a**

First Civil Settlement·Alta California·1777

1725

1726

1727

US Bicentennial 13 cents

1728

1729

1730

1731

1732

1733 **1732a**

1734

1735

1737

1738   1739   1740   1741   1742 1742a

1745   1746

1744

1747   1748   1748a

1750

1752

1749

1753

1751   1752a

1754   1755   1756

	Issues of 1980, Perf. 11		Un	U	PB/LP	#	FDC	Q(M̄)
	Windmills Booklet Issue							
1738	15¢ Virginia, 1720	02/07/80	.30	.15			1.00	
1739	15¢ Rhode Island, 1790	02/07/80	.30	.15			1.00	
1740	15¢ Massachusetts, 1793	02/07/80	.30	.15			1.00	
1741	15¢ Illinois, 1860	02/07/80	.30	.15			1.00	
1742	15¢ Texas, 1890	02/07/80	.30	.15			1.00	
a	Booklet pane of 10, #1738-42		3.50	*3.00*			3.50	
	#1737-42 issued only in booklets. All stamps are imperf. top or bottom, or top or bottom and right side.							
	Issues of 1978 (continued), Coil Stamp, Perf. 10 Vertically							
1743	(15¢) "A" orange Eagle (1735)	05/22/78	.25	.15	.65	(2)	1.00	
a	Imperf. pair		*100.00*		—	(2)		
	Black Heritage Issue, Harriet Tubman, Perf. 10.5 x 11							
1744	13¢ Harriet Tubman and Cart Carrying Slaves	02/01/78	.25	.15	3.25	(12)	1.00	157
	American Folk Art Issue, Quilts, Perf. 11							
1745	13¢ Basket design, red and orange	03/08/78	.25	.15			1.00	41
1746	13¢ Basket design, red	03/08/78	.25	.15			1.00	41
1747	13¢ Basket design, orange	03/08/78	.25	.15			1.00	41
1748	13¢ Basket design, brown	03/08/78	.25	.15			1.00	41
a	Block of 4, #1745-48		1.00	1.00	3.25	(12)	2.00	
	American Dance Issue							
1749	13¢ Ballet	04/26/78	.25	.15			1.00	39
1750	13¢ Theater	04/26/78	.25	.15			1.00	39
1751	13¢ Folk	04/26/78	.25	.15			1.00	39
1752	13¢ Modern	04/26/78	.25	.15			1.00	39
a	Block of 4, #1749-52		1.00	1.00	3.25	(12)	1.75	
	American Bicentennial Issue, French Alliance							
1753	13¢ King Louis XVI and Benjamin Franklin, by Charles Gabriel Sauvage	05/04/78	.25	.15	1.10	(4)	1.00	103
	Perf. 10.5 x 11							
1754	13¢ Early Cancer Detection	05/18/78	.25	.15	1.10	(4)	1.00	152
	Performing Arts Issue, Jimmie Rodgers, Perf. 11							
1755	13¢ Jimmie Rodgers with Locomotive, Guitar and Brakeman's Cap	05/24/78	.25	.15	3.25	(12)	1.00	95
	George M. Cohan							
1756	15¢ George M. Cohan, "Yankee Doodle Dandy" and Stars	07/03/78	.25	.15	3.50	(12)	1.00	152

Minimum value listed for a stamp is 15 cents; for a First Day Cover (FDC), $1.00. This minimum represents a fair-market price for having a dealer locate and provide a single stamp or cover from his or her stock. Dealers may charge less per stamp or cover for a group of such stamps or covers, or less for a single stamp or cover.

	Issues of 1978, Perf. 11		Un	U	PB	#	FDC	Q(M̄)
	CAPEX '78 Souvenir Sheet							
1757	13¢ Souvenir sheet of 8	06/10/78	2.10	2.10	2.25	(8)	2.75	15
a	13¢ Cardinal		.25	.15				15
b	13¢ Mallard		.25	.15				15
c	13¢ Canada Goose		.25	.15				15
d	13¢ Blue Jay		.25	.15				15
e	13¢ Moose		.25	.15				15
f	13¢ Chipmunk		.25	.15				15
g	13¢ Red Fox		.25	.15				15
h	13¢ Raccoon		.25	.15				15
i	Yellow, green, red, brown and black (litho.) omitted		5,000.00					
1758	15¢ Photography	06/26/78	.30	.15	4.00	(12)	1.25	163
1759	15¢ Viking Missions to Mars	07/20/78	.30	.15	1.35	(4)	2.00	159
	Wildlife Conservation Issue, American Owls							
1760	15¢ Great Gray Owl	08/26/78	.30	.15			1.00	47
1761	15¢ Saw-Whet Owl	08/26/78	.30	.15			1.00	47
1762	15¢ Barred Owl	08/26/78	.30	.15			1.00	47
1763	15¢ Great Horned Owl	08/26/78	.30	.15			1.00	47
a	Block of 4, #1760-63		1.25	1.25	1.40	(4)	2.00	
	American Trees Issue							
1764	15¢ Giant Sequoia	10/09/78	.30	.15			1.00	42
1765	15¢ White Pine	10/09/78	.30	.15			1.00	42
1766	15¢ White Oak	10/09/78	.30	.15			1.00	42
1767	15¢ Gray Birch	10/09/78	.30	.15			1.00	42
a	Block of 4, #1764-67		1.25	1.25	4.00	(12)	2.00	
b	As "a," imperf. horizontally		12,500.00					

Customers could buy this full pane with six souvenir sheets. **(#1757)**

a   b   c   d

1757   e   f   g   h

1758

1759

1760   **1761**

1762   **1763**   **1763a**

1764   **1765**

1766   **1767**   **1767a**

1768

1769

1770

1771

1772

1775　　**1776**

1773

1774

1777　　**1778**　　**1778a**

1779　　**1780**

1781　　**1782**　　**1782a**

1783　　**1784**

1785　　**1786**　　**1786a**

Issues of 1978, Perf. 11		Un	U	PB	#	FDC	Q(M̄)
Christmas Issues							
1768	15¢ Madonna and Child with Cherubim, by Andrea della Robbia 10/18/78	.30	.15	4.00	(12)	1.00	963
a	Imperf. pair	90.00					
1769	15¢ Child on Hobby Horse and Christmas Trees 10/18/78	.30	.15	4.00	(12)	1.00	917
a	Imperf. pair	100.00					
b	Vertical pair, imperf. horizontally	2,250.00					
	Pair with full horizontal gutter between	—					
Issues of 1979, Perf. 11							
1770	15¢ Robert F. Kennedy 01/12/79	.30	.15	1.40	(4)	3.00	159
Black Heritage Issue, Martin Luther King, Jr.							
1771	15¢ Martin Luther King, Jr., and Civil Rights Marchers 01/13/79	.30	.15	4.00	(12)	2.50	166
a	Imperf. pair	—					
1772	15¢ International Year of the Child 02/15/79	.30	.15	1.40	(4)	1.00	163
Literary Arts Issue, John Steinbeck, Perf. 10.5 x 11							
1773	15¢ John Steinbeck, by Philippe Halsman 02/27/79	.30	.15	1.40	(4)	1.00	155
1774	15¢ Albert Einstein 03/04/79	.30	.15	1.40	(4)	3.50	157
	Pair with full horizontal gutter between	—					
American Folk Art Issue, Pennsylvania Toleware, Perf. 11							
1775	15¢ Straight-Spout Coffeepot 04/19/79	.30	.15			1.00	44
1776	15¢ Tea Caddy 04/19/79	.30	.15			1.00	44
1777	15¢ Sugar Bowl 04/19/79	.30	.15			1.00	44
1778	15¢ Curved-Spout Coffeepot 04/19/79	.30	.15			1.00	44
a	Block of 4, #1775-78	1.25	1.25	3.25	(10)	2.00	
b	As "a," imperf. horizontally	4,250.00					
American Architecture Issue							
1779	15¢ Virginia Rotunda, by Thomas Jefferson 06/04/79	.30	.15			1.00	41
1780	15¢ Baltimore Cathedral, by Benjamin Latrobe 06/04/79	.30	.15			1.00	41
1781	15¢ Boston State House, by Charles Bulfinch 06/04/79	.30	.15			1.00	41
1782	15¢ Philadelphia Exchange, by William Strickland 06/04/79	.30	.15			1.00	41
a	Block of 4, #1779-82	1.25	1.25	1.40	(4)	2.00	
Endangered Flora Issue							
1783	15¢ Persistent Trillium 06/07/79	.30	.15			1.00	41
1784	15¢ Hawaiian Wild Broadbean 06/07/79	.30	.15			1.00	41
1785	15¢ Contra Costa Wallflower 06/07/79	.30	.15			1.00	41
1786	15¢ Antioch Dunes Evening Primrose 06/07/79	.30	.15			1.00	41
a	Block of 4, #1783-86	1.25	1.25	4.00	(12)	2.00	
b	As "a," imperf.	600.00					
	As "a," full vertical gutter between	—					

	Issues of 1979, Perf. 11		Un	U	PB	#	FDC	Q(M)
1787	15¢ Seeing Eye Dogs	06/15/79	.30	.15	6.50	(20)	1.00	162
a	Imperf. pair		400.00					
1788	15¢ Special Olympics	08/09/79	.30	.15	3.25	(10)	1.00	166
	American Bicentennial Issue, John Paul Jones, Perf. 11 x 12							
1789	15¢ John Paul Jones, by Charles Willson Peale	09/23/79	.30	.15	3.25	(10)	1.25	160
a	Perf. 11		.30	.15	3.75	(10)		
b	Perf. 12		2,250.00	1,000.00				
c	Vertical pair, imperf. horizontally		200.00					
d	As "a," vertical pair, imperf. horizontally		150.00					
	Numerous varieties of printer's waste of #1789 exist.							
	Olympic Summer Games Issue, Perf. 11 (See also #C97)							
1790	10¢ Javelin Thrower	09/05/79	.20	.20	3.00	(12)	1.00	67
1791	15¢ Runner	09/28/79	.30	.15			1.00	47
1792	15¢ Swimmer	09/28/79	.30	.15			1.00	47
1793	15¢ Rowers	09/28/79	.30	.15			1.00	47
1794	15¢ Equestrian Contestant	09/28/79	.30	.15			1.00	47
a	Block of 4, #1791-94		1.25	1.25	4.00	(12)	2.00	
b	As "a," imperf.		1,600.00					
	Issues of 1980, Olympic Winter Games Issue, Perf. 11 x 10.5							
1795	15¢ Speed Skater	02/01/80	.35	.15			1.00	52
1796	15¢ Downhill Skier	02/01/80	.35	.15			1.00	52
1797	15¢ Ski Jumper	02/01/80	.35	.15			1.00	52
1798	15¢ Hockey Goaltender	02/01/80	.35	.15			1.00	52
a	Perf. 11		1.05	—				
b	Block of 4, #1795-98		1.50	1.40	4.50	(12)	2.00	
c	Block of 4, #1795a-98a		4.25	—	13.00	(12)		
	Issues of 1979 (continued), Christmas Issue, Perf. 11							
1799	15¢ Virgin and Child with Cherubim, by Gerard David	10/18/79	.30	.15	4.00	(12)	1.00	874
a	Imperf. pair		100.00					
b	Vertical pair, imperf. horizontally		700.00					
c	Vertical pair, imperf. between		2,250.00					
1800	15¢ Santa Claus, Christmas Tree Ornament	10/18/79	.30	.15	4.00	(12)	1.00	932
a	Green and yellow omitted		750.00					
b	Green, yellow and tan omitted		800.00					
	Performing Arts Issue, Will Rogers							
1801	15¢ Will Rogers Portrait and Rogers as a Cowboy Humorist	11/04/79	.30	.15	4.00	(12)	1.50	161
a	Imperf. pair		225.00					
1802	15¢ Vietnam Veterans	11/11/79	.30	.15	3.25	(10)	4.00	173
	Issues of 1980 (continued), Performing Arts Issue, W.C. Fields							
1803	15¢ W.C. Fields Portrait and Fields as a Juggler	01/29/80	.30	.15	4.00	(12)	1.25	169
	Black Heritage Issue, Benjamin Banneker							
1804	15¢ Benjamin Banneker Portrait and Banneker as Surveyor	02/15/80	.30	.15	4.00	(12)	1.00	160
a	Horizontal pair, imperf. vertically		800.00					

1787   **1788**   **1789**

1791   **1792**

1790

1793   **1794**   **1794a**

1795   **1796**

1797   **1798**   **1798b**

1799   **1800**

1801   **1802**   **1803**   **1804**

1805  **1807**  **1809**

1813   **1816**

1806   **1808**   **1810**

1818

1821

Frances Perkins
USA **15c**

1822

Emily Bissell
Crusader Against Tuberculosis
USA **15c**

1823

1824   **1825**   **1826**

1827   **1828**

1829   **1830**   **1830a**

	Issues of 1980, Perf. 11		Un	U	PB/LP	#	FDC	Q(M̄)
	Letter Writing Issue							
1805	15¢ Letters Preserve Memories	02/25/80	.30	.15			1.00	39
1806	15¢ purple P.S. Write Soon	02/25/80	.30	.15			1.00	39
1807	15¢ Letters Lift Spirits	02/25/80	.30	.15			1.00	39
1808	15¢ green P.S. Write Soon	02/25/80	.30	.15			1.00	39
1809	15¢ Letters Shape Opinions	02/25/80	.30	.15			1.00	39
1810	15¢ red and blue P.S. Write Soon	02/25/80	.30	.15			1.00	39
a	Vertical Strip of 6, #1805-10		1.85	2.00	11.00	(36)	2.50	
	Issues of 1980-81, Americana Issue, Coil Stamps, Perf. 10 Vertically							
	(See also #1581-82, 1584-85, 1590-99, 1603-06, 1608, 1610-19, 1622-23, 1625)							
1811	1¢ dark blue, greenish Inkwell and Quill (1581)	03/06/80	.15	.15	.40	(2)	1.00	
a	Imperf. pair		*160.00*		*275.00*	(2)		
1812	Not assigned							
1813	3.5¢ Weaver Violins	06/23/80	.15	.15	1.00	(2)	1.00	
a	Untagged (Bureau precanceled)			.15				
b	Imperf. pair		*225.00*		*450.00*	(2)		
1814-15	Not assigned							
1816	12¢ red brown, *beige* Torch from Statue of Liberty (1594)	04/08/81	.25	.15	1.50	(2)	1.00	
a	Untagged (Bureau precanceled)			.25				
b	Imperf. pair		*200.00*		*400.00*	(2)		
1817	Not assigned							
	Issues of 1981, Perf. 11 x 10.5							
1818	(18¢) "B" Stamp	03/15/81	.35	.15	1.60	(4)	1.00	
	Booklet Stamp, Perf. 10							
1819	(18¢) "B" Stamp (1818), single from booklet	03/15/81	.40	.15			1.00	
a	Booklet pane of 8	03/15/81	3.50	*1.75*			3.00	
	Coil Stamp, Perf. 10 Vertically							
1820	(18¢) "B" Stamp (1818)	03/15/81	.40	.15	1.60	(2)	1.00	
a	Imperf. pair		*125.00*		—	(2)		
	Issues of 1980 (continued), Perf. 10.5 x 11							
1821	15¢ Frances Perkins	04/10/80	.30	.15	1.30	(4)	1.00	164
	Perf. 11							
1822	15¢ Dolley Madison	05/20/80	.30	.15	1.40	(4)	1.00	257
1823	15¢ Emily Bissell	05/31/80	.30	.15	1.30	(4)	1.00	96
a	Vertical pair, imperf. horizontally		*400.00*					
1824	15¢ Helen Keller/Anne Sullivan	06/27/80	.30	.15	1.30	(4)	1.00	154
1825	15¢ Veterans Administration	07/21/80	.30	.15	1.30	(4)	1.50	160
a	Horizontal pair, imperf. vertically		*500.00*					
	American Bicentennial Issue, General Bernardo de Galvez							
1826	15¢ Gen. de Galvez, Battle of Mobile	07/23/80	.30	.15	1.30	(4)	1.00	104
a	Red, brown and blue omitted		*800.00*					
b	Bl., brn., red and yel. omitted		*1,400.00*					
	Coral Reefs Issue							
1827	15¢ Brain Coral, Beaugregory Fish	08/26/80	.30	.15			1.00	51
1828	15¢ Elkhorn Coral, Porkfish	08/26/80	.30	.15			1.00	51
1829	15¢ Chalice Coral, Moorish Idol	08/26/80	.30	.15			1.00	51
1830	15¢ Finger Coral, Sabertooth Blenny	08/26/80	.30	.15			1.00	51
a	Block of 4, #1827-30		1.25	1.10	4.00	(12)	2.00	
b	As "a," imperf.		*1,250.00*					
c	As "a," imperf. between, vertically		—					
d	As "a," imperf. vertically		*3,000.00*					

	Issues of 1980, Perf. 11		Un	U	PB	#	FDC	Q(M̄)
1831	15¢ Organized Labor	09/01/80	.30	.15	3.50	(12)	1.00	167
a	Imperf. pair		375.00					
	Literary Arts Issue, Edith Wharton, Perf. 10.5 x 11							
1832	15¢ Edith Wharton Reading Letter	09/05/80	.30	.15	1.30	(4)	1.00	163
	Perf. 11							
1833	15¢ Education	09/12/80	.30	.15	1.90	(6)	1.00	160
a	Horizontal pair, imperf. vertically		250.00					
	American Folk Art Issue, Pacific Northwest Indian Masks							
1834	15¢ Heiltsuk, Bella Bella Tribe	09/25/80	.30	.15			1.00	39
1835	15¢ Chilkat Tlingit Tribe	09/25/80	.30	.15			1.00	39
1836	15¢ Tlingit Tribe	09/25/80	.30	.15			1.00	39
1837	15¢ Bella Coola Tribe	09/25/80	.30	.15			1.00	39
a	Block of 4, #1834-37		1.25	1.25	3.50	(10)	2.00	
	American Architecture Issue							
1838	15¢ Smithsonian Institution, by James Renwick	10/09/80	.30	.15			1.00	39
1839	15¢ Trinity Church, by Henry Hobson Richardson	10/09/80	.30	.15			1.00	39
1840	15¢ Pennsylvania Academy of Fine Arts, by Frank Furness	10/09/80	.30	.15			1.00	39
1841	15¢ Lyndhurst, by Alexander Jefferson Davis	10/09/80	.30	.15			1.00	39
a	Block of 4, #1838-41		1.25	1.25	1.50	(4)	2.00	
	Christmas Issue							
1842	15¢ Madonna and Child from Epiphany Window, Washington Cathedral	10/31/80	.30	.15	4.00	(12)	1.00	693
a	Imperf. pair		80.00					
	Pair with full vertical gutter between		—					
1843	15¢ Wreath and Toys	10/31/80	.30	.15	6.50	(20)	1.00	719
a	Imperf. pair		80.00					
b	Buff omitted		25.00					

Wagner Act of 1935 guaranteed workers the right to form labor unions

The National Labor Relations Act, commonly known as the Wagner Act, was passed by Congress in July 1935 to govern relations between labor and management in certain industries where interstate commerce was involved. With the express intent of eliminating strikes and other forms of labor unrest—which obstructed the free flow of goods in the country—the Act protected the right of employees to join unions and bargain collectively; prohibited unfair labor practices by employers, employees and unions; and created the National Labor Relations Board to administer the law. **(#1831)**

1831

1832

1834   **1835**

1833

1836   **1837**   **1837a**

1838   **1839**

1840   **1841**   **1841a**

1842   **1843**

1844

1845

1846

1847

1848

1849

1850

1851

1852

1853

1854

1855

1856

1857

1858

1859

1860

1861

1862

1863

1864

1865

1866

1867

1868

1869

	Issues of 1980-90, Perf. 11		Un	U	PB	#	FDC
	Great Americans Issue (See also #2168-73, 2176-80, 2182-86, 2188, 2190-92, 2194-97)						
1844	1¢ Dorothea Dix	09/23/83	.15	.15	.35	(6)	1.00
a	Imperf. pair		425.00				
b	Vertical pair, imperf. between		3,000.00				
	Perf. 11 x 10.5						
1845	2¢ Igor Stravinsky	11/18/82	.15	.15	.25	(4)	1.00
a	Vertical pair, full gutter between		—				
1846	3¢ Henry Clay	07/13/83	.15	.15	.40	(4)	1.00
1847	4¢ Carl Schurz	06/03/83	.15	.15	.45	(4)	1.00
1848	5¢ Pearl Buck	06/25/83	.15	.15	.50	(4)	1.00
	Perf. 11						
1849	6¢ Walter Lippman	09/19/85	.15	.15	.75	(6)	1.00
a	Vertical pair, imperf. between		2,500.00				
1850	7¢ Abraham Baldwin	01/25/85	.15	.15	.75	(6)	1.00
1851	8¢ Henry Knox	07/25/85	.15	.15	.80	(4)	1.00
1852	9¢ Sylvanus Thayer	06/07/85	.20	.15	1.25	(6)	1.00
1853	10¢ Richard Russell	05/31/84	.20	.15	1.50	(6)	1.00
a	Vertical pair, imperf. between		1,100.00				
b	Horizontal pair, imperf. between		2,250.00				
1854	11¢ Alden Partridge	02/12/85	.20	.15	1.10	(4)	1.00
	Perf. 11 x 10.5						
1855	13¢ Crazy Horse	01/15/82	.25	.15	1.50	(4)	1.25
	Perf. 11						
1856	14¢ Sinclair Lewis	03/21/85	.25	.15	2.00	(6)	1.00
a	Vertical pair, imperf. horizontally		150.00				
b	Horizontal pair, imperf. between		10.00				
c	Vertical pair, imperf. between		1,600.00				
	Perf. 11 x 10.5						
1857	17¢ Rachel Carson	05/28/81	.35	.15	1.50	(4)	1.00
1858	18¢ George Mason	05/07/81	.35	.15	2.25	(4)	1.00
1859	19¢ Sequoyah	12/27/80	.35	.15	2.25	(4)	1.25
1860	20¢ Ralph Bunche	01/12/82	.40	.15	3.00	(4)	1.00
1861	20¢ Thomas H. Gallaudet	06/10/83	.40	.15	3.00	(4)	1.25
	Perf. 11						
1862	20¢ Harry S. Truman	01/26/84	.40	.15	2.50	(6)	1.00
b	Overall tagging	1990	—	—			
1863	22¢ John J. Audubon	04/23/85	.40	.15	2.50	(6)	1.00
a	Vertical pair, imperf. horizontally		2,500.00				
b	Vertical pair, imperf. between		—				
c	Horizontal pair, imperf. between		2,500.00				
1864	30¢ Frank C. Laubach	09/02/84	.55	.15	3.50	(6)	1.25
	Perf. 11 x 10.5						
1865	35¢ Charles R. Drew, MD	06/03/81	.65	.15	3.00	(4)	1.25
1866	37¢ Robert Millikan	01/26/82	.70	.15	3.25	(4)	1.25
	Perf. 11						
1867	39¢ Grenville Clark	03/20/85	.70	.15	5.00	(6)	1.25
a	Vertical pair, imperf. horizontally		600.00				
b	Vertical pair, imperf. between		2,000.00				
1868	40¢ Lillian M. Gilbreth	02/24/84	.70	.15	˙4.50	(6)	1.25
1869	50¢ Chester W. Nimitz	02/22/85	.95	.15	4.50	(4)	2.00
1870-73 Not assigned							

	Issues of 1981, Perf. 11		Un	U	PB/PNC	#	FDC	Q(M̄)
1874	15¢ Everett Dirksen	01/04/81	.30	.15	1.40	(4)	1.00	160
	Black Heritage Issue, Whitney Moore Young							
1875	15¢ Whitney Moore Young at Desk	01/30/81	.30	.15	1.50	(4)	1.00	160
	Flower Issue							
1876	18¢ Rose	04/23/81	.35	.15			1.00	53
1877	18¢ Camellia	04/23/81	.35	.15			1.00	53
1878	18¢ Dahlia	04/23/81	.35	.15			1.00	53
1879	18¢ Lily	04/23/81	.35	.15			1.00	53
a	Block of 4, #1876-79		1.40	1.25	1.75	(4)	2.50	
	Wildlife Booklet Issue							
1880	18¢ Bighorn Sheep	05/14/81	.55	.15			1.00	
1881	18¢ Puma	05/14/81	.55	.15			1.00	
1882	18¢ Harbor Seal	05/14/81	.55	.15			1.00	
1883	18¢ Bison	05/14/81	.55	.15			1.00	
1884	18¢ Brown Bear	05/14/81	.55	.15			1.00	
1885	18¢ Polar Bear	05/14/81	.55	.15			1.00	
1886	18¢ Elk (Wapiti)	05/14/81	.55	.15			1.00	
1887	18¢ Moose	05/14/81	.55	.15			1.00	
1888	18¢ White-Tailed Deer	05/14/81	.55	.15			1.00	
1889	18¢ Pronghorn Antelope	05/14/81	.55	.15			1.00	
a	Booklet pane of 10, #1880-89		8.00	7.00			5.00	

#1880-89 issued only in booklets. All stamps are imperf. at one side or imperf. at one side and bottom.

	Flag and Anthem Issue							
1890	18¢ "...for amber waves of grain"	04/24/81	.35	.15	2.25	(6)	1.00	
a	Imperf. pair		125.00					
b	Vertical pair, imperf. horizontally		*1,100.00*					
	Coil Stamp, Perf. 10 Vertically							
1891	18¢ "...from sea to shining sea"	04/24/81	.35	.15	4.50	(3)	1.00	
a	Imperf. pair		20.00					

Beginning with #1891, all coil stamps except 1947 feature a small plate number at the bottom of the design at varying intervals in a roll, depending on the press used. The basic "plate number coil" (PNC) collecting unit is a strip of three stamps, with the plate number appearing on the middle stamp. PNC values are for the most common plate number.

	Booklet Stamps, Perf. 11							
1892	6¢ USA Circle of Stars, single from booklet (1893a)	04/24/81	.50	.15			1.00	
1893	18¢ "...for purple mountain majesties," single from booklet (1893a)	04/24/81	.30	.15			1.00	
a	Booklet pane of 8 (2 #1892 & 6 #1893)		3.00	2.25			2.50	
b	As "a," imperf. vertically between		*75.00*					

#1892-93 issued only in booklets. All stamps are imperf. at one side or imperf. at one side and bottom.

	Flag Over Supreme Court Issue							
1894	20¢ Flag Over Supreme Court	12/17/81	.40	.15	2.25	(6)	1.00	
a	Imperf. pair		40.00					
b	Vertical pair, imperf. horizontally		*650.00*					
c	Dark blue omitted		*90.00*					
d	Black omitted		*325.00*					
	Coil Stamp, Perf. 10 Vertically							
1895	20¢ Flag Over Supreme Court (1894)	12/17/81	.35	.15	4.25	(3)	1.00	
a	Imperf. pair		8.50					
b	Black omitted		65.00					
c	Blue omitted		*1,500.00*					
e	Untagged (Bureau precanceled)		.50	.50	57.50	(3)		

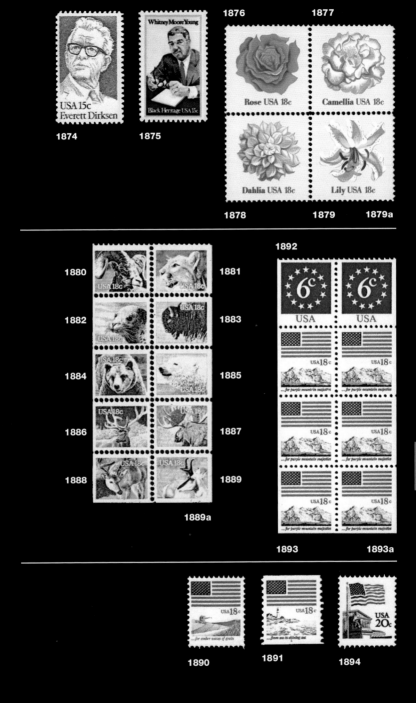

1874

1875

1876

1877

Rose USA 18c

Camellia USA 18c

Dahlia USA 18c

Lily USA 18c

1878

1879

1879a

1880

1881

1882

1883

1884

1885

1886

1887

1888

1889

1889a

1892

1893

1893a

1890

1891

1894

1897

1897A

1898

1898A

1899

1900

1901

1902

1903

1904

1905

1906

1907

1908

1909

1910

1911

	Issues of 1981-82, Perf. 11 x 10.5		Un	U	PB/PNC/LP #		FDC	Q(M̄)
	Booklet Stamp							
1896	20¢ Flag over Supreme Court (1894), single from booklet	12/17/81	.35	.15			1.00	
a	Booklet pane of 6	12/17/81	2.50	2.00			6.00	
b	Booklet pane of 10	06/01/82	4.25	3.25			10.00	
	Issues of 1981-84, Perf. 10 Vertically							
	Coil Stamps, Transportation Issue (See also #2123-36, 2225-26, 2228, 2231, 2252-66, 2452-53A, 2457, 2464, 2468)							
1897	1¢ Omnibus 1880s	08/19/83	.15	.15	.45	(3)	1.00	
b	Imperf. pair		700.00		—	(2)		
1897A	2¢ Locomotive 1870s	05/20/82	.15	.15	.50	(3)	1.50	
e	Imperf. pair		55.00		—	(2)		
1898	3¢ Handcar 1880s	03/25/83	.15	.15	.70	(3)	1.00	
1898A	4¢ Stagecoach 1890s	08/19/82	.15	.15	1.40	(3)	1.00	
b	Untagged (Bureau precanceled)		.15	.15	7.00	(3)		
c	As "b," imperf. pair		700.00					
d	Imperf. pair		925.00	—				
1899	5¢ Motorcycle 1913	10/10/83	.15	.15	1.10	(3)	2.00	
a	Imperf. pair		2,750.00					
1900	5.2¢ Sleigh 1880s	03/21/83	.15	.15	7.50	(3)	1.00	
a	Untagged (Bureau precanceled)		.15	.15	12.00	(3)		
1901	5.9¢ Bicycle 1870s	02/17/82	.20	.15	10.00	(3)	1.00	
a	Untagged (Bureau precanceled)		.20	.20	27.50	(3)		
b	As "a," imperf. pair		200.00		—	(2)		
1902	7.4¢ Baby Buggy 1880s	04/07/84	.20	.15	8.50	(3)	1.00	
a	Untagged (Bureau precanceled)		.20	.20	4.25	(3)		
1903	9.3¢ Mail Wagon 1880s	12/15/81	.30	.20	10.00	(3)	1.00	
a	Untagged (Bureau precanceled)		.25	.25	3.00	(3)		
b	As "a," imperf. pair		125.00		200.00	(2)		
1904	10.9¢ Hansom Cab 1890s	03/26/82	.25	.15	18.00	(3)	1.00	
a	Untagged (Bureau precanceled)		.25	.25	30.00	(3)		
b	As "a," imperf. pair		150.00		—	(2)		
1905	11¢ RR Caboose 1890s	02/03/84	.25	.15	4.00	(3)	1.50	
a	Untagged (Bureau precanceled)		.25	.15	2.25	(3)		
1906	17¢ Electric Auto 1917	06/25/81	.35	.15	2.25	(3)	1.00	
a	Untagged (Bureau precanceled)		.35	.35	4.00	(3)		
b	Imperf. pair		165.00		—	(2)		
c	As "a," imperf. pair		650.00		—	(2)		
1907	18¢ Surrey 1890s	05/18/81	.35	.15	3.25	(3)	1.00	
a	Imperf. pair		150.00		—	(2)		
1908	20¢ Fire Pumper 1860s	12/10/81	.35	.15	3.00	(3)	3.00 ·	
a	Imperf. pair		110.00		300.00	(2)		
	Values for plate # coil strips of 3 stamps for #1897-1908 are for the most common plate numbers. Other plate #s and strips of 5 stamps may have higher values.							
	Issue of 1983, Express Mail Booklet Issue, Perf. 10 Vertically							
1909	$9.35 Eagle and Moon, single from booklet	08/12/83	21.00	14.00			45.00	
a	Booklet pane of 3		65.00	—			125.00	
	#1909 issued only in booklets. All stamps are imperf. at top and bottom or imperf. at top, bottom and right side.							
	Issues of 1981, Perf. 10.5 x 11							
1910	18¢ American Red Cross	05/01/81	.35	.15	1.50	(4)	1.00	165
	Perf. 11							
1911	18¢ Savings and Loans	05/08/81	.35	.15	1.50	(4)	1.00	107

Issues of 1981, Perf. 11		Un	U	PB	#	FDC	Q(M̄)
Space Achievement Issue							
1912	18¢ Exploring the Moon—Moon Walk 05/21/81	.35	.15			1.00	42
1913	18¢ Benefiting Mankind (upper left)—Columbia Space Shuttle 05/21/81	.35	.15			1.00	42
1914	18¢ Benefiting Mankind—Space Shuttle Deploying Satellite 05/21/81	.35	.15			1.00	42
1915	18¢ Understanding the Sun—Skylab 05/21/81	.35	.15			1.00	42
1916	18¢ Probing the Planets—Pioneer 11 05/21/81	.35	.15			1.00	42
1917	18¢ Benefiting Mankind—Columbia Space Shuttle Lifting Off 05/21/81	.35	.15			1.00	42
1918	18¢ Benefiting Mankind—Space Shuttle Preparing to Land 05/21/81	.35	.15			1.00	42
1919	18¢ Comprehending the Universe—Telescope 05/21/81	.35	.15			1.00	42
a	Block of 8, #1912-19	3.00	3.00	3.25	(8)	3.00	
b	As "a," imperf.	9,000.00					
1920	18¢ Professional Management 06/18/81	.35	.15	1.50	(4)	1.00	99
Preservation of Wildlife Habitats Issue							
1921	18¢ Save Wetland Habitats—Great Blue Heron 06/26/81	.35	.15			1.00	45
1922	18¢ Save Grassland Habitats—Badger 06/26/81	.35	.15			1.00	45
1923	18¢ Save Mountain Habitats—Grizzly Bear 06/26/81	.35	.15			1.00	45
1924	18¢ Save Woodland Habitats—Ruffled Grouse 06/26/81	.35	.15			1.00	45
a	Block of 4, #1921-24	1.50	1.25	2.00	(4)	2.50	
1925	18¢ International Year of the Disabled 06/29/81	.35	.15	1.50	(4)	1.00	100
a	Vertical pair, imperf. horizontally	2,750.00					
1926	18¢ Edna St. Vincent Millay 07/10/81	.35	.15	1.50	(4)	1.00	100
a	Black omitted	425.00	—				
1927	18¢ Alcoholism 08/19/81	.40	.15	13.00	(6)	1.25	98
a	Imperf. pair	450.00					
b	Vertical pair, imperf. horizontally	1,750.00					

Like the phoenix from the flames

The logo of the National Council on Alcoholism and Drug Dependence, Inc. (NCADD) combines the medical caduceus, which is a symbol of health, and a key, which signifies unlocking the doors of understanding. For the NCADD, the wings of the caduceus represent the wings of the phoenix, a mythical bird who, like so many people in recovery from the diseases of alcoholism and other drug addictions, rose from the ashes of its own destruction to face a new life. **(#1927)**

1912   **1913**   **1914**   **1915**

1916   **1917**   **1918**   **1919 1919a**

1920

1921   **1922**

1923   **1924 1924a**

1925

1926

1927

1981

1928   1929

1930   1931   1931a

1932   1933

1934   1935   1936

1937   1938   1938a

1939   1940

1941

	Issues of 1981, Perf. 11		Un	U	PB	#	FDC	Q(M)
	American Architecture Issue							
1928	18¢ NYU Library, by Sanford White	08/28/81	.40	.15			1.00	42
1929	18¢ Biltmore House, by Richard Morris Hunt	08/28/81	.40	.15			1.00	42
1930	18¢ Palace of the Arts, by Bernard Maybeck	08/28/81	.40	.15			1.00	42
1931	18¢ National Farmer's Bank, by Louis Sullivan	08/28/81	.40	.15			1.00	42
a	Block of 4, #1928-31		1.65	1.50	2.10	(4)	2.50	
	American Sports Issue, Babe Zaharias and Bobby Jones, Perf. 10.5 x 11							
1932	18¢ Babe Zaharias Holding Trophy	09/22/81	.35	.15	3.00	(4)	6.00	102
1933	18¢ Bobby Jones Teeing off	09/22/81	.35	.15	3.00	(4)	7.50	99
	Perf. 11							
1934	18¢ Frederic Remington	10/09/81	.35	.15	1.60	(4)	1.00	101
a	Vertical pair, imperf. between		275.00					
b	Brown omitted		550.00					
1935	18¢ James Hoban	10/13/81	.35	.15	1.60	(4)	1.00	101
1936	20¢ James Hoban	10/13/81	.35	.15	1.65	(4)	1.00	167
	American Bicentennial Issue, Yorktown-Virginia Capes							
1937	18¢ Battle of Yorktown 1781	10/16/81	.35	.15			1.00	81
1938	18¢ Battle of the Virginia Capes 1781	10/16/81	.35	.15			1.00	81
a	Attached pair, #1937-38		.90	.75	2.00	(4)	1.50	
b	As "a," black omitted		450.00					
	Christmas Issue							
1939	20¢ Madonna and Child, by Botticelli	10/28/81	.40	.15	1.75	(4)	1.00	598
a	Imperf. pair		125.00					
b	Vertical pair, imperf. horizontally		1,650.00					
1940	20¢ Felt Bear on Sleigh	10/28/81	.40	.15	1.75	(4)	1.00	793
a	Imperf. pair		350.00					
b	Vertical pair, imperf. horizontally		—					
1941	20¢ John Hanson	11/05/81	.40	.15	1.75	(4)	1.00	167

Babe Zaharias

The greatest female athlete of the first half of the 20th century

Babe Didrikson Zaharias was born Mildred Ella Didriksen (changed to s-o-n in adulthood) on June 26, 1914, in Port Arthur, Texas. She excelled in track and field as well as baseball, swimming, figure skating and even football. Babe won gold medals in the javelin and the 80-meter hurdles in the 1932 Olympics before she began playing golf exclusively in 1935. Babe won every major women's golf championship and helped found the Ladies Professional Golf Association. In 1950, the Associated Press voted her the greatest woman athlete of the first half of the 20th century. She married professional wrestler George Zaharias in 1938 and died of cancer at the age of 42 in 1956. **(#1932)**

Interesting Fact: Babe got her nickname—a reference to Babe Ruth—after hitting five home runs in a baseball game.

	Issues of 1981, Perf. 11		Un	U	PB/LP	#	FDC	Q(M̄)
	Desert Plants Issue							
1942	20¢ Barrel Cactus	12/11/81	.35	.15			1.00	48
1943	20¢ Agave	12/11/81	.35	.15			1.00	48
1944	20¢ Beavertail Cactus	12/11/81	.35	.15			1.00	48
1945	20¢ Saguaro	12/11/81	.35	.15			1.00	48
a	Block of 4, #1942-45		1.50	1.25	1.90	(4)	2.50	
b	As "a," deep brown omitted		7,500.00					
c	#1945 vertical pair, imperf.		5,250.00					
	Perf. 11 x 10.5							
1946	(20¢) "C" Stamp	10/11/81	.40	.15	2.00	(4)	1.00	
	Coil Stamp, Perf. 10 Vertically							
1947	(20¢) "C" brown Eagle (1946)	10/11/81	.60	.15	1.50	(2)	1.00	
a	Imperf. pair		2,000.00		—	(2)		
	Booklet Stamp, Perf. 11 x 10.5							
1948	(20¢) "C" brown Eagle (1946), single from booklet	10/11/81	.40	.15			1.00	
a	Booklet pane of 10	10/11/81	4.50	3.00			3.50	
	Issues of 1982, Bighorn Sheep Booklet Issue, Perf. 11							
1949	20¢ Bighorn Sheep, single from booklet	01/08/82	.50	.15			1.00	
a	Booklet pane of 10		5.00	3.50			6.00	
b	As "a," imperf. between		110.00					
	#1949 issued only in booklets. All stamps are imperf. at one side or imperf. at one side and bottom.							
1950	20¢ Franklin D. Roosevelt	01/30/82	.40	.15	1.75	(4)	1.00	164
	Perf. 11 x 10.5							
1951	20¢ Love	02/01/82	.65	.15	3.00	(4)	1.00	447
a	Perf. 11		.40	.15	1.75	(4)		
b	Imperf. pair		350.00					
c	Blue omitted		225.00					
	Perf. 11							
1952	20¢ George Washington	02/22/82	.40	.15	1.75	(4)	1.00	181

Head-to-head combat

Bighorn sheep are perhaps best known for the battles between the males. Horn size determines a ram's dominance as he charges his opponent. The rams weigh approximately 200 pounds, but they can charge at speeds up to 20 miles per hour, and head-to-head combat lasting as long as 25.5 hours has been observed. These lengthy battles for dominance end with the victor gaining access to the females for mating purposes. **(#1949)**

Interesting Fact: Native Americans and early settlers prized bighorn meat as the most palatable of American big-game species.

1943

1942   **1944**   **1945**   **1945a**

1949

1946

1951

1950

1952

	Issues of 1982, Perf. 10.5 x 11		Un	U	FDC	Q(M̄)
	State Birds & Flowers Issue					
1953	20¢ Alabama: Yellowhammer and Camellia	04/14/82	.50	.25	1.25	13
1954	20¢ Alaska: Willow Ptarmigan and Forget-Me-Not	04/14/82	.50	.25	1.25	13
1955	20¢ Arizona: Cactus Wren and Saguaro Cactus Blossom	04/14/82	.50	.25	1.25	13
1956	20¢ Arkansas: Mockingbird and Apple Blossom	04/14/82	.50	.25	1.25	13
1957	20¢ California: California Quail and California Poppy	04/14/82	.50	.25	1.25	13
1958	20¢ Colorado: Lark Bunting and Rocky Mountain Columbine	04/14/82	.50	.25	1.25	13
1959	20¢ Connecticut: Robin and Mountain Laurel	04/14/82	.50	.25	1.25	13
1960	20¢ Delaware: Blue Hen Chicken and Peach Blossom	04/14/82	.50	.25	1.25	13
1961	20¢ Florida: Mockingbird and Orange Blossom	04/14/82	.50	.25	1.25	13
1962	20¢ Georgia: Brown Thrasher and Cherokee Rose	04/14/82	.50	.25	1.25	13
1963	20¢ Hawaii: Hawaiian Goose and Hibiscus	04/14/82	.50	.25	1.25	13
1964	20¢ Idaho: Mountain Bluebird and Syringa	04/14/82	.50	.25	1.25	13
1965	20¢ Illinois: Cardinal and Violet	04/14/82	.50	.25	1.25	13
1966	20¢ Indiana: Cardinal and Peony	04/14/82	.50	.25	1.25	13
1967	20¢ Iowa: Eastern Goldfinch and Wild Rose	04/14/82	.50	.25	1.25	13
1968	20¢ Kansas: Western Meadowlark and Sunflower	04/14/82	.50	.25	1.25	13
1969	20¢ Kentucky: Cardinal and Goldenrod	04/14/82	.50	.25	1.25	13
1970	20¢ Louisiana: Brown Pelican and Magnolia	04/14/82	.50	.25	1.25	13
1971	20¢ Maine: Chickadee and White Pine Cone and Tassel	04/14/82	.50	.25	1.25	13
1972	20¢ Maryland: Baltimore Oriole and Black-Eyed Susan	04/14/82	.50	.25	1.25	13
1973	20¢ Massachusetts: Black-Capped Chickadee and Mayflower	04/14/82	.50	.25	1.25	13
1974	20¢ Michigan: Robin and Apple Blossom	04/14/82	.50	.25	1.25	13
1975	20¢ Minnesota: Common Loon and Showy Lady Slipper	04/14/82	.50	.25	1.25	13
1976	20¢ Mississippi: Mockingbird and Magnolia	04/14/82	.50	.25	1.25	13
1977	20¢ Missouri: Eastern Bluebird and Red Hawthorn	04/14/82	.50	.25	1.25	13

	Issues of 1982, Perf. 10.5 x 11		Un	U	FDC	Q(M)
	State Birds & Flowers Issue (continued)					
1978	20¢ Montana: Western Meadowlark & Bitterroot	04/14/82	.50	.25	1.25	13
1979	20¢ Nebraska: Western Meadowlark & Goldenrod	04/14/82	.50	.25	1.25	13
1980	20¢ Nevada: Mountain Bluebird & Sagebrush	04/14/82	.50	.25	1.25	13
1981	20¢ New Hampshire: Purple Finch & Lilac	04/14/82	.50	.25	1.25	13
1982	20¢ New Jersey: American Goldfinch & Violet	04/14/82	.50	.25	1.25	13
1983	20¢ New Mexico: Roadrunner & Yucca Flower	04/14/82	.50	.25	1.25	13
1984	20¢ New York: Eastern Bluebird & Rose	04/14/82	.50	.25	1.25	13
1985	20¢ North Carolina: Cardinal & Flowering Dogwood	04/14/82	.50	.25	1.25	13
1986	20¢ North Dakota: Western Meadowlark & Wild Prairie Rose	04/14/82	.50	.25	1.25	13
1987	20¢ Ohio: Cardinal & Red Carnation	04/14/82	.50	.25	1.25	13
1988	20¢ Oklahoma: Scissor-tailed Flycatcher & Mistletoe	04/14/82	.50	.25	1.25	13
1989	20¢ Oregon: Western Meadowlark & Oregon Grape	04/14/82	.50	.25	1.25	13
1990	20¢ Pennsylvania: Ruffed Grouse & Mountain Laurel	04/14/82	.50	.25	1.25	13
1991	20¢ Rhode Island: Rhode Island Red & Violet	04/14/82	.50	.25	1.25	13
1992	20¢ South Carolina: Carolina Wren & Carolina Jessamine	04/14/82	.50	.25	1.25	13
1993	20¢ South Dakota: Ring-Necked Pheasant & Pasqueflower	04/14/82	.50	.25	1.25	13
1994	20¢ Tennessee: Mockingbird & Iris	04/14/82	.50	.25	1.25	13
1995	20¢ Texas: Mockingbird & Bluebonnet	04/14/82	.50	.25	1.25	13
1996	20¢ Utah: California Gull & Sego Lily	04/14/82	.50	.25	1.25	13
1997	20¢ Vermont: Hermit Thrush & Red Clover	04/14/82	.50	.25	1.25	13
1998	20¢ Virginia: Cardinal & Flowering Dogwood	04/14/82	.50	.25	1.25	13
1999	20¢ Washington: American Goldfinch & Rhododendron	04/14/82	.50	.25	1.25	13
2000	20¢ West Virginia: Cardinal & Rhododendron Maximum	04/14/82	.50	.25	1.25	13
2001	20¢ Wisconsin: Robin & Wood Violet	04/14/82	.50	.25	1.25	13
2002	20¢ Wyoming: Western Meadowlark & Indian Paintbrush	04/14/82	.50	.25	1.25	13
a	Any single, perf. 11		.55	.30		
b	Pane of 50 (with plate #)		25.00	—	30.00	
c	Pane of 50, perf. 11		27.50	—		
d	Pane of 50, imperf.		—			

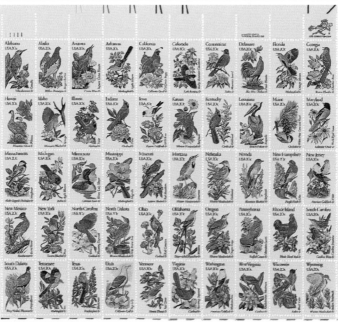

Example of 2002b.

Montana USA 20c *Western Meadowlark &* Bitterroot	Nebraska USA 20c *Western Meadowlark &* Goldenrod	Nevada USA 20c *Mountain Bluebird &* Sagebrush	New Hampshire USA 20c *Purple Finch &* Lilac	New Jersey USA 20c *American Goldfinch &* Violet
1978	**1979**	**1980**	**1981**	**1982**

New Mexico USA 20c *Roadrunner &* Yucca Flower	New York USA 20c *Eastern Bluebird &* Rose	North Carolina USA 20c *Cardinal &* Flowering Dogwood	North Dakota USA 20c *Western Meadowlark &* Wild Prairie Rose	Ohio USA 20c *Cardinal &* Red Carnation
1983	**1984**	**1985**	**1986**	**1987**

Oklahoma USA 20c *Scissor-tailed Flycatcher &* Mistletoe	Oregon USA 20c *Western Meadowlark &* Oregon Grape	Pennsylvania USA 20c *Ruffed Grouse &* Mountain Laurel	Rhode Island USA 20c *Rhode Island Red &* Violet	South Carolina USA 20c *Carolina Wren &* Carolina Jasmine
1988	**1989**	**1990**	**1991**	**1992**

South Dakota USA 20c *Ring-Necked Pheasant &* Pasqueflower	Tennessee USA 20c *Mockingbird &* Iris	Texas USA 20c *Mockingbird &* Bluebonnet	Utah USA 20c *California Gull &* Sego Lily	Vermont USA 20c *Hermit Thrush &* Red Clover
1993	**1994**	**1995**	**1996**	**1997**

Virginia USA 20c *Cardinal &* Flowering Dogwood	Washington USA 20c *American Goldfinch &* Rhododendron	West Virginia USA 20c *Cardinal &* Rhododendron Maximum	Wisconsin USA 20c *Robin &* Wood Violet	Wyoming USA 20c *Western Meadowlark &* Indian Paintbrush
1998	**1999**	**2000**	**2001**	**2002**

2003

2004

2005

2006

2007

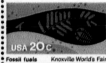

2008

2009

2009a

2010

2012

2011

2013

2014

2015

2016

2017

2019

2020

2018

2021

2022

2022a

	Issues of 1982, Perf. 11		Un	U	PB/PNC/LP	#	FDC	Q(M̄)
2003	20¢ USA/The Netherlands	04/20/82	.40	.15	3.50	(6)	1.00	109
a	Imperf. pair		325.00					
2004	20¢ Library of Congress	04/21/82	.40	.15	1.75	(4)	1.00	113
	Coil Stamp, Perf. 10 Vertically							
2005	20¢ Consumer Education	04/27/82	.55	.15	30.00	(3)	1.00	
a	Imperf. pair		100.00		400.00	(2)		

Value for plate no. coil strip of 3 stamps is for most common plate nos. Other plate nos. and strips of 5 stamps may have higher values.

	Knoxville World's Fair Issue, Perf. 11							
2006	20¢ Solar Energy	04/29/82	.40	.15			1.00	31
2007	20¢ Synthetic Fuels	04/29/82	.40	.15			1.00	31
2008	20¢ Breeder Reactor	04/29/82	.40	.15			1.00	31
2009	20¢ Fossil Fuels	04/29/82	.40	.15			1.00	31
a	Block of 4, #2006-09		1.65	1.50	2.00	(4)	2.50	
2010	20¢ Horatio Alger	04/30/82	.40	.15	1.75	(4)	1.00	108
2011	20¢ Aging Together	05/21/82	.40	.15	1.75	(4)	1.00	173
	Performing Arts Issue, The Barrymores							
2012	20¢ Portraits of John, Ethel and Lionel Barrymore	06/08/82	.40	.15	1.75	(4)	1.00	107
2013	20¢ Dr. Mary Walker	06/10/82	.40	.15	1.75	(4)	1.00	109
2014	20¢ International Peace Garden	06/30/82	.40	.15	1.75	(4)	1.00	183
a	Black and green omitted		275.00					
2015	20¢ America's Libraries	07/13/82	.40	.15	1.75	(4)	1.00	169
a	Vertical pair, imperf. horizontally		325.00					
	Black Heritage Issue, Jackie Robinson, Perf. 10.5 x 11							
2016	20¢ Jackie Robinson Portrait and Robinson Stealing Home Plate	08/02/82	1.10	.15	5.25	(4)	5.50	164
	Perf. 11							
2017	20¢ Touro Synagogue	08/22/82	.40	.15	11.00	(20)	1.00	110
a	Imperf. pair		2,500.00					
2018	20¢ Wolf Trap Farm Park	09/01/82	.40	.15	1.75	(4)	1.00	111
	American Architecture Issue							
2019	20¢ Fallingwater, by Frank Lloyd Wright	09/30/82	.40	.15			1.00	41
2020	20¢ Illinois Institute of Technology, by Ludwig Mies van der Rohe	09/30/82	.40	.15			1.00	41
2021	20¢ Gropius House, by Walter Gropius	09/30/82	.40	.15			1.00	41
2022	20¢ Dulles Airport by Eero Saarinen	09/30/82	.40	.15			1.00	41
a	Block of 4, #2019-22		1.75	1.60	2.25	(4)	2.50	

The stamp listings contain a number of "a," "b," "c," etc. additions which include recognized varieties and errors. These listings are as complete as space permits.

	Issues of 1982, Perf. 11		Un	U	PB	#	FDC	Q(M̄)
2023	20¢ St. Francis of Assisi	10/07/82	.40	.15	1.75	(4)	1.25	174
2024	20¢ Ponce de Leon	10/12/82	.40	.15	3.25	(6)	1.00	110
a	Imperf. pair		600.00					
	Christmas Issue							
2025	13¢ Puppy and Kitten	11/03/82	.25	.15	1.40	(4)	1.00	234
a	Imperf. pair		650.00					
2026	20¢ Madonna and Child, by Tiepolo	10/28/82	.40	.15	12.00	(20)	1.00	703
a	Imperf. pair		150.00					
b	Horizontal pair, imperf. vertically		—					
c	Vertical pair, imperf. horizontally		—					
	Seasons Greetings Issue							
2027	20¢ Children Sledding	10/28/82	.45	.15			1.00	197
2028	20¢ Children Building a Snowman	10/28/82	.45	.15			1.00	197
2029	20¢ Children Skating	10/28/82	.45	.15			1.00	197
2030	20¢ Children Trimming a Tree	10/28/82	.45	.15			1.00	197
a	Block of 4, #2027-30		2.00	1.50	2.50	(4)	2.50	
b	As "a," imperf.		3,000.00					
c	As "a," imperf. horizontally		3,250.00					
	Issues of 1983							
2031	20¢ Science & Industry	01/19/83	.40	.15	1.75	(4)	1.00	119
a	Black omitted		1,400.00					
	Balloons Issue							
2032	20¢ Intrepid, 1861	03/31/83	.40	.15			1.00	57
2033	20¢ Hot Air Ballooning (wording lower right)	03/31/83	.40	.15			1.00	57
2034	20¢ Hot Air Ballooning (wording upper left)	03/31/83	.40	.15			1.00	57
2035	20¢ Explorer II, 1935	03/31/83	.40	.15			1.00	57
a	Block of 4, #2032-35		1.65	1.50	1.75	(4)	2.50	
b	As "a," imperf.		—					
2036	20¢ U.S./Sweden Treaty	03/24/83	.40	.15	1.75	(4)	1.00	118
2037	20¢ Civilian Conservation Corps	04/05/83	.40	.15	1.75	(4)	1.00	114
a	Imperf. pair		2,500.00					
2038	20¢ Joseph Priestley	04/13/83	.40	.15	1.75	(4)	1.00	165
2039	20¢ Voluntarism	04/20/83	.40	.15	3.00	(6)	1.25	120
a	Imperf. pair		800.00					
2040	20¢ Concord—German Immigration, Apr. 29	04/29/83	.40	.15	1.75	(4)	1.00	117

2023

2024

2025

2026

2027　　**2028**

2029　　**2030**　　**2030a**

2033

2031

2032　　**2034**　　**2035**　**2035a**

2036

2037

2038

2039

2040

2041

2042

2043

2044

2045

2046

2047

2048   **2049**

2050   **2051**   **2051a**

2052

2055   **2056**

2053

2054

2057   **2058**   **2058a**

	Issues of 1983, Perf. 11		Un	U	PB	#	FDC	Q(M̄)
2041	20¢ Brooklyn Bridge	05/17/83	.40	.15	1.75	(4)	1.00	182
2042	20¢ Tennessee Valley Authority	05/18/83	.40	.15	11.00	(20)	1.00	114
2043	20¢ Physical Fitness	05/14/83	.40	.15	3.00	(6)	1.00	112
	Black Heritage Issue, Scott Joplin							
2044	20¢ Scott Joplin Portrait and Joplin Playing the Piano	06/09/83	.40	.15	1.75	(4)	1.00	115
a	Imperf. pair		550.00					
2045	20¢ Medal of Honor	06/07/83	.40	.15	1.75	(4)	3.00	109
a	Red omitted		325.00					
	American Sports Issue, Babe Ruth, Perf. 10.5 x 11							
2046	20¢ Babe Ruth Hitting a Home Run	07/06/83	1.10	.15	6.50	(4)	5.00	185
	Literary Arts Issue, Nathaniel Hawthorne, Perf. 11							
2047	20¢ Nathaniel Hawthorne, by Cephus Giovanni Thompson	07/08/83	.40	.15	1.70	(4)	1.00	111
	Olympic Summer Games Issue (See also #2082-85, C101-12)							
2048	13¢ Discus Thrower	07/28/83	.35	.15			1.00	99
2049	13¢ High Jumper	07/28/83	.35	.15			1.00	99
2050	13¢ Archer	07/28/83	.35	.15			1.00	99
2051	13¢ Boxers	07/28/83	.35	.15			1.00	99
a	Block of 4, #2048-51		1.50	1.25	1.75	(4)	2.50	
	American Bicentennial Issue, Treaty of Paris							
2052	20¢ Signing of Treaty of Paris (John Adams, Benjamin Franklin and John Jay observing David Hartley), by Benjamin West	09/02/83	.40	.15	1.75	(4)	1.00	104
2053	20¢ Civil Service	09/09/83	.40	.15	3.00	(6)	1.00	115
2054	20¢ Metropolitan Opera	09/14/83	.40	.15	1.75	(4)	1.00	113
	American Inventors Issue							
2055	20¢ Charles Steinmetz and Curve on Graph	09/21/83	.40	.15			1.00	48
2056	20¢ Edwin Armstrong and Frequency Modulator	09/21/83	.40	.15			1.00	48
2057	20¢ Nikola Tesla and Induction Motor	09/21/83	.40	.15			1.00	48
2058	20¢ Philo T. Farnsworth and First Television Camera	09/21/83	.40	.15			1.00	48
a	Block of 4, #2055-58		1.60	1.25	2.40	(4)	2.50	
b	As "a," black omitted		450.00					

The long-awaited Brooklyn Bridge connects the boroughs of Manhattan and Brooklyn

Spanning the East River between Brooklyn and Manhattan, the Brooklyn Bridge was, at 1,595 feet, the longest suspension bridge in the world when it opened on May 24, 1883, and the first to be built using steel cables. After designer John A. Roebling's death in 1869 due to complications from an injury sustained while surveying the site, his son and partner Washington A. Roebling was named chief engineer. Despite suffering a crippling attack of the bends in 1872, Washington Roebling was able, with the help of his wife, Emily, to see the project through to completion. An extraordinary feat of 19th-century engineering, the Brooklyn Bridge remains a celebrated New York City landmark. **(#2041)**

	Issues of 1983, Perf. 11		Un	U	PB	#	FDC	Q(Ⓜ)
	Streetcars Issue							
2059	20¢ First American Streetcar	10/08/83	.40	.15			1.00	52
2060	20¢ Early Electric Streetcar	10/08/83	.40	.15			1.00	52
2061	20¢ "Bobtail" Horsecar	10/08/83	.40	.15			1.00	52
2062	20¢ St. Charles Streetcar	10/08/83	.40	.15			1.00	52
a	Block of 4, #2059-62		1.70	1.40	2.00	(4)	2.50	
b	As "a," black omitted		*475.00*					
c	As "a," black omitted on #2059, 2061		—					
	Christmas Issue							
2063	20¢ Niccolini-Cowper Madonna, by Raphael	10/28/83	.40	.15	1.75	(4)	1.00	716
2064	20¢ Santa Claus	10/28/83	.40	.15	3.00	(6)	1.00	849
a	Imperf. pair		*175.00*					
2065	20¢ Martin Luther	11/11/83	.40	.15	1.75	(4)	2.50	165
	Issues of 1984							
2066	20¢ 25th Anniversary of Alaska Statehood	01/03/84	.40	.15	1.75	(4)	1.00	120
	Winter Olympic Games Issue, Perf. 10.5 x 11							
2067	20¢ Ice Dancing	01/06/84	.45	.15			1.00	80
2068	20¢ Alpine Skiing	01/06/84	.45	.15			1.00	80
2069	20¢ Nordic Skiing	01/06/84	.45	.15			1.00	80
2070	20¢ Hockey	01/06/84	.45	.15			1.00	80
a	Block of 4, #2067-70		1.85	1.50	2.50	(4)	2.50	
	Perf. 11							
2071	20¢ Federal Deposit Insurance Corporation	01/12/84	.40	.15	1.75	(4)	1.00	103

The magic of Christmas lives through Santa Claus

The spirit of the Christmas season involves bringing gifts to children around the world. Santa Claus, also know as Saint Nicholas or Kriss Kringle, is believed to deliver holiday presents on Christmas Eve wearing his red suit with white trim and driving his sleigh pulled by eight reindeer. This legend of Santa Claus has been passed down to generations of children, and when they believe in this generous gift-giver, the magic of the Christmas season remains alive. The American story of Santa Claus was told in the poem, "The Night Before Christmas," written by Clement Clarke Moore in 1823. **(#2064)**

2059 **2060**

2061 **2062** **2062a**

2064

2063

2065

2067 **2068**

2066

2071

2069 **2070** **2070a**

2072

2073

2074

2075

2076   2077

2080

2081

2078   2079   2079a

2082   2083

2086

2087

2084   2085   2085a

	Issues of 1984, Perf. 11 x 10.5		Un	U	PB	#	FDC	Q(M̄)
2072	20¢ Love	01/31/84	.40	.15	11.50	(20)	2.00	555
a	Horizontal pair, imperf. vertically		175.00					
	Black Heritage Issue, Carter G. Woodson, Perf. 11							
2073	20¢ Carter G. Woodson Holding History Book	02/01/84	.40	.15	1.75	(4)	1.00	120
a	Horizontal pair, imperf. vertically		1,750.00					
2074	20¢ Soil and Water Conservation	02/06/84	.40	.15	1.75	(4)	1.00	107
2075	20¢ 50th Anniversary of Credit Union Act	02/10/84	.40	.15	1.75	(4)	1.00	107
	Orchids Issue							
2076	20¢ Wild Pink	03/05/84	45	.15			1.00	77
2077	20¢ Yellow Lady's-Slipper	03/05/84	.45	.15			1.00	77
2078	20¢ Spreading Pogonia	03/05/84	.45	.15			1.00	77
2079	20¢ Pacific Calypso	03/05/84	.45	.15			1.00	77
a	Block of 4, #2076-79		1.85	1.50	2.10	(4)	2.50	
2080	20¢ 25th Anniversary of Hawaii Statehood	03/12/84	.40	.15	1.70	(4)	1.00	120
2081	20¢ National Archives	04/16/84	.40	.15	1.70	(4)	1.00	108
	Olympic Summer Games Issue (See also #2048-52, C101-12)							
2082	20¢ Diving	05/04/84	.50	.15			1.00	78
2083	20¢ Long Jump	05/04/84	.50	.15			1.00	78
2084	20¢ Wrestling	05/04/84	.50	.15			1.00	78
2085	20¢ Kayak	05/04/84	.50	.15			1.00	78
a	Block of 4, #2082-85		2.25	1.90	3.50	(4)	2.50	
2086	20¢ Louisiana World Exposition	05/11/84	.40	.15	1.75	(4)	1.00	130
2087	20¢ Health Research	05/17/84	.40	.15	1.75	(4)	1.00	120

Researching a cure for the common cold to the rarest genetic disorder

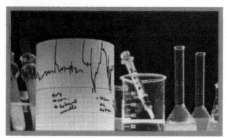

There are many government and private agencies and companies that fund and conduct health-related research, but the National Institutes of Health (NIH) is the largest supporter of medical research in the U.S. and one of the largest in the world. An agency of the U.S. Department of Health and Human Services, the NIH is made up of 24 individual organizations and is associated with medical research in the factors, treatment and prevention of disease. Other functions of the NIH include training researchers and fostering communication of medical information. **(#2087)**

Interesting Fact: The NIH has grown from a one-room lab with a $300 annual budget in 1887 to more than 50 buildings on more than 300 acres with a budget of more than $13.6 billion in 1998.

Issues of 1984, Perf. 11		Un	U	PB	#	FDC	Q(M)
Performing Arts Issue, Douglas Fairbanks							
2088	20¢ Douglas Fairbanks Portrait and Fairbanks in Pirate Role 05/23/84	.40	.15	14.00	(20)	1.00	117
American Sports Issue, Jim Thorpe							
2089	20¢ Jim Thorpe on Football Field 05/24/84	.40	.15	2.00	(4)	3.00	116
Performing Arts Issue, John McCormack							
2090	20¢ John McCormack Portrait and McCormack in Tenor Role 06/06/84	.40	.15	1.75	(4)	1.00	117
2091	20¢ 25th Anniversary of St. Lawrence Seaway 06/26/84	.40	.15	1.75	(4)	1.00	120
2092	20¢ Migratory Bird Hunting and Preservation Act 07/02/84	.50	.15	2.50	(4)	1.25	124
a	Horizontal pair, imperf. vertically	425.00					
2093	20¢ Roanoke Voyages 07/13/84	.40	.15	1.75	(4)	1.00	120
	Pair with full horizontal gutter between	—					
Literary Arts Issue, Herman Melville							
2094	20¢ Herman Melville 08/01/84	.40	.15	1.75	(4)	1.50	117
2095	20¢ Horace Moses 08/06/84	.45	.15	3.50	(6)	1.00	117
2096	20¢ Smokey the Bear 08/13/84	.40	.15	2.00	(4)	3.50	96
a	Horizontal pair, imperf. between	300.00					
b	Vertical pair, imperf. between	300.00					
c	Block of 4, imperf. between vertically and horizontally	5,500.00					
American Sports Issue, Roberto Clemente							
2097	20¢ Clemente in Pirates Cap, Puerto Rican Flag in Background 08/17/84	1.40	.15	7.00	(4)	8.00	119
a	Horizontal pair, imperf. vertically	1,800.00					
American Dogs Issue							
2098	20¢ Beagle and Boston Terrier 09/07/84	.40	.15			1.25	54
2099	20¢ Chesapeake Bay Retriever and Cocker Spaniel 09/07/84	.40	.15			1.25	54
2100	20¢ Alaskan Malamute and Collie 09/07/84	.40	.15			1.25	54
2101	20¢ Black and Tan Coonhound and American Foxhound 09/07/84	.40	.15			1.25	54
a	Block of 4, #2098-2101	1.75	1.75	2.75	(4)	3.00	

These pets love to fetch

The Chesapeake Bay retriever and the cocker spaniel are two kinds of sporting dogs that can be trained to fetch balls or maybe even your slippers. The Chesapeake Bay retriever, standing about 23 to 26 inches high and weighing about 70 pounds, is much bigger than its 15-inch-high cocker spaniel friend who weighs about 30 pounds. Both breeds are considered friendly and are therefore popular family pets. **(#2099)**

2088   2089   2090

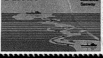

2091   2092

2093

2094   2095   2096   2097

2098   2099

2100   2101   2101a

2102

2103

2104

2105

2106

2107

2108

2109

2110

2111

2114

2115b

2116

	Issues of 1984, Perf. 11		Un	U	PB/PNC	#	FDC	Q(M)
2102	20¢ Crime Prevention	09/26/84	.40	.15	1.75	(4)	1.00	120
2103	20¢ Hispanic Americans	10/31/84	.40	.15	1.75	(4)	1.00	108
a	Vertical pair, imperf. horizontally		1,750.00					
2104	20¢ Family Unity	10/01/84	.40	.15	14.00	(20)	1.00	118
a	Horizontal pair, imperf. vertically		550.00					
2105	20¢ Eleanor Roosevelt	10/11/84	.40	.15	1.75	(4)	1.00	113
2106	20¢ A Nation of Readers	10/16/84	.40	.15	1.75	(4)	1.00	117
	Christmas Issue							
2107	20¢ Madonna and Child, by Fra Filippo Lippi	10/30/84	.40	.15	1.70	(4)	1.00	751
2108	20¢ Santa Claus	10/30/84	.40	.15	1.70	(4)	1.00	786
a	Horizontal pair, imperf. vertically		950.00					
	Perf. 10.5							
2109	20¢ Vietnam Veterans' Memorial	11/10/84	.40	.15	1.90	(4)	4.00	105
	Issues of 1985, Perf. 11 **Performing Arts Issue, Jerome Kern**							
2110	22¢ Jerome Kern Portrait and Kern Studying Sheet Music	01/23/85	.40	.15	1.75	(4)	1.00	125
2111	(22¢) "D" Stamp	02/01/85	.55	.15	4.50	(6)	1.00	
a	Imperf. pair		50.00					
b	Vertical pair, imperf. horizontally		1,350.00					
	Coil Stamp, Perf. 10 Vertically							
2112	(22¢) "D" green Eagle (2111)	02/01/85	.60	.15	6.00	(3)	1.00	
a	Imperf. pair		50.00					
	Booklet Stamp, Perf. 11							
2113	(22¢) "D" green Eagle (2111), single from booklet	02/01/85	.80	.15			1.00	
a	Booklet pane of 10	02/01/85	8.50				7.50	
b	As "a," imperf. between horizontally		—					
	Issues of 1985-87, Flag Over Capitol Issue							
2114	22¢ Flag Over Capitol	03/29/85	.40	.15	1.90	(4)	1.00	
	Pair with full horizontal gutter between		—					
	Coil Stamp, Perf. 10 Vertically							
2115	22¢ Flag Over Capitol (2114)	03/29/85	.40	.15	3.75	(3)	1.00	
a	Imperf. pair		12.50				1.00	
b	Inscribed "T" at bottom	05/23/87	.50	.15	4.00	(3)		
c	Black field of stars		—	—				
	#2115b issued for test on prephosphored paper. Paper is whiter and colors are brighter than on 2115.							
	Booklet Stamp, Perf. 10 Horizontally							
2116	22¢ Flag over Capitol, single from booklet		.50	.15			1.00	
a	Booklet pane of 50	03/29/85	2.50	1.25			3.50	
	#2116 issued only in booklets. All stamps are imperf. at both sides or imperf. at both sides and bottom.							

	Issues of 1985, Perf. 10 vertically		Un	U	PNC	#	FDC
	Seashells Booklet Issue						
2117	22¢ Frilled Dogwinkle	04/04/85	.40	.15			1.00
2118	22¢ Reticulated Helmet	04/04/85	.40	.15			1.00
2119	22¢ New England Neptune	04/04/85	.40	.15			1.00
2120	22¢ Calico Scallop	04/04/85	.40	.15			1.00
2121	22¢ Lightning Whelk	04/04/85	.40	.15			1.00
a	Booklet pane of 10		4.00	2.50			7.50
b	As "a," violet omitted		850.00				
c	As "a," imperf. between vertically		600.00				
e	Strip of 5, #2117-21		2.00	—			
	Express Mail Booklet Issue						
2122	$10.75 Eagle and Moon, booklet single	04/29/85	17.00	7.00			40.00
a	Booklet pane of 3		52.50	—			95.00
	#2122 issued only in booklets. All stamps are imperf. at top and bottom or at top, bottom and one side.						
	Issues of 1985-89, Coil Stamps, Transportation Issue (See also #1897-1908, 2225-31, 2252-66, 2451-68)						
2123	3.4¢ School Bus 1920s	06/08/85	.15	.15	.95	(3)	1.00
a	Untagged (Bureau precanceled)		.15	.15	6.50	(3)	
2124	4.9¢ Buckboard 1880s	06/21/85	.15	.15	1.00	(3)	1.00
a	Untagged (Bureau precanceled)		.20	.20	1.75	(3)	
2125	5.5¢ Star Route Truck 1910s	11/01/86	.15	.15	1.90	(3)	1.00
a	Untagged (Bureau precanceled)		.15	.15	1.75	(3)	
2126	6¢ Tricycle 1880s	05/06/85	.15	.15	1.40	(3)	1.00
a	Untagged (Bureau precanceled)		.15	.15	1.75	(3)	
b	As "a," imperf. pair		200.00				
2127	7.1¢ Tractor 1920s	02/06/87	.15	.15	2.50	(3)	1.00
a	Untagged (Bureau precanceled "Nonprofit org.")		.15	.15	3.25	(3)	
a	Untagged (Bureau precanceled "Nonprofit 5-Digit ZIP + 4")	05/26/89	.15	.15	2.00	(3)	5.00
2128	8.3¢ Ambulance 1860s	06/21/85	.20	.15	1.40	(3)	1.00
a	Untagged (Bureau precanceled)		.20	.20	1.65	(3)	
2129	8.5¢ Tow Truck 1920s	01/24/87	.20	.15	2.75	(3)	1.00
a	Untagged (Bureau precanceled)		.20	.20	3.00	(3)	
2130	10.1¢ Oil Wagon 1890s	04/18/85	.25	.15	2.50	(3)	1.00
a	Untagged (Bureau precanceled, black)		.25	.25	2.75	(3)	1.00
a	Untagged (Bureau precanceled, red)		.25	.25	2.25	(3)	1.00
b	As "a," black precancel, imperf. pair		100.00				
b	As "a," red precancel, imperf. pair		15.00				
2131	11¢ Stutz Bearcat 1933	06/11/85	.25	.15	1.65	(3)	1.25
2132	12¢ Stanley Steamer 1909	04/02/85	.25	.15	2.00	(3)	1.00
a	Untagged (Bureau precanceled)		.25	.25	2.50	(3)	
b	As "a," type II		.25	.25	20.00	(3)	
	Type II has "Stanley Steamer 1909" 1/2mm shorter (17 1/2mm) than #2132 (18mm).						
2133	12.5¢ Pushcart 1880s	04/18/85	.25	.15	2.75	(3)	1.25
a	Untagged (Bureau precanceled)		.25	.25	3.00	(3)	
b	As "a," imperf. pair		50.00				
2134	14¢ Iceboat 1880s	03/23/85	.30	.15	2.50	(3)	1.25
a	Imperf. pair		100.00				
2135	17¢ Dog Sled 1920s	08/20/86	.30	.15	3.00	(3)	1.25
a	Imperf. pair		550.00				
2136	25¢ Bread Wagon 1880s	11/22/86	.45	.15	3.25	(3)	1.25
a	Imperf. pair		10.00				

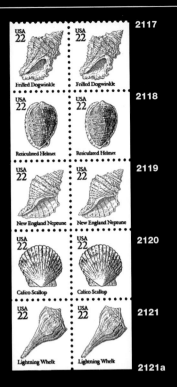

2117

2118

2119

2120

2121

2121a

2122

2123

2124

2125

2126

2127

2128

2129

2130

2131

2132

2133

2134

2135

2136

277

2137

2138   2139

2140   2141   2141a

2142

2143

2144

2145

2146

2147

2149

2150

2152

2153

Issues of 1985, Perf. 11		Un	U	PB/PNC	#	FDC	Q(M̄)
Black Heritage Issue, Mary McLeod Bethune							
2137	22¢ Mary McLeod Bethune Portrait 03/05/85	.40	.15	2.25	(4)	1.00	120
American Folk Art Issue, Duck Decoys							
2138	22¢ Broadbill Decoy 03/22/85	.60	.15			1.00	75
2139	22¢ Mallard Decoy 03/22/85	.60	.15			1.00	75
2140	22¢ Canvasback Decoy 03/22/85	.60	.15			1.00	75
2141	22¢ Redhead Decoy 03/22/85	.60	.15			1.00	75
a	Block of 4, #2138–41	3.75	2.25	6.00	(4)	2.75	
2142	22¢ Winter Special Olympics 03/25/85	.40	.15	1.75	(4)	1.00	121
a	Vertical pair, imperf. horizontally	650.00					
2143	22¢ Love 04/17/85	.40	.15	1.70	(4)	2.00	730
a	Imperf. pair	1,750.00					
2144	22¢ Rural Electrification Administration 05/11/85	.45	.15	25.00	(20)	1.00	125
2145	22¢ AMERIPEX '86 05/25/85	.40	.15	1.75	(4)	1.00	203
a	Red, black and blue omitted	200.00					
b	Red and black omitted	1,250.00					
2146	22¢ Abigail Adams 06/14/85	.40	.15	1.90	(4)	1.00	126
a	Imperf. pair	275.00					
2147	22¢ Frederic A. Bartholdi 07/18/85	.40	.15	1.90	(4)	1.00	130
2148	Not assigned						
Coil Stamps, Perf. 10 Vertically							
2149	18¢ George Washington, Washington Monument 11/06/85	.35	.15	3.25	(3)	1.25	
a	Untagged (Bureau precanceled)	.35	.35	3.25	(3)		
b	Imperf. pair	950.00					
c	As "a," imperf. pair	800.00		4.50	(3)		
2150	21.1¢ Sealed Envelopes 10/22/85	.40	.15	3.25	(3)	1.25	
a	Untagged (Bureau precanceled)	.40	.40	3.50	(3)		
2151	Not assigned						
Perf. 11							
2152	22¢ Korean War Veterans 07/26/85	.40	.15	1.90	(4)	3.00	120
2153	22¢ Social Security Act, 50th Anniversary 08/14/85	.40	.15	1.90	(4)	1.00	120

The "Super Bowl of Stamp Shows"

The AMERIPEX '86 International Stamp Show, held May 22 to June 1, 1986, was the largest stamp show that had ever been held in the Western Hemisphere, earning nicknames like the "Super Bowl of Stamp Shows" and the "World's Fair of Stamps." The show featured 4,000 frames of competitive stamp displays and 500 frames of invited world-class exhibits, each holding 16 album pages. In the U.S., shows of this nature are usually held only once every 10 years. **(#2145)**

	Issues of 1985, Perf. 11		Un	U	PB	#	FDC	Q(M)
2154	22¢ World War I Veterans	08/26/85	.40	.15	2.25	(4)	3.00	120
	American Horses Issue							
2155	22¢ Quarter Horse	09/25/85	.90	.15			1.25	37
2156	22¢ Morgan	09/25/85	.90	.15			1.25	37
2157	22¢ Saddlebred	09/25/85	.90	.15			1.25	37
2158	22¢ Appaloosa	09/25/85	.90	.15			1.25	37
a	Block of 4, #2155-58		5.50	4.50	8.50	(4)	2.50	
2159	22¢ Public Education	10/01/85	.45	.15	2.75	(4)	1.00	120
	International Youth Year Issue							
2160	22¢ YMCA Youth Camping	10/07/85	.60	.15			1.00	33
2161	22¢ Boy Scouts	10/07/85	.60	.15			2.00	33
2162	22¢ Big Brothers/Big Sisters	10/07/85	.60	.15			1.00	33
2163	22¢ Camp Fire	10/07/85	.60	.15			1.00	33
a	Block of 4, #2160-63		2.75	2.25	4.50	(4)	2.50	
2164	22¢ Help End Hunger	10/15/85	.45	.15	2.00	(4)	1.00	120
	Christmas Issue							
2165	22¢ Genoa Madonna, by Luca Della Robbia	10/30/85	.40	.15	1.75	(4)	1.00	759
a	Imperf. pair		100.00					
2166	22¢ Poinsettia Plants	10/30/85	.40	.15	1.70	(4)	1.00	758
a	Imperf. pair		130.00					

Breaking the myth of this holiday flower

Poinsettias have been viewed as poisonous after an alleged incident in 1919 when an Army officer's child died after eating the leaf. Since then, efforts to dispel this myth continue, as individuals have been known to eat part of the poinsettia publicly to demonstrate its non-poisonous nature. In spite of this, poinsettias are always in great demand around the holiday season as their red flowers represent the seasonal colors well. The plant is native to Mexico and Central America where it was named for Joel R. Poinsett who introduced it while he was a minister to Mexico in the late 1820s. **(#2166)**

2154

2155 **2156**

2157 **2158** **2158a**

2159

2160 **2161**

2162 **2163** **2163a**

2164

2165

2166

2167

2168

2169

2170

2171

2172

2173

2175

2176

2177

2178

2179

2180

2181

2182

2183

2184

2185

2186

2187

2188

2189

2190

2191

2192

2193

2194A

2195

2196

Issues of 1986, Perf. 11			Un	U	PB	#	FDC	Q(M)
2167	22¢ Arkansas Statehood	01/03/86	.40	.15	2.00	(4)	1.00	130
a	Vertical pair, imperf. horizontally		—					
Issues of 1986-91, Great Americans Issue (See also #1844-69)								
2168	1¢ Margaret Mitchell	06/30/86	.15	.15	.25	(4)	1.25	
2169	2¢ Mary Lyon	02/28/87	.15	.15	.25	(4)	1.00	
2170	3¢ Paul Dudley White, MD	09/15/86	.15	.15	.30	(4)	1.00	
2171	4¢ Father Flanagan	07/14/86	.15	.15	.35	(4)	1.00	
2172	5¢ Hugo L. Black	02/27/86	.15	.15	.40	(4)	1.00	
2173	5¢ Luis Munoz Marin	02/18/90	.15	.15	.50	(4)	1.25	
2174	Not assigned							
2175	10¢ Red Cloud	08/15/87	.20	.15	.85	(4)	1.25	
a	Tagging omitted	1990	.30	.15				
2176	14¢ Julia Ward Howe	02/12/87	.25	.15	1.10	(4)	1.00	
2177	15¢ Buffalo Bill Cody	06/06/88	.30	.15	1.30	(4)	2.00	
a	Overall tagging	1990	.30	—				
2178	17¢ Belva Ann Lockwood	06/18/86	.30	.15	1.45	(4)	1.00	
	Perf. 11 x 11.8							
2179	20¢ Virginia Apgar	10/24/94	.40	.15	2.00	(4)	1.25	
	Perf. 11							
2180	21¢ Chester Carlson	10/21/88	.40	.15	1.75	(4)	1.25	
2181	23¢ Mary Cassatt	11/04/88	.45	.15	2.00	(4)	1.25	
2182	25¢ Jack London	01/11/86	.45	.15	2.00	(4)	1.25	
a	Booklet pane of 10	05/03/88	4.75	3.75			6.00	
b	Tagging omitted	1990	—	—				
2183	28¢ Sitting Bull	09/28/89	.50	.15	2.50	(4)	1.25	
2184	29¢ Earl Warren	03/09/92	.50	.15	2.50	(4)	1.25	
2185	29¢ Thomas Jefferson	04/13/93	.50	.15	2.50	(4)	1.25	
2186	35¢ Dennis Chavez	04/03/91	.65	.15	3.25	(4)	1.25	
2187	40¢ Claire Lee Chennault	09/06/90	.70	.15	3.25	(4)	2.00	
2188	45¢ Harvey Cushing, MD	06/17/88	.85	.15	3.50	(4)	1.25	
a	Overall tagging	1990	1.65	—				
2189	52¢ Hubert H. Humphrey	06/03/91	1.00	.15	4.00	(4)	1.35	
2190	56¢ John Harvard	09/03/86	1.00	.15	4.00	(4)	2.50	
2191	65¢ H.H. 'Hap' Arnold	11/05/88	1.20	.20	5.00	(4)	1.50	
2192	75¢ Wendell Willkie	02/16/92	1.30	.20	5.50	(4)	1.50	
2193	$1 Bernard Revel	09/23/86	2.25	.50	9.50	(4)	2.00	
2194	$1 Johns Hopkins	06/07/89	1.80	.50	7.00	(4)	3.00	
b	Overall tagging	1990	1.75	—				
2195	$2 William Jennings Bryan	03/19/86	3.25	.50	13.00	(4)	5.00	
2196	$5 Bret Harte	08/25/87	7.50	1.00	28.00	(4)	20.00	
	Booklet Stamp, Perf. 10							
2197	25¢ Jack London (2182), single from booklet		.45	.15			1.25	
a	Booklet pane of 6	05/03/88	3.00	2.25			4.00	

	Issues of 1986, Perf. 10 Vertically		Un	U	PB	#	FDC	Q(M)
	United States—Sweden Stamp Collecting Booklet Issue							
2198	22¢ Handstamped Cover	01/23/86	.45	.15			1.00	17
2199	22¢ Boy Examining Stamp Collection	01/23/86	.45	.15			1.00	17
2200	22¢ #836 Under Magnifying Glass	01/23/86	.45	.15			1.00	17
2201	22¢ 1986 Presidents Miniature Sheet	01/23/86	.45	.15			1.00	17
a	Booklet pane of 4, #2198-2201		2.00	1.75			4.00	17
b	As "a," black omitted on #2198, 2201		55.00					
c	As "a," blue omitted on #2198-2200		2,500.00					
d	As "a," buff omitted		—					
	#2198-2201 issued only in booklets. All stamps are imperf. at top and bottom or imperf. at top, bottom and right side.							
	Perf. 11							
2202	22¢ Love	01/30/86	.40	.15	1.75	(4)	1.75	949
	Black Heritage Issue, Sojourner Truth							
2203	22¢ Sojourner Truth Portrait and Truth Lecturing	02/04/86	.40	.15	1.75	(4)	1.00	130
2204	22¢ Republic of Texas, 150th Anniversary	03/02/86	.40	.15	1.75	(4)	1.00	137
a	Horizontal pair, imperf. vertically		1,250.00					
b	Dark red omitted		2,750.00					
	Fish Booklet Issue, Perf. 10 Horizontally							
2205	22¢ Muskellunge	03/21/86	.50	.15			1.00	44
2206	22¢ Atlantic Cod	03/21/86	.50	.15			1.00	44
2207	22¢ Largemouth Bass	03/21/86	.50	.15			1.00	44
2208	22¢ Bluefin Tuna	03/21/86	.50	.15			1.00	44
2209	22¢ Catfish	03/21/86	.50	.15			1.00	44
a	Booklet pane of 5, #2205-09		5.00	2.75			2.50	44
	#2205-09 issued only in booklets. All stamps are imperf. at sides or imperf. at sides and bottom.							
	Perf. 11							
2210	22¢ Public Hospitals	04/11/86	.40	.15	1.75	(4)	1.00	130
a	Vertical pair, imperf. horizontally		300.00					
b	Horizontal pair, imperf. vertically		1,350.00					
	Performing Arts Issue, Duke Ellington							
2211	22¢ Duke Ellington Portrait and Piano Keys	04/29/86	.40	.15	1.90	(4)	1.75	130
a	Vertical pair, imperf. horizontally		1,000.00					
2212-15	Not assigned							

Minimum value listed for a stamp is 15 cents; for a First Day Cover (FDC), $1.00. This minimum represents a fair-market price for having a dealer locate and provide a single stamp or cover from his or her stock. Dealers may charge less per stamp or cover for a group of such stamps or covers, or less for a single stamp or cover.

2198 2199 2200 2201 2201a

2202 2203 2204

2205

2210

2211

2206

2207

2208

2209

2216a

2216b

2216c

2216d

2216e

2216f

2216g

2216h

2216i

2217a

2217b

2217c

2217d

2217e

2217f

2217g

2217h

2217i

Issues of 1986, Perf. 11		Un	U	FDC	Q(M)
AMERIPEX '86 Issue, Presidents Miniature Sheets					
2216	Sheet of 9	05/22/86	3.75	—		4.00	6
a	22¢ George Washington		.40	.25	1.00	
b	22¢ John Adams		.40	.25	1.00	
c	22¢ Thomas Jefferson		.40	.25	1.00	
d	22¢ James Madison		.40	.25	1.00	
e	22¢ James Monroe		.40	.25	1.00	
f	22¢ John Quincy Adams		.40	.25	1.00	
g	22¢ Andrew Jackson		.40	.25	1.00	
h	22¢ Martin Van Buren		.40	.25	1.00	
i	22¢ William H. Harrison		.40	.25	1.00	
j	Blue omitted		3,500.00			
k	Black inscription omitted		2,000.00			
l	Imperf.		10,500.00			
2217	Sheet of 9	05/22/86	3.75	—		4.00	6
a	22¢ John Tyler		.40	.25	1.00	
b	22¢ James Polk		.40	.25	1.00	
c	22¢ Zachary Taylor		.40	.25	1.00	
d	22¢ Millard Fillmore		.40	.25	1.00	
e	22¢ Franklin Pierce		.40	.25	1.00	
f	22¢ James Buchanan		.40	.25	1.00	
g	22¢ Abraham Lincoln		.40	.25	1.00	
h	22¢ Andrew Johnson		.40	.25	1.00	
i	22¢ Ulysses S. Grant		.40	.25	1.00	

#2216

#2217

Issues of 1986, Perf. 11		Un	U	FDC	Q(M)
AMERIPEX '86 Issue (continued), Presidents Miniature Sheets					
2218	Sheet of 9	05/22/86	3.75	—	4.00	6
a	22¢ Rutherford B. Hayes		.40	.25	1.00	
b	22¢ James A. Garfield		.40	.25	1.00	
c	22¢ Chester A. Arthur		.40	.25	1.00	
d	22¢ Grover Cleveland		.40	.25	1.00	
e	22¢ Benjamin Harrison		.40	.25	1.00	
f	22¢ William McKinley		.40	.25	1.00	
g	22¢ Theodore Roosevelt		.40	.25	1.00	
h	22¢ William H. Taft		.40	.25	1.00	
i	22¢ Woodrow Wilson		.40	.25	1.00	
j	Brown omitted		—			
k	Black inscription omitted		3,000.00			
2219	Sheet of 9	05/22/86	3.75	—	4.00	6
a	22¢ Warren G. Harding		.40	.25	1.00	
b	22¢ Calvin Coolidge		.40	.25	1.00	
c	22¢ Herbert Hoover		.40	.25	1.00	
d	22¢ Franklin D. Roosevelt		.40	.25	1.00	
e	22¢ White House		.40	.25	1.00	
f	22¢ Harry S. Truman		.40	.25	1.00	
g	22¢ Dwight D. Eisenhower		.40	.25	1.00	
h	22¢ John F. Kennedy		.40	.25	1.00	
i	22¢ Lyndon B. Johnson		.40	.25	1.00	

#2218

#2219

2218a   **2218b**   **2218c**   **2218d**   **2218e**

2218f   **2218g**   **2218h**   **2218i**

2219a   **2219b**   **2219c**   **2219d**   **2219e**

2219f   **2219g**   **2219h**   **2219i**

2220   2221

2224

2225

2226

2222   2223   2223a

2235   2236

2239

2240   2241

2237   2238   2238a

2242   2243   2243a

2244

2245

2247

2246

2248

2249

2250

2251

	Issues of 1986, Perf. 11		Un	U	PB/PNC	#	FDC	Q(M̄)
	Arctic Explorers Issue							
2220	22¢ Elisha Kent Kane	05/28/86	.65	.15			1.00	33
2221	22¢ Adolphus W. Greely	05/28/86	.65	.15			1.00	33
2222	22¢ Vilhjalmur Stefansson	05/28/86	.65	.15			1.00	33
2223	22¢ Robt. Peary, Matt. Henson	05/28/86	.65	.15			1.00	33
a	Block of 4, #2220-23		2.75	2.25	4.50	(4)	2.50	
b	As "a," black omitted		9,500.00					
2224	22¢ Statue of Liberty	07/04/86	.40	.15	2.25	(4)	3.00	221
	Issues of 1986-87, Reengraved Transportation Issue, Coil Stamps, Perf. 10 Vertically							
	(See also #1897-1908, 2123-36, 2252-66, 2452-53A, 2457, 2464, 2468)							
2225	1¢ Omnibus	11/26/86	.15	.15	.80	(3)	1.00	
2226	2¢ Locomotive	03/06/87	.15	.15	.65	(3)	1.50	
2227, 2229-30, 2232-34 Not assigned								
2228	4¢ Stagecoach (1898A)	08/86	.15	.15	1.40	(3)		
2231	8.3¢ Ambulance (2128)							
	(Bureau precanceled)	08/29/86	.20	.20	3.75	(3)		
	On #2228, "Stagecoach 1890s" is 17mm long; on #1898A, it is 19¹/2mm long. On #2231, "Ambulance 1860s" is 18mm long; on #2128, it is 18¹/2mm long.							
	American Folk Art Issue, Navajo Blankets, Perf. 11							
2235	22¢ Navajo Art, four "+" marks horizontally through middle	09/04/86	.45	.15			1.00	60
2236	22¢ Navajo Art, vertical diamond pattern	09/04/86	.45	.15			1.00	60
2237	22¢ Navajo Art, horizontal diamond pattern	09/04/86	.45	.15			1.00	60
2238	22¢ Navajo Art, jagged line horizontally through middle	09/04/86	.45	.15			1.00	60
a	Block of 4, #2235-38		2.25	2.00	3.00	(4)	2.50	
b	As "a," black omitted		450.00					
	Literary Arts Issue, T.S. Eliot							
2239	22¢ T.S. Eliot Portrait	09/26/86	.40	.15	1.90	(4)	1.00	132
	American Folk Art Issue, Wood-Carved Figurines							
2240	22¢ Highlander Figure	10/01/86	.40	.15			1.00	60
2241	22¢ Ship Figurehead	10/01/86	.40	.15			1.00	60
2242	22¢ Nautical Figure	10/01/86	.40	.15			1.00	60
2243	22¢ Cigar Store Figure	10/01/86	.40	.15			1.00	60
a	Block of 4, #2240-43		1.75	1.75	3.00	(4)	2.50	
b	As "a," imperf. vertically		1,500.00					
	Christmas Issue							
2244	22¢ Madonna and Child	10/24/86	.40	.15	2.00	(4)	1.00	690
2245	22¢ Village Scene	10/24/86	.40	.15	1.90	(4)	1.00	882
	Issues of 1987							
2246	22¢ Michigan Statehood	01/26/87	.40	.15	1.90	(4)	1.00	167
	Pair with full vertical gutter between		—					
2247	22¢ Pan American Games	01/29/87	.40	.15	1.90	(4)	1.00	167
a	Silver omitted		1,500.00					
	Perf. 11.5 x 11							
2248	22¢ Love	01/30/87	.40	.15	1.90	(4)	1.75	842
	Black Heritage Issue, Jean Baptiste Point Du Sable, Perf. 11							
2249	22¢ Portrait of Du Sable and Chicago Settlement	02/20/87	.40	.15	1.90	(4)	1.00	143
	Performing Arts Issue, Enrico Caruso							
2250	22¢ Caruso as the Duke of Mantua in *Rigoletti*	02/27/87	.40	.15	1.90	(4)	1.00	130
2251	22¢ Girl Scouts	03/12/87	.40	.15	1.90	(4)	2.50	150

Issues of 1987-88, Perf. 10 Vertically		Un	U	PNC	#	FDC	Q(M)
Coil Stamps, Transportation Issue (See also #1897-1908, 2123-36, 2225-31, 2451-68)							
2252	3¢ Conestoga Wagon 1800s	02/29/88	.15	.15	.90	(3)	1.00	
2253	5¢ Milk Wagon 1900s	09/25/87	.15	.15	1.00	(3)	1.00	
2254	5.3¢ Elevator 1900s, Bureau precanceled	09/16/88	.15	.15	1.25	(3)	1.25	
2255	7.6¢ Carreta 1770s, Bureau precanceled	08/30/88	.15	.15	2.25	(3)	1.25	
2256	8.4¢ Wheel Chair 1920s, Bureau precanceled	08/12/88	.15	.15	2.00	(3)	1.25	
a	Imperf. pair		750.00					
2257	10¢ Canal Boat 1880s	04/11/87	.20	.15	1.40	(3)	1.00	
2258	13¢ Patrol Wagon 1880s, Bureau precanceled	10/29/88	.25	.25	2.75	(3)	1.50	
2259	13.2¢ Coal Car 1870s, Bureau precanceled	07/19/88	.25	.25	2.75	(3)	1.50	
a	Imperf. pair		100.00					
2260	15¢ Tugboat 1900s	07/12/88	.25	.15	2.25	(3)	1.25	
2261	16.7¢ Popcorn Wagon 1902, Bureau precanceled	07/07/88	.30	.30	3.25	(3)	1.25	
a	Imperf. pair		225.00					
2262	17.5¢ Racing Car 1911	09/25/87	.30	.15	3.25	(3)	1.00	
a	Untagged (Bureau precanceled)		.30	.30	3.50	(3)		
b	Imperf. pair		2,000.00					
2263	20¢ Cable Car 1880s	10/28/88	.35	.15	3.25	(3)	1.25	
a	Imperf. pair		75.00					
2264	20.5¢ Fire Engine 1920s, Bureau precanceled	09/28/88	.40	.40	3.25	(3)	2.00	
2265	21¢ Railroad Mail Car 1920s, Bureau precanceled	08/16/88	.40	.40	3.50	(3)	1.50	
a	Imperf. pair		65.00					
2266	24.1¢ Tandem Bicycle 1890s, Bureau precanceled	10/26/88	.45	.45	3.50	(3)	1.50	
Issues of 1987 (continued), Special Occasions Booklet Issue, Perf. 10								
2267	22¢ Congratulations!	04/20/87	.55	.15			1.00	1,222
2268	22¢ Get Well!	04/20/87	.55	.15			1.00	611
2269	22¢ Thank you!	04/20/87	.55	.15			1.00	611
2270	22¢ Love You, Dad!	04/20/87	.55	.15			1.00	611
2271	22¢ Best Wishes!	04/20/87	.55	.15			1.00	611
2272	22¢ Happy Birthday!	04/20/87	.55	.15			1.00	1,222
2273	22¢ Love You, Mother!	04/20/87	.55	.15			1.00	611
2274	22¢ Keep In Touch!	04/20/87	.55	.15			1.00	611
a	Booklet pane of 10, #2268-71, 2273-74 and 2 each of #2267, 2272		8.00	5.00			5.00	611

#2267-74 issued only in booklets. All stamps are imperf. at one or two sides or imperf. at sides and bottom.

Conestoga Wagon 1800s
USA 3
2252

Milk Wagon 1900s
5 USA
2253

Elevator 1900s
5.3 USA
Nonprofit
Carrier Route Sort
2254

Carreta 1770s
7.6 USA
Nonprofit
2255

Wheel Chair 1920s
8.4 USA
Nonprofit
2256

Canal Boat 1880s
10 USA
2257

Patrol Wagon 1880s
USA 13
Presorted
First-Class
POLICE PATROL
2258

Coal Car 1870s
13.2 Bulk Rate
USA
2259

Tugboat 1900s
USA 15
2260

Popcorn Wagon 1902
16.7 USA
Bulk Rate
2261

Racing Car 1911
USA 17.5
2262

Cable Car 1880s
USA 20
2263

Fire Engine 1900s
20.5 USA
ZIP+4
Presort
2264

Railroad Mail Car 1920s
Presorted
First-Class
21 USA
2265

Tandem Bicycle 1890s
24.1 USA
ZIP+4
2266

2267
Congratulations! USA 22

2268
Get Well! USA 22

2269
Thank You! USA 22

2270
Love You, Dad! USA 22

2271
Best Wishes! USA 22

2272
Happy Birthday! USA 22

2273
Love You, Mother! USA 22

2274
Keep In Touch! USA 22

Happy Birthday! USA 22

Congratulations! USA 22

2274a

2275

2276

2277

2278

2279

2280

2281

2283

2283c

2282a

2285b

2284   **2285**

	Issues of 1987, Perf. 11		Un	U	PB/PNC	#	FDC	Q(M̄)
2275	22¢ United Way	04/28/87	.40	.15	1.90	(4)	1.00	157
2276	22¢ Flag with Fireworks	05/09/87	.40	.15	1.90	(4)	1.00	
a	Booklet pane of 20	11/30/87	8.50	—			8.00	
	Issues of 1988-89 (All issued in 1988 except #2280 on prephosphored paper)							
2277	(25¢) "E" Stamp	03/22/88	.45	.15	2.00	(4)	1.25	
2278	25¢ Flag with Clouds	05/06/88	.40	.15	1.90	(4)	1.25	
	Pair with full vertical gutter between		—					
	Coil Stamps, Perf. 10 Vertically							
2279	(25¢) "E" Earth	03/22/88	.45	.15	2.50	(3)	1.25	
a	Imperf. pair		90.00					
2280	25¢ Flag over Yosemite	05/20/88	.45	.15	3.50	(3)	1.25	
	Prephosphored paper	02/14/89	.45	.15	3.50	(3)	1.25	
a	Imperf. pair		27.50					
b	Black trees		100.00	—				
2281	25¢ Honeybee	09/02/88	.45	.15	3.25	(3)	1.25	
a	Imperf. pair		40.00					
b	Black omitted		65.00					
d	Pair, imperf. between		1,000.00					
	Booklet Stamp, Perf. 10							
2282	(25¢) "E" Earth (#2277), single from booklet		.50	.15			1.25	
a	Booklet pane of 10	03/22/88	6.50	3.50			6.00	
	Pheasant Booklet Issue, Perf. 11							
2283	25¢ Pheasant, single from booklet		.50	.15			1.25	
a	Booklet pane of 10	04/29/88	6.00	3.50			6.00	
b	Single, red removed from sky		6.00	.15				
c	As "b," booklet pane of 10		70.00	—				
d	As "a," imperf. horizontally between		2,250.00					
	#2283 issued only in booklets. All stamps have one or two imperf. edges. Imperf. and part perf. pairs and panes exist from printer's waste.							
	Owl and Grosbeak Booklet Issue, Perf. 10							
2284	25¢ Grosbeak, single from booklet		.45	.15			1.25	
2285	25¢ Owl, single from booklet		.45	.15			1.25	
b	Booklet pane of 10, 5 each of #2284, 2285	05/28/88	4.50	—			6.00	
	#2284 and 2285 issued only in booklets. All stamps are imperf. at one side or imperf. at one side and bottom.							
2285A	25¢ Flag with Clouds (#2278), single from booklet		.45	.15			1.25	
c	Booklet pane of 6	07/05/88	2.75	—			4.00	

Many species of pheasants

Approximately 50 species of pheasants are known to exist, and many of them are long-tailed birds found in fields and open woodlands. Most males are brightly colored, while females are duller. Unlike many birds, the male pheasant mates with several females. Unfortunately, some species have been hunted to the verge of extinction. **(#2283)**

Issues of 1987, Perf. 11			Un	U		FDC	Q(M̄)
American Wildlife Issue							
2286	22¢ Barn Swallow	06/13/87	.85	.15		1.50	13
2287	22¢ Monarch Butterfly	06/13/87	.85	.15		1.50	13
2288	22¢ Bighorn Sheep	06/13/87	.85	.15		1.50	13
2289	22¢ Broad-tailed Hummingbird	06/13/87	.85	.15		1.50	13
2290	22¢ Cottontail	06/13/87	.85	.15		1.50	13
2291	22¢ Osprey	06/13/87	.85	.15		1.50	13
2292	22¢ Mountain Lion	06/13/87	.85	.15		1.50	13
2293	22¢ Luna Moth	06/13/87	.85	.15		1.50	12
2294	22¢ Mule Deer	06/13/87	.85	.15		1.50	13
2295	22¢ Gray Squirrel	06/13/87	.85	.15		1.50	13
2296	22¢ Armadillo	06/13/87	.85	.15		1.50	13
2297	22¢ Eastern Chipmunk	06/13/87	.85	.15		1.50	13
2298	22¢ Moose	06/13/87	.85	.15		1.50	13
2299	22¢ Black Bear	06/13/87	.85	.15		1.50	13
2300	22¢ Tiger Swallowtail	06/13/87	.85	.15		1.50	13
2301	22¢ Bobwhite	06/13/87	.85	.15		1.50	13
2302	22¢ Ringtail	06/13/87	.85	.15		1.50	13
2303	22¢ Red-winged Blackbird	06/13/87	.85	.15		1.50	13
2304	22¢ American Lobster	06/13/87	.85	.15		1.50	13
2305	22¢ Black-tailed Jack Rabbit	06/13/87	.85	.15		1.50	13
2306	22¢ Scarlet Tanager	06/13/87	.85	.15		1.50	13
2307	22¢ Woodchuck	06/13/87	.85	.15		1.50	13
2308	22¢ Roseate Spoonbill	06/13/87	.85	.15		1.50	13
2309	22¢ Bald Eagle	06/13/87	.85	.15		1.50	13
2310	22¢ Alaskan Brown Bear	06/13/87	.85	.15		1.50	13

Woodchuck

Did you know that *woodchuck* is simply another name for *groundhog*?

Because the groundhog is honored each year with its own day on February 2, *groundhog* is the more familiar name for *woodchuck*. According to popular legend, if the groundhog emerges from its burrow on Groundhog Day and does see its shadow, there will be six more weeks of winter. If it does not see its shadow, an early spring is predicted. Found across Canada, in eastern and central United States and in Alaska, woodchucks can be destructive to agricultural areas because they like to feed mainly on green vegetation. **(#2307)**

Interesting Fact: Whistle-pig *is another name for* woodchuck.

22 USA Barn Swallow
22 USA Monarch
22 USA Bighorn Sheep
22 USA Broad-tailed Hummingbird
22 USA Cottontail

2286   2287   2288   2289   2290

22 USA Osprey
22 USA Mountain Lion
22 USA Luna Moth
22 USA Mule Deer
22 USA Gray Squirrel

2291   2292   2293   2294   2295

22 USA Armadillo
22 USA Eastern Chipmunk
22 USA Moose
22 USA Black Bear
22 USA Tiger Swallowtail

2296   2297   2298   2299   2300

22 USA Bobwhite
22 USA Ringtail
22 USA Red-winged Blackbird
22 USA American Lobster
22 USA Black-tailed Jack Rabbit

2301   2302   2303   2304   2305

22 USA Scarlet Tanager
22 USA Woodchuck
22 USA Roseate Spoonbill
22 USA Bald Eagle
22 USA Alaskan Brown Bear

2306   2307   2308   2309   2310

22 USA Iiwi	22 USA Badger	22 USA Pronghorn	22 USA River Otter	22 USA Ladybug
2311	2312	2313	2314	2315
22 USA Beaver	22 USA White-tailed Deer	22 USA Blue Jay	22 USA Pika	22 USA Bison
2316	2317	2318	2319	2320
22 USA Snowy Egret	22 USA Gray Wolf	22 USA Mountain Goat	22 USA Deer Mouse	22 USA Black-tailed Prairie Dog
2321	2322	2323	2324	2325
22 USA Box Turtle	22 USA Wolverine	22 USA American Elk	22 USA California Sea Lion	22 USA Mockingbird
2326	2327	2328	2329	2330
22 USA Raccoon	22 USA Bobcat	22 USA Black-footed Ferret	22 USA Canada Goose	22 USA Red Fox
2331	2332	2333	2334	2335

	Issues of 1987, Perf. 11		Un	U	FDC	Q(M̄)
	American Wildlife Issue (continued)					
2311	22¢ Iiwi	06/13/87	.85	.15	1.50	13
2312	22¢ Badger	06/13/87	.85	.15	1.50	13
2313	22¢ Pronghorn	06/13/87	.85	.15	1.50	13
2314	22¢ River Otter	06/13/87	.85	.15	1.50	13
2315	22¢ Ladybug	06/13/87	.85	.15	1.50	13
2316	22¢ Beaver	06/13/87	.85	.15	1.50	13
2317	22¢ White-tailed Deer	06/13/87	.85	.15	1.50	13
2318	22¢ Blue Jay	06/13/87	.85	.15	1.50	13
2319	22¢ Pika	06/13/87	.85	.15	1.50	13
2320	22¢ Bison	06/13/87	.85	.15	1.50	13
2321	22¢ Snowy Egret	06/13/87	.85	.15	1.50	13
2322	22¢ Gray Wolf	06/13/87	.85	.15	1.50	13
2323	22¢ Mountain Goat	06/13/87	.85	.15	1.50	13
2324	22¢ Deer Mouse	06/13/87	.85	.15	1.50	13
2325	22¢ Black-tailed Prairie Dog	06/13/87	.85	.15	1.50	13
2326	22¢ Box Turtle	06/13/87	.85	.15	1.50	13
2327	22¢ Wolverine	06/13/87	.85	.15	1.50	13
2328	22¢ American Elk	06/13/87	.85	.15	1.50	13
2329	22¢ California Sea Lion	06/13/87	.85	.15	1.50	13
2330	22¢ Mockingbird	06/13/87	.85	.15	1.50	13
2331	22¢ Raccoon	06/13/87	.85	.15	1.50	13
2332	22¢ Bobcat	06/13/87	.85	.15	1.50	13
2333	22¢ Black-footed Ferret	06/13/87	.85	.15	1.50	13
2334	22¢ Canada Goose	06/13/87	.85	.15	1.50	13
2335	22¢ Red Fox	06/13/87	.85	.15	1.50	13
a	Pane of 50, #2286-2335		47.50		50.00	
b	Any single, red omitted		—			

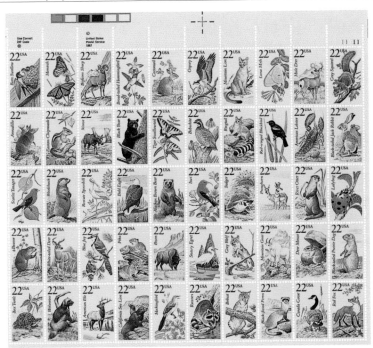

Example of 2335a.

	Issues of 1987-90, Perf. 11		Un	U	PB	#	FDC	Q(M̄)
	Constitution Bicentennial Issue, Ratification of the Constitution							
2336	22¢ Delaware	07/04/87	.40	.15	2.00	(4)	1.00	168
2337	22¢ Pennsylvania	08/26/87	.40	.15	2.25	(4)	1.00	187
2338	22¢ New Jersey	09/11/87	.40	.15	2.00	(4)	1.00	184
a	Black omitted		6,000.00					
2339	22¢ Georgia	01/06/88	.40	.15	2.00	(4)	1.00	169
2340	22¢ Connecticut	01/09/88	.40	.15	2.00	(4)	1.00	155
2341	22¢ Massachusetts	02/06/88	.40	.15	2.00	(4)	1.00	102
2342	22¢ Maryland	02/15/88	.40	.15	2.25	(4)	1.00	103
2343	25¢ South Carolina	05/23/88	.45	.15	2.00	(4)	1.25	162
2344	25¢ New Hampshire	06/21/88	.45	.15	2.00	(4)	1.25	153
2345	25¢ Virginia	06/25/88	.45	.15	2.25	(4)	1.25	160
2346	25¢ New York	07/26/88	.45	.15	2.00	(4)	1.25	183
2347	25¢ North Carolina	08/22/89	.45	.15	2.00	(4)	1.25	
2348	25¢ Rhode Island	05/29/90	.45	.15	2.00	(4)	1.25	164
2349	22¢ Friendship with Morocco	07/18/87	.40	.15	1.75	(4)	1.00	157
a	Black omitted		350.00					
	Issues of 1987, Literary Arts Issue, William Faulkner							
2350	22¢ Portrait of Faulkner	08/03/87	.40	.15	1.75	(4)	1.00	156
	American Folk Art Issue, Lacemaking							
2351	22¢ Squash Blossoms	08/14/87	.45	.15			1.00	41
2352	22¢ Floral Piece	08/14/87	.45	.15			1.00	41
2353	22¢ Floral Piece	08/14/87	.45	.15			1.00	41
2354	22¢ Dogwood Blossoms	08/14/87	.45	.15			1.00	41
a	Block of 4, #2351-54		1.90	1.90	3.25	(4)	2.75	
b	As "a," white omitted		1,000.00					

A European art comes to America

Lacemaking is an art that originated in Italy and Flanders in the 15th century. Many laces are named for their place of origin—such as Chantilly, Mechlin, Venetian—and can be made of linen, cotton, silk, wool or even gold or silver threads. Lacemaking has long been a part of the American tradition, with lace decorations on linens and clothing being its most popular applications. **(#2351-2354)**

Dec 7, 1787 USA
Delaware 22
2336

Dec 12, 1787 22 USA
Pennsylvania
2337

Dec 18, 1787 USA
New Jersey 22
2338

22 USA
January 2, 1788
Georgia
2339

22 USA
January 9, 1788
Connecticut
2340

22 USA
Feb 6, 1788
Massachusetts
2341

April 28, 1788 USA
Maryland 22
2342

25 USA
May 23, 1788
South Carolina
2343

25 USA
June 21, 1788
New Hampshire
2344

June 25, 1788 USA
Virginia 25
2345

July 26, 1788 USA
New York 25
2346

25 USA
November 21, 1789
North Carolina
2347

25 USA
May 29, 1790
Rhode Island
2348

2351 **2352**

Friendship
with Morocco
1787-1987
USA 22
2349

William Faulkner
USA 22
2350

Lacemaking USA 22
Lacemaking USA 22
Lacemaking USA 22
Lacemaking USA 22

2353   **2354**   **2354a**

The Bicentennial of the Constitution of the United States of America
1787-1987 USA 22

2355

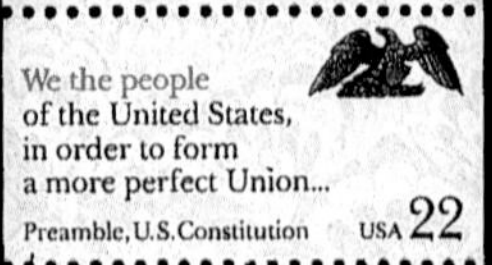

We the people of the United States, in order to form a more perfect Union...
Preamble, U.S. Constitution USA 22

2356

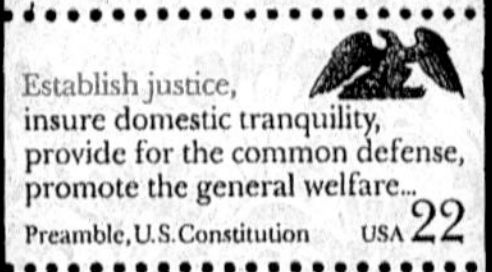

Establish justice, insure domestic tranquility, provide for the common defense, promote the general welfare...
Preamble, U.S. Constitution USA 22

2357

And secure the blessings of liberty to ourselves and our posterity...
Preamble, U.S. Constitution USA 22

2358

Do ordain and establish this Constitution for the United States of America.
Preamble, U.S. Constitution USA 22

2359

2359a

U.S. Constitution
We the People
1787-1987 22 USA

2360

CPA
Certified Public Accountant
22 USA

2361

Stourbridge Lion 1829 USA 22

2362

Best Friend of Charleston 1830 USA 22

2363

John Bull 1831 USA 22

2364

Brother Jonathan 1832 USA 22

2365

Gowan & Marx 1839 USA 22

2366

2366a

CHRISTMAS 22 USA
Moroni, National Gallery

2367

USA 22 GREETINGS

2368

	Issues of 1987, Perf. 10 Horizontally		Un	U	PB	#	FDC	Q(M)
	Constitution Bicentennial Issue, Drafting of the Constitution Booklet Issue							
2355	22¢ "The Bicentennial..."	08/28/87	.50	.15			1.00	122
2356	22¢ "We the people..."	08/28/87	.50	.15			1.00	122
2357	22¢ "Establish justice..."	08/28/87	.50	.15			1.00	122
2358	22¢ "And secure..."	08/28/87	.50	.15			1.00	122
2359	22¢ "Do ordain..."	08/28/87	.50	.15			1.00	122
a	Booklet pane of 5, #2355-59		3.00	2.50			3.00	122
	#2355-59 issued only in booklets. All stamps are imperf. at sides or imperf. at sides and bottom.							
	Signing of the Constitution, Perf. 11							
2360	22¢ Constitution and Signer's Hand-Holding Quill Pen	09/17/87	.40	.15	2.00	(4)	1.00	169
2361	22¢ Certified Public Accountants	09/21/87	1.90	.15	9.00	(4)	3.50	163
a	Black omitted		900.00					
	Locomotives Booklet Issue, Perf. 10 Horizontally							
2362	22¢ Stourbridge Lion, 1829	10/01/87	.55	.15			1.50	143
2363	22¢ Best Friend of Charleston, 1830	10/01/87	.55	.15			1.50	143
2364	22¢ John Bull, 1831	10/01/87	.55	.15			1.50	143
2365	22¢ Brother Jonathan, 1832	10/01/87	.55	.15			1.50	143
2366	22¢ Gowan & Marx, 1839	10/01/87	.55	.15			1.50	143
a	Booklet pane of 5, #2362-66		2.75	2.50			4.50	143
b	As "a," black omitted on #2366		—					
	#2362-66 issued only in booklets. All stamps are imperf. at sides or imperf. at sides and bottom.							
	Christmas Issue, Perf. 11							
2367	22¢ Madonna and Child, by Moroni	10/23/87	.40	.15	2.00	(4)	1.00	529
2368	22¢ Christmas Ornaments	10/23/87	.40	.15	1.75	(4)	1.00	978
	Pair with full vertical gutter between		—					

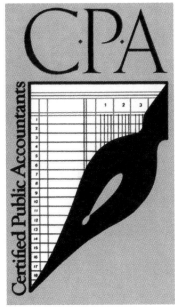

CPA's forensic accounting

One of the hottest growth areas for certified public accountants is forensic accounting. A forensic accountant's job is surprisingly similar to that of a forensic pathologist like television's *Quincy*. A forensic accountant dissects records to determine if any fraud or abuses have taken place. Also known as an investigative accountant, the forensic accountant searches for evidence of criminal conduct, such as the misappropriation of assets or fraudulent financial reporting. In addition to investigating, the forensic accountant can assist lawyers in the litigation process by serving as an expert witness or consultant. **(#2361)**

Interesting Fact: Depending on whether you take statistics from the U.S. Department of Labor's Bureau of Labor Statistics or the U.S. Census, data from 1994 places the number of accountants and auditors between 850,000 and 1.5 million.

Issues of 1988, Perf. 11		Un	U	PB	#	FDC	Q(M̄)
	Winter Olympic Games Issue						
2369	22¢ Skier and Olympic Rings	01/10/88	.40	.15	1.75	(4)	1.00	159
2370	22¢ Australia Bicentennial	01/10/88	.40	.15	1.75	(4)	1.00	146
	Black Heritage Issue, James Weldon Johnson						
2371	22¢ Portrait of Johnson and Music from "Lift Ev'ry Voice and Sing"	02/02/88	.40	.15	1.75	(4)	1.00	97
	American Cats Issue						
2372	22¢ Siamese and Exotic Shorthair	02/05/88	.45	.15			2.00	40
2373	22¢ Abyssinian and Himalayan	02/05/88	.45	.15			2.00	40
2374	22¢ Maine Coon and Burmese	02/05/88	.45	.15			2.00	40
2375	22¢ American Shorthair and Persian	02/05/88	.45	.15			2.00	40
a	Block of 4, #2372-75		1.90	1.90	3.00	(4)	4.50	
	American Sports Issue, Knute Rockne						
2376	22¢ Rockne Holding Football on Field	03/09/88	.40	.15	2.25	(4)	3.50	97
	Francis Ouimet						
2377	25¢ Portrait of Ouimet and Ouimet Hitting Fairway Shot	06/13/88	.45	.15	2.50	(4)	3.50	153
2378	25¢ Love	07/04/88	.45	.15	1.90	(4)	1.75	841
2379	45¢ Love	08/08/88	.65	.20	3.25	(4)	1.75	180
	Summer Olympic Games Issue						
2380	25¢ Gymnast on Rings	08/19/88	.45	.15	1.90	(4)	1.25	157

The 'short and long' about this pair of domestic felines

Both Abyssinian and Himalayan cats are popular domestic breeds, but their similarities seem to end there. The Abyssinian is believed to be of Egyptian origin and, with its slender legs, long tail and short, fine hair, resembles the sacred cats of ancient Egypt. The Himalayan was developed by breeding Persians to Siamese to combine the Siamese point coloring with Persian body type. The Himalayan has long hair, short legs, and a broad, round head. Both Abyssinians and Himalayans are considered affectionate but can be shy with strangers. **(#2373)**

2370

2369

2371

2372   **2373**

2374   **2375**   **2375a**

2378

2376   **2377**   **2379**

2380

2381 1928 Locomobile

2382 1929 Pierce-Arrow

2383 1931 Cord

2384 1932 Packard

2385 1935 Duesenberg

2385a

2390   2391

2392   2393   2393a

2386   2387

Nathaniel Palmer

Lt. Charles Wilkes

Richard E. Byrd

Lincoln Ellsworth

2388   2389   2389a

	Issues of 1988, Perf. 10 Horizontally		Un	U	PB	#	FDC	Q(M̄)
	Classic Cars Booklet Issue							
2381	25¢ 1928 Locomobile	08/25/88	.50	.15			1.25	127
2382	25¢ 1929 Pierce-Arrow	08/25/88	.50	.15			1.25	127
2383	25¢ 1931 Cord	08/25/88	.50	.15			1.25	127
2384	25¢ 1932 Packard	08/25/88	.50	.15			1.25	127
2385	25¢ 1935 Duesenberg	08/25/88	.50	.15			1.25	127
a	Booklet pane of 5, #2381-85		5.50	2.25			3.00	127
	#2381-85 issued only in booklets. All stamps are imperf. at sides or imperf. at sides and bottom.							
	Antarctic Explorers Issue, Perf. 11							
2386	25¢ Nathaniel Palmer	09/14/88	.65	.15			1.25	41
2387	25¢ Lt. Charles Wilkes	09/14/88	.65	.15			1.25	41
2388	25¢ Richard E. Byrd	09/14/88	.65	.15			1.25	41
2389	25¢ Lincoln Ellsworth	09/14/88	.65	.15			1.25	41
a	Block of 4, #2386-89		2.75	2.00	4.50	(4)	3.00	
b	As "a," black omitted		1,500.00					
c	As "a," imperf. horizontally		3,000.00					
	American Folk Art Issue, Carousel Animals							
2390	25¢ Deer	10/01/88	.65	.15			2.50	76
2391	25¢ Horse	10/01/88	.65	.15			2.50	76
2392	25¢ Camel	10/01/88	.65	.15			2.50	76
2393	25¢ Goat	10/01/88	.65	.15			2.50	76
a	Block of 4, #2390-93		3.00	2.00	3.75	(4)	5.00	

America's first mass-produced front-wheel-drive automobile

The L-29 Cord was introduced in June 1929 as America's first mass-produced front-wheel-drive automobile. It was so well received that the company had 3,000 orders on hand by September, a record for vehicles priced above $3,000. The styling themes of the body, designed by Alan Leamy, were evident throughout the car, including the interior and the dash. The car was long and low, nearly 10 inches lower than most of its contemporaries. **(#2383)**

Interesting Fact: By the time the L-29 was discontinued in 1932, 5,015 had been produced. Between 200 and 300 exist today.

	Issues of 1988, Perf. 11		Un	U	PB	#	FDC	Q(M)
2394	$8.75 Express Mail	10/04/88	13.50	8.00	54.00	(4)	25.00	
	Special Occasions Booklet Issue							
2395	25¢ Happy Birthday	10/22/88	.50	.15			1.25	120
2396	25¢ Best Wishes	10/22/88	.50	.15			1.25	120
a	Booklet pane of 6, 3 #2395 and 3 #2396 with gutter between		3.75	—			4.00	
2397	25¢ Thinking of You	10/22/88	.50	.15			2.00	120
2398	25¢ Love You	10/22/88	.50	.15			2.00	120
a	Booklet pane of 6, 3 #2397 and 3 #2398 with gutter between		3.75	3.25			5.00	
b	As "a," imperf. horizontally		—					
	#2395-98a issued only in booklets. All stamps are imperf. on one side or on one side and top or bottom.							
	Christmas Issue							
2399	25¢ Madonna and Child, by Botticelli	10/20/88	.45	.15	1.90	(4)	1.25	844
a	Gold omitted		30.00					
2400	25¢ One-Horse Open Sleigh and Village Scene	10/20/88	.45	.15	1.90	(4)	1.25	1,038
	Pair with full vertical gutter between		—					

The father of Express Mail

To speed the delivery of mail, in 1836 Congress authorized U.S. Postmaster General Amos Kendall to start an Express Mail service at 75¢ per half-ounce letter, which was three times the regular postage rate. Beginning with the first route from New Orleans to New York City, the service grew to five routes and used an innovative combination of horses, trains and steamboats. Advances in aviation during World War II contributed to further expansion in mail delivery and led to the initiation of new air routes around the world. Today, overnight and second-day delivery services are a multibillion-dollar industry in the U.S. alone. **(#2394)**

2394

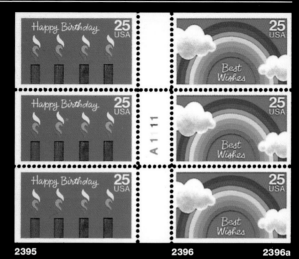

2395   2396   2396a

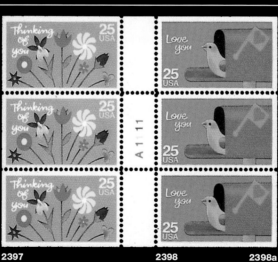

2397   2398   2398a

2399

2400

2401

2402

2403

2404

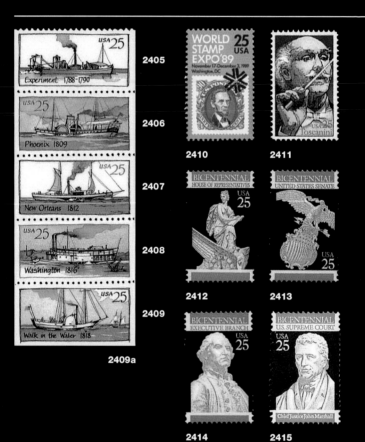

2405

2406

2407

2408

2409

2409a

2410

2411

2412

2413

2414

2415

2416

2417

2418

	Issues of 1989, Perf. 11		Un	U	PB	#	FDC	Q(M̄)
2401	25¢ Montana Statehood	01/15/89	.45	.15	2.00	(4)	1.25	165
	Black Heritage Issue, A. Philip Randolph							
2402	25¢ Portrait of Randolph, Pullman Porters and Railroad Cars	02/03/89	.45	.15	2.00	(4)	1.25	152
2403	25¢ North Dakota Statehood	02/21/89	.45	.15	1.90	(4)	1.25	163
2404	25¢ Washington Statehood	02/22/89	.45	.15	2.00	(4)	1.25	265
	Steamboats Booklet Issue, Perf. 10 Horizontally							
2405	25¢ Experiment 1788-90	03/03/89	.45	.15			1.25	159
2406	25¢ Phoenix 1809	03/03/89	.45	.15			1.25	159
2407	25¢ New Orleans 1812	03/03/89	.45	.15			1.25	159
2408	25¢ Washington 1816	03/03/89	.45	.15			1.25	159
2409	25¢ Walk in the Water 1818	03/03/89	.45	.15			1.25	159
a	Booklet pane of 5, #2405-09		2.25	1.75			4.00	159
	#2405-09 issued only in booklets. All stamps are imperf. at sides or imperf. at sides and bottom.							
	Perf. 11							
2410	25¢ World Stamp Expo '89	03/16/89	.45	.15	1.90	(4)	1.25	164
	Performing Arts Issue, Arturo Toscanini							
2411	25¢ Portrait of Toscanini Conducting with Baton	03/25/89	.45	.15	2.00	(4)	1.25	152
	Issues of 1989-90, Constitution Bicentennial Issue							
2412	25¢ U.S. House of Representatives	04/04/89	.45	.15	1.90	(4)	1.25	139
2413	25¢ U.S. Senate	04/06/89	.45	.15	2.00	(4)	1.25	138
2414	25¢ Executive Branch, George Washington	04/16/89	.45	.15	2.00	(4)	1.25	139
2415	25¢ Supreme Court, Chief Justice John Marshall	02/02/90	.45	.15	1.90	(4)	1.25	151
	Issues of 1989 (continued)							
2416	25¢ South Dakota Statehood	05/03/89	.45	.15	1.90	(4)	1.25	165
	American Sports Issue, Lou Gehrig							
2417	25¢ Portrait of Gehrig, Gehrig Swinging Bat	06/10/89	.50	.15	2.75	(4)	4.00	263
	Literary Arts Issue, Ernest Hemingway							
2418	25¢ Portrait of Hemingway, African Landscape in Background	07/17/89	.45	.15	2.00	(4)	1.25	192

Stamp facts and history

Large national or international stamp exhibitions, where one gets to see many excellent and rare collections, are a great educational source for stamp collectors. The radical concept of prepaid postage with a fixed rate based on weight rather than distance traveled was proposed in Great Britain by Rowland Hill in 1837 in a pamphlet called "Post Office Reform." The first stamp, known as the "Penny Black" because of its value and color, was issued in Britain in May 1840. Today, there are millions of stamps from every country on innumerable subjects. For this reason collectors specialize in any of a number of different categories. **(#2410)**

Interesting Fact: Early stamps were printed on sheets of paper without perforations, and it was necessary to use a scissors, or some other device, to cut them apart.

	Issues of 1989		Un	U	PB	#	FDC	Q(M̄)
	Perf. 11 x 11.5, Priority Mail Issue							
2419	$2.40 Moon Landing	07/20/89	4.00	2.00	16.00	(4)	9.00	
a	Black omitted		*3,000.00*					
b	Imperf. pair		*1,000.00*					
	Perf. 11							
2420	25¢ Letter Carriers	08/30/89	.45	.15	1.90	(4)	1.25	188
	Constitution Bicentennial Issue, Drafting of the Bill of Rights							
2421	25¢ Stylized U.S. Flag, Eagle With Quill Pen in Mouth	09/25/89	.45	.15	3.00	(4)	1.25	192
a	Black omitted		375.00					
	Prehistoric Animals Issue							
2422	25¢ Tyrannosaurus	10/01/89	.65	.15			1.50	102
2423	25¢ Pteranodon	10/01/89	.65	.15			1.50	102
2424	25¢ Stegosaurus	10/01/89	.65	.15			1.50	102
2425	25¢ Brontosaurus	10/01/89	.65	.15			1.50	102
a	Block of 4, #2422-25		3.00	2.00	3.00	(4)	3.00	
b	As "a," black omitted		*1,250.00*					
	America/PUAS Issue (See also #C121)							
2426	25¢ Southwest Carved Figure (A.D. 1150-1350), Emblem of the Postal Union of the Americas	10/12/89	.45	.15	2.00	(4)	1.25	137
	Christmas Issue, Perf. 11.5							
2427	25¢ Madonna and Child, by Caracci	10/19/89	.45	.15	2.00	(4)	1.25	913
a	Booklet pane of 10		4.75	—			6.00	
	Perf. 11							
2428	25¢ Sleigh Full of Presents	10/19/89	.45	.15	1.90	(4)	1.25	900
a	Vertical pair, imperf. horizontally		*2,000.00*					
	Booklet Stamp Issue, Perf. 11.5							
2429	25¢ Single from booklet pane (#2428)	10/19/89	.45	.15			1.25	399
a	Booklet pane of 10		4.75	—			6.00	40
b	As "a," imperf. horiz. between		—					
c	As "a," red omitted		—					
	In #2429, runners on sleigh are twice as thick as in 2428; bow on package at rear of sleigh is same color as package; board running underneath sleigh is pink.							
2430	Not assigned							
	Self-Adhesive, Die-Cut							
2431	25¢ Eagle and Shield	11/10/89	.50	.20			1.25	75
a	Booklet pane of 18		11.00					
b	Vertical pair, no die-cutting between		*850.00*					
2432	Not assigned							

2420

2421

2419

2422   **2423**

2426

2424   **2425**   **2425a**

2427

2428

2431

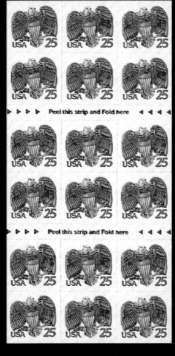

2431a

2431 (coil)

WORLD STAMP EXPO '89℠

The classic 1869 U.S. Abraham Lincoln stamp is reborn in these four larger versions commemorating World Stamp Expo '89, held in Washington, D.C. during the 20th Universal Postal Congress of the UPU. These stamps show the issued colors and three of the trial proof color combinations.

©USPS 1989℠

2433

2434   **2435**

2439

2440

2436   **2437**   **2437a**

2442

2443

20th Universal Postal Congress

A review of historical methods of delivering the mail in the United States is the theme of these four stamps issued in commemoration of the convening of the 20th Universal Postal Congress in Washington, D.C. from November 13 through December 15, 1989. The United States, as host nation to the Congress for the first time in ninety-two years, welcomed more than 1,000 delegates from most of the member nations of the Universal Postal Union to the major international event.

2438

	Issues of 1989		Un	U	PB	#	FDC	Q(M̄)
	World Stamp Expo '89 Issue Souvenir Sheet, Imperf.							
2433	Reproduction of #122, 90¢ Lincoln, and three essays of #122	11/17/89	12.00	9.00			7.00	2
a-d	Single stamp from sheet		2.00	1.75				
	20th UPU Congress Issues, Classic Mail Transportation, Perf. 11 (See also #C122-25)							
2434	25¢ Stagecoach	11/19/89	.45	.15			1.25	41
2435	25¢ Paddlewheel Steamer	11/19/89	.45	.15			1.25	41
2436	25¢ Biplane	11/19/89	.45	.15			1.25	41
2437	25¢ Depot-Hack Type Automobile	11/19/89	.45	.15			1.25	41
a	Block of 4, #2434-37		2.00	2.00	3.75	(4)	3.00	
b	As "a," dark blue omitted		1,250.00					
	Souvenir Sheet, Imperf. (See also #C126)							
2438	Designs of #2434-37	11/28/89	4.00	1.75			2.00	2
a-d	Single stamp from sheet		.65	.25				
	Issues of 1990, Perf. 11							
2439	25¢ Idaho Statehood	01/06/90	.45	.15	2.00	(4)	1.25	173
	Perf. 12.5 x 13							
2440	25¢ Love	01/18/90	.45	.15	2.00	(4)	1.25	886
a	Imperf. pair		850.00					
	Booklet Stamp, Perf. 11.5							
2441	25¢ Love, single from booklet	01/18/90	.45	.15			1.25	995
a	Booklet pane of 10	01/18/90	4.75	—			6.00	
b	As "a," bright pink omitted		2,250.00					
	Black Heritage Issue, Ida B. Wells, Perf. 11							
2442	25¢ Portrait of Ida B. Wells, Marchers in Background	02/01/90	.45	.15	2.00	(4)	1.25	153
	Beach Umbrella Booklet Issue, Perf. 11.5 x 11							
2443	15¢ Beach Umbrella, single from booklet	02/03/90	.30	.15			1.25	
a	Booklet pane of 10	02/03/90	3.00	2.00			4.25	
b	As "a," blue omitted		2,000.00					

#2443 issued only in booklets. All stamps are imperf. at one side or imperf. at one side and bottom.

Not just for special people

In ancient times, umbrellas, which were usually large and carried by bearers, were marks of honor used only for important persons. During the late 16th century in Italy, the usage of an umbrella was to distinguish the pope and clergy. During the 19th and 20th centuries, an umbrella, which was quite small and commonly called a parasol, was carried by fashionable women to offer shade from the sun. Today, umbrellas are so commonly used that you can see them even on the beach. **(#2443)**

	Issues of 1990, Perf. 11		Un	U	PB	#	FDC	Q(M̄)
2444	25¢ Wyoming Statehood	02/23/90	.45	.15	2.00	(4)	1.25	169
	Classic Films Issue							
2445	25¢ The Wizard of Oz	03/23/90	1.00	.15			2.50	44
2446	25¢ Gone With the Wind	03/23/90	1.00	.15			2.50	44
2447	25¢ Beau Geste	03/23/90	1.00	.15			2.50	44
2448	25¢ Stagecoach	03/23/90	1.00	.15			2.50	44
a	Block of 4, #2445-48		4.50	3.50	5.50	(4)	5.00	
	Literary Arts Issue, Marianne Moore							
2449	25¢ Portrait of Marianne Moore	04/18/90	.45	.15	2.00	(4)	1.25	150
2450	Not assigned							
	Issues of 1990-95, Transportation Issue, Coil Stamps, Perf. 9.8 Vertically							
2451	4¢ Steam Carriage 1866	01/25/91	.15	.15	1.10	(3)	1.25	
a	Imperf. pair		700.00					
2452	5¢ Circus Wagon 1900s, intaglio printing	08/31/91	.15	.15	1.25	(3)	1.50	
2452B	5¢ Circus Wagon (2452), gravure printing	12/08/92	.15	.15	1.50	(3)	1.50	
2452D	5¢ Circus Wagon (2452), gravure printing	03/20/95	.15	.15	1.65	(3)	1.50	
2453	5¢ Canoe 1800s, precanceled, intaglio printing	05/25/91	.15	.15	1.75	(3)	1.25	
2454	5¢ Canoe 1800s, precanceled, gravure printing	10/22/91	.15	.15	1.50	(3)	1.25	
2455-56	Not assigned							
2457	10¢ Tractor Trailer, Bureau precanceled, intaglio printing	05/25/91	.20	.20	1.90	(3)	1.25	
2458	10¢ Tractor Trailer, Bureau precanceled, gravure printing	05/25/94	.20	.20	2.00	(3)	1.25	
2459-62	Not assigned							
2463	20¢ Cog Railway Car 1870s	06/09/95	.40	.15	3.50	(3)	1.25	
a	Imperf. pair		150.00					
2464	23¢ Lunch Wagon 1890s	04/12/91	.45	.15	3.50	(3)	1.25	
a	Imperf. pair		200.00					
2465	Not assigned		*					
2466	32¢ Ferryboat 1900s	06/02/95	.60	.15	5.75	(3)	1.25	
2467	Not assigned							
2468	$1 Seaplane 1914	04/20/90	1.75	.50	8.00	(3)	2.50	
2469	Not assigned							
	Issues of 1990, Lighthouses Booklet Issue, Perf. 10 Vertically							
2470	25¢ Admiralty Head, WA	04/26/90	.45	.15			1.25	147
2471	25¢ Cape Hatteras, NC	04/26/90	.45	.15			1.25	147
2472	25¢ West Quoddy Head, ME	04/26/90	.45	.15			1.25	147
2473	25¢ American Shoals, FL	04/26/90	.45	.15			1.25	147
2474	25¢ Sandy Hook, NJ	04/26/90	.45	.15			1.25	147
a	Booklet pane of 5, #2470-74		2.50	2.00			4.00	147
b	As "a," white (USA 25) omitted		75.00					

2444

2445

2446

2449

2447

2448   **2448a**

2451

2452

2452D

2453

2454

2457

2463

2464

2466

2468

2474a

2470   **2471**   **2472**   **2473**   **2474**

2475

2476 **2477** **2478**

2479

2480 **2481** **2482** **2483**

2484 **2485** **2486**

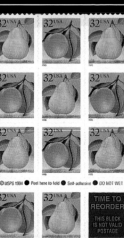

2487-88a

2487 **2488**

2489

2490 **2491** **2492**

OLYMPIAN OLYMPIAN OLYMPIAN OLYMPIAN OLYMPIAN

2496 **2497** **2498** **2499** **2500** **2500a**

2501 **2502** **2503** **2504** **2505** **2505a**

	Issues of 1990-1995		Un	U	PB	#	FDC	Q(M̄)
	Self-Adhesive Issue, Die-Cut							
2475	25¢ Flag, single from pane	05/18/90	.50	.25			1.25	36
a	Pane of 12	05/18/90	6.00					
	Flora and Fauna Issues, Perf. 11							
2476	1¢ American Kestrel	06/22/91	.15	.15	.15	(4)	1.25	
2477	1¢ American Kestrel	05/10/95	.15	.15	.15	(4)	1.25	
2478	3¢ Eastern Bluebird	06/22/91	.15	.15	.30	(4)	1.25	
	Perf. 11.5 x 11							
2479	19¢ Fawn	03/11/91	.35	.15	1.75	(4)	1.25	
2480	30¢ Cardinal	06/22/91	.50	.15	2.25	(4)	1.25	
	Perf. 11							
2481	45¢ Pumpkinseed Sunfish	12/02/92	.80	.15	3.90	(4)	1.75	
a	Black omitted		*650.00*	—				
2482	$2 Bobcat	06/01/90	3.00	1.25	12.00	(4)	5.00	
	Perf. 10.9 x 9.8							
2483	20¢ Blue Jay	06/15/95	.40	.15			1.25	
a	Booklet pane of 10		4.00	—				
	Wood Duck Booklet Issue, Perf. 10							
2484	29¢ Black and multicolored	04/12/91	.50	.15			1.25	
a	Booklet pane of 10		5.50				5.00	
	Perf. 11							
2485	29¢ Red and multicolored	04/12/91	.50	.15			1.25	
a	Booklet pane of 10		5.50	4.00			5.00	
	#2484-85a issued only in bklts. All stamps are imperf. top or bottom, or top or bottom and right edge.							
	Perf. 10 x 11							
2486	29¢ African Violet	10/08/93	.50	.15			1.25	
a	Booklet pane of 10		5.50	4.00			5.00	
2487	32¢ Peach	07/08/95	.60	.15			1.25	
2488	32¢ Pear	07/08/95	.60	.15			1.25	
a	Booklet pane, 5 each #2487-88		6.00	—			7.50	
b	Pair, #2487-88		1.25	.30				
	Issues of 1993 (Self-Adhesive), Die-Cut							
2489	29¢ Red Squirrel	06/25/93	.50	.15			1.25	
2490	29¢ Red Rose	08/19/93	.50	.15			1.25	
2491	29¢ Pine Cone	11/05/93	.50	.15			1.25	
	Serpentine Die-Cut							
2492	32¢ Pink Rose	06/02/95	.60	.15			1.25	
a	Booklet pane of 20 plus label		12.00					
	Issues of 1990, Olympians Issue, Perf. 11							
2496	25¢ Jesse Owens	07/06/90	.60	.15			1.25	36
2497	25¢ Ray Ewry	07/06/90	.60	.15			1.25	36
2498	25¢ Hazel Wightman	07/06/90	.60	.15			1.25	36
2499	25¢ Eddie Eagan	07/06/90	.60	.15			1.25	36
2500	25¢ Helene Madison	07/06/90	.60	.15			1.25	36
a	Strip of 5, #2496-2500		3.25	2.50	7.00	(10)	3.00	7
	Indian Headdresses Booklet Issue							
2501	25¢ Assiniboine Headdress	08/17/90	.55	.15			1.25	124
2502	25¢ Cheyenne Headdress	08/17/90	.55	.15			1.25	124
2503	25¢ Comanche Headdress	08/17/90	.55	.15			1.25	124
2504	25¢ Flathead Headdress	08/17/90	.55	.15			1.25	124
2505	25¢ Shoshone Headdress	08/17/90	.55	.15			1.25	124
a	Booklet pane of 10, 2 each of #2501-05		5.75	—			6.00	62
b	As "a," black omitted		—					
	#2501-05 issued only in booklets. All stamps imperf. top or bottom, or top or bottom and right edge.							

	Issues of 1990, Perf. 11		Un	U	PB	#	FDC	Q(M̄)
	Micronesia/Marshall Islands Issue							
2506	25¢ Canoe and Flag of the Federated States of Micronesia	09/28/90	.45	.15			1.25	76
2507	25¢ Stick Chart, Canoe and Flag of the Marshall Islands	09/28/90	.45	.15			1.25	76
a	Pair, #2506-07		.90	.60	2.25	(4)	2.00	61
b	As "a" black omitted		4,000.00					
	Creatures of the Sea Issue							
2508	25¢ Killer Whales	10/03/90	.45	.15			1.25	70
2509	25¢ Northern Sea Lions	10/03/90	.45	.15			1.25	70
2510	25¢ Sea Otter	10/03/90	.45	.15			1.25	70
2511	25¢ Common Dolphin	10/03/90	.45	.15			1.25	70
a	Block of 4, #2508-11		1.90	1.75	2.50	(4)	3.00	70
b	As "a," black omitted		1,250.00					
	America/PUAS Issue, (See also #C127)							
2512	25¢ Grand Canyon	10/12/90	.45	.15	2.00	(4)	1.25	151
2513	25¢ Dwight D. Eisenhower	10/13/90	.45	.15	2.00	(4)	1.25	143
a	Imperf. pair		2,000.00					
	Christmas Issue, Perf. 11.5							
2514	25¢ Madonna and Child, by Antonello	10/18/90	.45	.15	2.00	(4)	1.25	500
a	Booklet pane of 10		5.00				5.00	23
	Perf. 11							
2515	25¢ Christmas Tree	10/18/90	.45	.15	2.00	(4)	1.25	599
	Booklet Stamp, Perf. 11.5 x 11 on two or three sides							
2516	Single (2515) from booklet pane	10/18/90	.45	.15			1.25	
a	Booklet pane of 10	10/18/90	5.00	—			6.00	32
	Issues of 1991, Perf. 13							
2517	(29¢) "F" Stamp	01/22/91	.50	.15	2.50	(4)	1.25	
	Coil Stamp, Perf. 10 Vertically							
2518	(29¢) "F" Tulip (2517)	01/22/91	.50	.15	3.75	(3)	1.25	
	Booklet Stamps, Perf. 11 on two or three sides							
2519	(29¢) "F", single from booklet		.50	.15			1.25	
a	Booklet pane of 10	01/22/91	6.50	4.50			7.25	
2520	(29¢) "F", single from booklet		.50	.15			1.25	
a	Booklet pane of 10	01/22/91	7.00	4.50			7.25	
	#2519 has bull's-eye perforations that measure approximately 11.2. #2520 has less-pronounced black lines in the leaf, which is a much brighter green than on #2519.							
	Perf. 11							
2521	(4¢) Makeup Rate	01/22/91	.15	.15	.40	(4)	1.25	
	Self-Adhesive, Die-Cut, Imperf.							
2522	(29¢) F Flag, single from pane		.50	.25			1.25	
a	Pane of 12	01/22/91	7.00					
	Coil Stamps, Perf. 10 Vertically							
2523	29¢ Flag Over Mt. Rushmore, intaglio printing	03/29/91	.50	.15	4.25	(3)	1.25	
b	Imperf. pair		20.00					
2523A	29¢ Flag Over Mt. Rushmore, gravure printing	07/04/91	.50	.15	4.50	(3)	1.25	

2506   2507   2507a

2508   2509   2511a

2510   2511

2512

2513

2514

2515

2517   2519   2520   2521

2522

2523   2523A

2524

2525

2526

2528

2529

2529C

2530

2531

2531A

2532

2533

2534

2535

2539

2540

2537

2538

2543

2542

322

	Issues of 1991, Perf. 11		Un	U	PB	#	FDC	Q(M̅)
2524	29¢ Tulip	04/05/91	.50	.15	2.25	(4)	1.25	
a	Perf. 13		.60	.15				
	Coil Stamps, Roulette 10 Vertically							
2525	29¢ Tulip	08/16/91	.50	.15	4.50	(3)	1.25	
	Issues of 1992, Perf. 10 Vertically							
2526	29¢ Tulip	03/03/92	.50	.15	4.75	(3)	1.25	
	Issues of 1991, Booklet Stamp, Perf. 11 on two or three sides							
2527	29¢ Tulip (2524), single from bklt.		.50	.15			1.25	
a	Booklet pane of 10	04/05/91	5.50	3.50			5.00	
b	As "a," vertically imperf. between		*1,500.00*					
	Flag With Olympic Rings Booklet Issue, Perf. 11							
2528	29¢ U.S. Flag, Olympic Rings, single from booklet	04/21/91	.50	.15			1.25	
a	Booklet pane of 10	04/21/91	5.25	3.50			5.00	
	Issues of 1991-94, Perf. 10 Vertically							
2529	19¢ Fishing Boat	08/08/91	.35	.15	4.00	(3)	1.25	
a	New printing, Type II	1993	.35	.15	4.00	(3)		
b	As "a," untagged		1.00	.40	*9.50*	(3)		
	Perf. 9.8							
2529C	19¢ Fishing Boat	06/25/94	.50	.15	4.00	(3)	1.25	
	Type II stamps have finer dot pattern, smoother edges along type. #2529C has only one loop of rope tying up boat.							
	Issue of 1991, Ballooning Booklet Issue, Perf. 10							
2530	19¢ Overhead View of Balloon, single from booklet	05/17/91	.35	.15			1.25	
a	Booklet pane of 10	05/17/91	3.50	2.75			5.00	
	#2530 was issued only in booklets. All stamps are imperf. on one side or on one side and bottom.							
	Perf. 11							
2531	29¢ Flags on Parade	05/30/91	.50	.15	2.25	(4)	1.25	
	Self-Adhesive, Die-Cut, Imperf.							
2531A	29¢ Liberty Torch, single stamp from pane	06/25/91	.55	.25			1.25	
b	Pane of 18	06/25/91	10.50					
	Perf. 11							
2532	50¢ Founding of Switzerland	02/22/91	1.00	.25	5.00	(4)	1.35	100
2533	29¢ Vermont Statehood	03/01/91	.50	.15	2.50	(4)	1.50	0.1
2534	29¢ Savings Bonds	04/30/91	.50	.15	2.50	(4)	1.25	151
	Perf. 12.5 x 13							
2535	29¢ Love	05/09/91	.50	.15	2.50	(4)	1.25	631
	Booklet Stamp, Perf. 11 on two or three sides							
2536	29¢ (2535), single from booklet		.50	.15			1.25	
a	Booklet pane of 10	05/09/91	5.25	3.50			5.00	
	Perf. 11							
2537	52¢ Love	05/09/91	.90	.20	4.50	(4)	1.35	200
	Issues of 1991-93, Literary Arts Issue, William Saroyan							
2538	29¢ Portrait of Saroyan	05/22/91	.50	.15	2.50	(4)	1.25	161
2539	$1 USPS Logo/Olympic Rings	09/29/91	1.75	.50	7.00	(4)	2.25	
2540	$2.90 Priority Mail	07/07/91	5.00	2.50	20.00	(4)	4.50	
2541	$9.95 Domestic Express Mail	06/16/91	15.00	7.50	60.00	(4)	12.50	
2542	$14 International Express Mail	08/31/91	22.50	10.00	90.00	(4)	18.50	
2543	$2.90 Space Vehicle	06/03/93	5.00	2.25	22.50	(4)	4.50	

	Issues of 1995, Perf. 11.2		Un	U	PB	#	FDC	Q(M)
2544	$3 Space Shuttle *Challenger*	06/22/95	5.25	2.25	21.00	(4)	5.00	
	Express Mail Rate, Perf. 11							
2544A	$10.75 Space Shuttle *Endeavour*	08/04/95	17.50	7.50			13.00	
	Issues of 1991, Fishing Flies Booklet Issue, Perf. 11 Horizontally							
2545	29¢ Royal Wulff	05/31/91	.55	.15			1.25	149
2546	29¢ Jock Scott	05/31/91	.55	.15			1.25	149
2547	29¢ Apte Tarpon Fly	05/31/91	.55	.15			1.25	149
2548	29¢ Lefty's Deceiver	05/31/91	.55	.15			1.25	149
2549	29¢ Muddler Minnow	05/31/91	.55	.15			1.25	149
a	Booklet pane of 5, #2545-49		3.00	2.50			3.00	149

#2545-49 were issued only in booklets. All stamps are imperf. at sides or imperf. at sides and bottom.

	Performing Arts Issue, Cole Porter, Perf. 11		Un	U	PB	#	FDC	Q(M)
2550	29¢ Portrait of Porter at Piano, Sheet Music	06/08/91	.50	.15	2.50	(4)	1.25	150
a	Vertical pair, imperf. horizontally		650.00					
2551	29¢ Operations Desert Shield/ Desert Storm	07/02/91	.50	.15	2.50	(4)	2.00	200
	Booklet Stamp, Perf. 11 on one or two sides							
2552	29¢ Operations Desert Shield/Desert Storm (2551), single from booklet	07/02/91	.50	.15			2.00	200
a	Booklet pane of 5	07/02/91	2.75	2.25			4.50	40
	Summer Olympic Games Issue, Perf. 11							
2553	29¢ Pole Vaulter	07/12/91	.50	.15			1.25	34
2554	29¢ Discus Thrower	07/12/91	.50	.15			1.25	34
2555	29¢ Women Sprinters	07/12/91	.50	.15			1.25	34
2556	29¢ Javelin Thrower	07/12/91	.50	.15			1.25	34
2557	29¢ Women Hurdlers	07/12/91	.50	.15			1.25	34
a	Strip of 5, #2553-57		2.75	2.25	7.50	(10)	3.00	34
2558	29¢ Numismatics	08/13/91	.50	.15	2.50	(4)	1.25	150
	World War II Issue, 1941: A World at War, Miniature Sheet, Perf. 11							
2559	Sheet of 10 and central label	09/03/91	5.25	4.50			6.00	15
a	29¢ Burma Road		.50	.30			1.50	15
b	29¢ America's First Peacetime Draft		.50	.30			1.50	15
c	29¢ Lend-Lease Act		.50	.30			1.50	15
d	29¢ Atlantic Charter		.50	.30			1.50	15
e	29¢ Arsenal of Democracy		.50	.30			1.50	15
f	29¢ Destroyer *Reuben James*		.50	.30			1.50	15
g	29¢ Civil Defense		.50	.30			1.50	15
h	29¢ Liberty Ship		.50	.30			1.50	15
i	29¢ Pearl Harbor		.50	.30			1.50	15
j	29¢ U.S. Declaration of War		.50	.30			1.50	15

2544

2544A

Cole Porter USA 29

2550

29 USA
Royal Wulff

2545

29 USA
Jock Scott

2546

29 USA
Apte Tarpon Fly

2547

29 USA
Lefty's Deceiver

2548

29 USA
Muddler Minnow

2549

2549a

Honoring Those Who Served
USA 29
Desert Shield ★ Desert Storm

2551

29 USA
NUMISMATICS

2558

2553

2554

2555

2556

2557   2557a

a

29 USA
Burma Road, 717-mile lifeline to China

b

29 USA
America's first peacetime draft, 1940

c

29 USA
U.S. supports allies with Lend-Lease Act

d

29 USA
Atlantic Charter sets war aims of allies

e

29 USA
America becomes "arsenal of democracy"

1941: A World at War

f

29 USA
Destroyer Reuben James sunk October 31

g

29 USA
Civil Defense mobilizes Americans at home

h

29 USA
First Liberty ship delivered December 30

i

29 USA
Japanese bomb Pearl Harbor, December 7

j

29 USA
U.S. declares war on Japan, December 8

2559

2561

2560

2567

2562 **2563** **2564** **2565** **2566** **2566a**

2568 **2569** **2570** **2571** **2572**

2573 **2574** **2575** **2576** **2577** **2577a**

2578

2579 **2580** **2581** **2581a**

2582 **2583** **2584** **2585**

	Issues of 1991, Perf. 11		Un	U	PB	#	FDC	Q(M̄)
2560	29¢ Basketball	08/28/91	.55	.15	2.50	(4)	2.00	150
2561	29¢ District of Columbia	09/07/91	.50	.15	2.50	(4)	1.25	149
	Comedians Booklet Issue, Perf. 11 on two or three sides							
2562	29¢ Stan Laurel and Oliver Hardy	08/29/91	.50	.15			1.25	140
2563	29¢ Edgar Bergen and Dummy Charlie McCarthy	08/29/91	.50	.15			1.25	140
2564	29¢ Jack Benny	08/29/91	.50	.15			1.25	140
2565	29¢ Fanny Brice	08/29/91	.50	.15			1.25	140
2566	29¢ Bud Abbott and Lou Costello	08/29/91	.50	.15			1.25	140
a	Booklet pane of 10, 2 each of #2562-66		5.50	—			5.00	70
b	As "a," scarlet and bright violet omitted		900.00					

#2562-66 issued only in booklets. All stamps are imperf. at top or bottom, or at top or bottom and right side.

	Black Heritage Issue, Jan Matzeliger, Perf. 11							
2567	29¢ Portrait of Matzeliger and Shoe-Lasting Machine Diagram	09/15/91	.50	.15	2.50	(4)	1.25	149
	Space Exploration Booklet Issue							
2568	29¢ Mercury, Mariner 10	10/01/91	.50	.15			1.25	33
2569	29¢ Venus, Mariner 2	10/01/91	.50	.15			1.25	33
2570	29¢ Earth, Landsat	10/01/91	.50	.15			1.25	33
2571	29¢ Moon, Lunar Orbiter	10/01/91	.50	.15			1.25	33
2572	29¢ Mars, Viking Orbiter	10/01/91	.50	.15			1.25	33
2573	29¢ Jupiter, Pioneer 11	10/01/91	.50	.15			1.25	33
2574	29¢ Saturn, Voyager 2	10/01/91	.50	.15			1.25	33
2575	29¢ Uranus, Voyager 2	10/01/91	.50	.15			1.25	33
2576	29¢ Neptune, Voyager 2	10/01/91	.50	.15			1.25	33
2577	29¢ Pluto	10/01/91	.50	.15			1.25	33
a	Booklet pane of 10, #2568-77		5.50	—			5.00	33

#2568-77 issued only in booklets. All stamps are imperf. at top or bottom, or at top or bottom and right side.

	Christmas Issue, Perf. 11							
2578	29¢ Madonna and Child, by Romano	10/17/91	.50	.15	2.50	(4)	1.25	401
a	Booklet pane of 10		5.80	—				30
2579	29¢ Santa Claus Sliding Down Chimney	10/17/91	.50	.15	2.50	(4)	1.25	900
	Booklet Stamps							
2580	29¢ Santa Claus (2579), Type I, single from booklet	10/17/91	1.75	.15			1.25	
2581	29¢ Santa Claus (2579), Type II, single from booklet	10/17/91	1.75	.15			1.25	
a	Pair, #2580, 2581	10/17/91	3.50	.25				28

The extreme left brick in top row of chimney is missing from Type II, #2581.

2582	29¢ Santa Claus Checking List, single from booklet	10/17/91	.50	.15			1.25	
a	Booklet pane of 4	10/17/91	2.00	—			2.50	28
2583	29¢ Santa Claus Leaving Present Under Tree, single from booklet	10/17/91	.50	.15			1.25	
a	Booklet pane of 4	10/17/91	2.00	—			2.50	28
2584	29¢ Santa Claus Going Up Chimney, single from booklet	10/17/91	.50	.15			1.25	
a	Booklet pane of 4	10/17/91	2.00	—			2.50	28
2585	29¢ Santa Claus Flying Away in Sleigh, single from booklet	10/17/91	.50	.15			1.25	
a	Booklet pane of 4	10/17/91	2.00	—			2.50	28

#2582-85 issued only in booklets. All stamps are imperf. at top or bottom, or at top or bottom and right side.

	Issue of 1995, Perf. 11.2		Un	U	PB	#	FDC	Q(M̄)
2587	32¢ James K. Polk	11/02/95	.60	.15			1.25	
	Issues of 1994, Perf. 11.5							
2590	$1 Victory at Saratoga	05/05/94	1.90	.50	7.60	(4)	2.00	
2592	$5 Washington and Jackson	08/19/94	8.00	2.50	40.00	(4)	9.00	
	Issue of 1992, Perf. 10							
2593	29¢ Pledge of Allegiance	09/08/92	.50	.15			1.25	
a	Booklet of 10		5.25	4.25			5.00	
	Issue of 1993, Perf. 11 x 10							
2594	29¢ Pledge of Allegiance	04/08/93	.50	.15			1.25	
a	Booklet of 10		5.25	4.25				
	Issues of 1992, Self-Adhesive Booklet and Coil Stamps							
2595	29¢ Eagle and Shield (brown lettering)	09/25/92	.50	.25			1.25	
a	Pane of 17 + label		13.00					
2596	29¢ Eagle and Shield (green lettering)	09/25/92	.50	.25			1.25	
a	Pane of 17 + label		12.00					
2597	29¢ Eagle and Shield (red lettering)	09/25/92	.50	.25			1.25	
a	Pane of 17 + label		10.00					
	Issues of 1994, Perf. 10							
2598	29¢ Eagle, Self-Adhesive	02/04/94	.50	.15			1.25	
2599	29¢ Statue of Liberty	06/24/94	.50	.15			1.25	
	Issues of 1991-93, Perf. 10 Vertically							
2602	10¢ Eagle and Shield (inscribed "Bulk Rate USA")	12/13/91	.20	.15	3.00	(3)	1.25	
2603	10¢ Eagle and Shield (inscribed "USA Bulk Rate")	05/29/93	.20	.20	3.50	(3)	1.25	
2604	10¢ Eagle and Shield (metallic, inscribed "USA Bulk Rate")	05/29/93	.20	.20	3.50	(3)	1.25	
2605	23¢ Flag, Presorted First-Class	09/27/91	.40	.40	3.75	(3)	1.25	
	Issues of 1992, Perf. 11							
2606	23¢ USA	07/21/92	.40	.40	4.50	(3)	1.25	
2607	23¢ USA (Bureau) (In #2607, "23" is 7mm long)	10/09/92	.40	.40	4.50	(3)	1.25	
2608	23¢ USA (violet)	05/14/93	.40	.40	4.50	(3)	1.25	
2609	29¢ Flag Over White House	04/23/92	.50	.15	5.00	(3)	1.25	
	Winter Olympic Games Issue							
2611	29¢ Hockey	01/11/92	.50	.15			1.25	32
2612	29¢ Figure Skating	01/11/92	.50	.15			1.25	32
2613	29¢ Speed Skating	01/11/92	.50	.15			1.25	32
2614	29¢ Skiing	01/11/92	.50	.15			1.25	32
2615	29¢ Bobsledding	01/11/92	.50	.15			1.25	32
a	Strip of 5, #2611-15		2.75	2.25	6.00	(10)	3.00	
2616	29¢ World Columbian Stamp Expo	01/24/92	.50	.15	2.50	(4)	1.25	149
	Black Heritage Issue, W.E.B. DuBois							
2617	29¢ W.E.B. DuBois	01/31/92	.50	.15	2.50	(4)	1.25	150
2618	29¢ Love	02/06/92	.50	.15	2.50	(4)	1.25	835
2619	29¢ Olympic Baseball	04/03/92	.50	.15	2.75	(4)	1.25	160

2587

2590

2592

2593

2594

2595

2596

2597

2598

2599

2602

2603

2604

2605

2606

2607

2608

2609

2611

2612

2613

2614

2615

2615a

2616

2617

2618

2619

2622   2623   2623a

2624

2625

2626

2627

2628

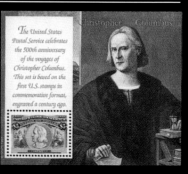

2629

Issues of 1992, Perf. 11		Un	U	PB	#	FDC	Q(M̄)
First Voyage of Christopher Columbus Issue							
2620	29¢ Seeking Queen Isabella's Support 04/24/92	.50	.15			1.25	40
2621	29¢ Crossing The Atlantic 04/24/92	.50	.15			1.25	40
2622	29¢ Approaching Land 04/24/92	.50	.15			1.25	40
2623	29¢ Coming Ashore 04/24/92	.50	.15			1.25	40
a	Block of 4, #2620-23	2.00	1.90	2.50	(4)	2.75	
The Voyages of Columbus Souvenir Sheets, Perf. 10.5							
2624	First Sighting of Land, sheet of 3 05/22/92	1.75	—			2.10	2
a	1¢ deep blue	.15	.15			1.25	
b	4¢ ultramarine	.15	.15			1.25	
c	$1 salmon	1.65	1.00			2.00	
2625	Claiming a New World, sheet of 3 05/22/92	6.75	—			8.10	2
a	2¢ brown violet	.15	.15			1.25	
b	3¢ green	.15	.15			1.25	
c	$4 crimson lake	6.50	4.00			8.00	
2626	Seeking Royal Support, sheet of 3 05/22/92	1.40	—			1.70	2
a	5¢ chocolate	.15	.15			1.25	
b	30¢ orange brown	.50	.30			1.25	
c	50¢ slate blue	.80	.50			1.50	
2627	Royal Favor Restored, sheet of 3 05/22/92	5.25	—			6.25	2
a	6¢ purple	.15	.15			1.25	
b	8¢ magenta	.15	.15			1.25	
c	$3 yellow green	4.75	3.00			6.00	
2628	Reporting Discoveries, sheet of 3 05/22/92	3.75	—			4.50	2
a	10¢ black brown	.15	.15			1.25	
b	15¢ dark green	.25	.15			1.25	
c	$2 brown red	3.25	2.00			4.00	
2629	$5 Christopher Columbus, sheet of 1 05/22/92	8.50	—			10.00	2

Christopher Columbus, man of mystery

The quincentenary of the Columbus voyage of 1492 led to many celebrations honoring this courageous explorer, but our knowledge of him remains surrounded by many contradictions. We do not know for certain his place of birth or his native language. We have no known likeness of him made in his lifetime; therefore, his

appearance is known only through the writings of his son Ferdinand and other contemporaries. These physical descriptions were similar, but very general. He is described as having a long face with high cheekbones, a curved nose, light gray or blue eyes and a ruddy complexion. His reddish hair turned white after he reached 30. His depiction through the centuries was left to the imagination and interpretation of the artist, and he was portrayed at times with a beard, curly hair and even a ruffled collar. This image was taken from an old engraving by T. Johnson based on a 16th century representation by Lorenzo Lotto. **(#2629)**

1992

	Issues of 1992, Perf. 11		Un	U	PB	#	FDC	Q($\overline{\text{M}}$)
2630	29¢ New York Stock Exchange Bicentennial	05/17/92	.50	.15	2.50	(4)	1.75	148
	Space Adventures Issue							
2631	29¢ Cosmonaut, US Space Shuttle	05/29/92	.50	.15			1.50	37
2632	29¢ Astronaut, Russian Space Station	05/29/92	.50	.15			1.50	37
2633	29¢ Sputnik, Vostok, Apollo Command and Lunar Modules	05/29/92	.50	.15			1.50	37
2634	29¢ Soyuz, Mercury and Gemini Spacecraft	05/29/92	.50	.15			1.50	37
a	Block of 4, #2631-34		2.00	1.75	2.50	(4)	2.75	
2635	29¢ Alaska Highway, 50th Anniversary	05/30/92	.50	.15	2.50	(4)	1.25	147
a	Black (engr.) omitted		750.00					
2636	29¢ Kentucky Statehood Bicentennial	06/01/92	.50	.15	2.50	(4)	1.25	160
	Summer Olympic Games Issue							
2637	29¢ Soccer	06/11/92	.50	.15			1.25	32
2638	29¢ Gymnastics	06/11/92	.50	.15			1.25	32
2639	29¢ Volleyball	06/11/92	.50	.15			1.25	32
2640	29¢ Boxing	06/11/92	.50	.15			1.25	32
2641	29¢ Swimming	06/11/92	.50	.15			1.25	32
a	Strip of 5, #2637-41		2.50	2.25	5.50	(10)	3.00	
	Hummingbirds Issue							
2642	29¢ Ruby-Throated	06/15/92	.50	.15			1.25	88
2643	29¢ Broad-Billed	06/15/92	.50	.15			1.25	88
2644	29¢ Costa's	06/15/92	.50	.15			1.25	88
2645	29¢ Rufous	06/15/92	.50	.15			1.25	88
2646	29¢ Calliope	06/15/92	.50	.15			1.25	88
a	Booklet pane of 5, #2642-46		2.75	2.25			3.00	

The NYSE bicentennial

In 1792, 24 brokers and merchants met under a buttonwood tree in New York City, and this meeting was the beginning of the New York Stock Exchange (NYSE). The Buttonwood Agreement, which served as the basis for trading securities using common commissions, was signed at this meeting. Twenty-five years later, the New York Stock & Exchange Board was created from the Buttonwood Agreement. In 1863, the name was shortened to the NYSE. The bicentennial of the NYSE, today's largest securities marketplace, was celebrated on stamp. **(#2630)**

Interesting Fact: The first company listed on the NYSE was the Bank of New York.

2630

2631   2632

2633   2634   2634a

2635

2636

2637   2638   2639   2640   2641   2641a

2642   2643   2644   2645   2646   2646a

2647	2648	2649	2650	2651

2652	2653	2654	2655	2656

2657	2658	2659	2660	2661

2662	2663	2664	2665	2666

2667	2668	2669	2670	2671

Issues of 1992, Perf. 11		Un	U	FDC	Q(M)
Wildflowers Issue					
2647	29¢ Indian Paintbrush	07/24/92	.50	.15	1.25	11
2648	29¢ Fragrant Water Lily	07/24/92	.50	.15	1.25	11
2649	29¢ Meadow Beauty	07/24/92	.50	.15	1.25	11
2650	29¢ Jack-in-the-Pulpit	07/24/92	.50	.15	1.25	11
2651	29¢ California Poppy	07/24/92	.50	.15	1.25	11
2652	29¢ Large-Flowered Trillium	07/24/92	.50	.15	1.25	11
2653	29¢ Tickseed	07/24/92	.50	.15	1.25	11
2654	29¢ Shooting Star	07/24/92	.50	.15	1.25	11
2655	29¢ Stream Violet	07/24/92	.50	.15	1.25	11
2656	29¢ Bluets	07/24/92	.50	.15	1.25	11
2657	29¢ Herb Robert	07/24/92	.50	.15	1.25	11
2658	29¢ Marsh Marigold	07/24/92	.50	.15	1.25	11
2659	29¢ Sweet White Violet	07/24/92	.50	.15	1.25	11
2660	29¢ Claret Cup Cactus	07/24/92	.50	.15	1.25	11
2661	29¢ White Mountain Avens	07/24/92	.50	.15	1.25	11
2662	29¢ Sessile Bellwort	07/24/92	.50	.15	1.25	11
2663	29¢ Blue Flag	07/24/92	.50	.15	1.25	11
2664	29¢ Harlequin Lupine	07/24/92	.50	.15	1.25	11
2665	29¢ Twinflower	07/24/92	.50	.15	1.25	11
2666	29¢ Common Sunflower	07/24/92	.50	.15	1.25	11
2667	29¢ Sego Lily	07/24/92	.50	.15	1.25	11
2668	29¢ Virginia Bluebells	07/24/92	.50	.15	1.25	11
2669	29¢ Ohi'a Lehua	07/24/92	.50	.15	1.25	11
2670	29¢ Rosebud Orchid	07/24/92	.50	.15	1.25	11
2671	29¢ Showy Evening Primrose	07/24/92	.50	.15	1.25	11

Meadow beauty native to eastern North America

The meadow beauty flower species can commonly be found along the coast of Georgia and more rarely up to the pine barrens of New Jersey. Also known as awned meadow beauty because of the point at the tip of the round petal, the rose-colored meadow beauty blooms from June to September. Most other relatives to the meadow beauty, part of the melastoma family, are found in tropical areas. **(#2649)**

	Issues of 1992, Perf. 11		Un	U		FDC	Q(M̄)
	Wildflowers Issue (continued)						
2672	29¢ Fringed Gentian	07/24/92	.50	.15		1.25	11
2673	29¢ Yellow Lady's Slipper	07/24/92	.50	.15		1.25	11
2674	29¢ Passionflower	07/24/92	.50	.15		1.25	11
2675	29¢ Bunchberry	07/24/92	.50	.15		1.25	11
2676	29¢ Pasqueflower	07/24/92	.50	.15		1.25	11
2677	29¢ Round-Lobed Hepatica	07/24/92	.50	.15		1.25	11
2678	29¢ Wild Columbine	07/24/92	.50	.15		1.25	11
2679	29¢ Fireweed	07/24/92	.50	.15		1.25	11
2680	29¢ Indian Pond Lily	07/24/92	.50	.15		1.25	11
2681	29¢ Turk's Cap Lily	07/24/92	.50	.15		1.25	11
2682	29¢ Dutchman's Breeches	07/24/92	.50	.15		1.25	11
2683	29¢ Trumpet Honeysuckle	07/24/92	.50	.15		1.25	11
2684	29¢ Jacob's Ladder	07/24/92	.50	.15		1.25	11
2685	29¢ Plains Prickly Pear	07/24/92	.50	.15		1.25	11
2686	29¢ Moss Campion	07/24/92	.50	.15		1.25	11
2687	29¢ Bearberry	07/24/92	.50	.15		1.25	11
2688	29¢ Mexican Hat	07/24/92	.50	.15		1.25	11
2689	29¢ Harebell	07/24/92	.50	.15		1.25	11
2690	29¢ Desert Five Spot	07/24/92	.50	.15		1.25	11
2691	29¢ Smooth Solomon's Seal	07/24/92	.50	.15		1.25	11
2692	29¢ Red Maids	07/24/92	.50	.15		1.25	11
2693	29¢ Yellow Skunk Cabbage	07/24/92	.50	.15		1.25	11
2694	29¢ Rue Anemone	07/24/92	.50	.15		1.25	11
2695	29¢ Standing Cypress	07/24/92	.50	.15		1.25	11
2696	29¢ Wild Flax	07/24/92	.50	.15		1.25	11
a	Pane of 50, #2647-96		25.00	—		30.00	11

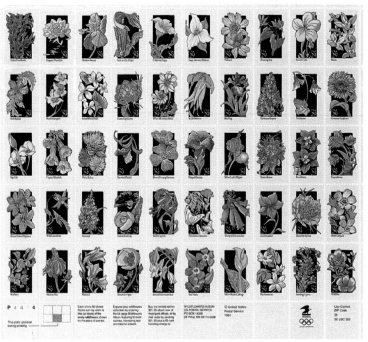

Example of #2696a.

Fringed Gentian

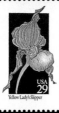
Yellow Lady's Slipper

Passionflower

Bunchberry

Pasqueflower

2672   **2673**   **2674**   **2675**   **2676**

Round-lobed Hepatica

Wild Columbine

Fireweed

Indian Pond Lily

Turk's Cap Lily

2677   **2678**   **2679**   **2680**   **2681**

Dutchman's Breeches

Trumpet Honeysuckle

Jacob's Ladder

Plains Prickly Pear

Moss Campion

2682   **2683**   **2684**   **2685**   **2686**

Bearberry

Mexican Hat

Harebell

Desert Five Spot

Smooth Solomon's Seal

2687   **2688**   **2689**   **2690**   **2691**

Red Maids

Yellow Skunk Cabbage

Rue Anemone

Standing Cypress

Wild Flax

2692   **2693**   **2694**   **2695**   **2696**

a 29 USA — *B-25s take off to raid Tokyo April 18, 1942*

b 29 USA — *Food and other essentials rationed, 1942*

c 29 USA — *U.S. wins Battle of the Coral Sea May 1942*

d 29 USA — *Corregidor falls to Japanese, May 6, 1942*

e 29 USA — *Japan invades Aleutian Islands, June 1942*

1942: Into the Battle

f 29 USA — *Allies decipher secret enemy codes, 1942*

g 29 USA — *Yorktown lost, U.S. wins at Midway, 1942*

h 29 USA — *Millions of women join war effort, 1942*

i 29 USA — *Marines land on Guadalcanal Aug. 7, 1942*

j 29 USA — *Allies land in North Africa November 1942*

2697

2698 — Dorothy Parker, American Writer 1893-1967

2699 — Theodore von Kármán, Aerospace Scientist

2700 — Minerals USA 29 — Azurite

2701 — Minerals USA 29 — Copper

2702 — Minerals USA 29 — Variscite

2703 — Minerals USA 29 — Wulfenite

2703a

2704 — Explorer of California 1542, Juan Rodríguez CABRILLO

Issues of 1992, Perf. 11		Un	U	PB	#	FDC	Q(M̄)
World War II Issue, 1942: Into the Battle, Miniature Sheet, Perf. 11							
2697 Sheet of 10 and central label	08/17/92	5.25	4.50			6.50	12
a 29¢ B-25s Take Off to Raid Tokyo		.50	.30			1.25	12
b 29¢ Food and Other Commodities Rationed		.50	.30			1.25	12
c 29¢ U.S. Wins Battle of the Coral Sea		.50	.30			1.25	12
d 29¢ Corregidor Falls to Japanese		.50	.30			1.25	12
e 29¢ Japan Invades Aleutian Islands		.50	.30			1.25	12
f 29¢ Allies Decipher Secret Enemy Codes		.50	.30			1.25	12
g 29¢ *Yorktown* Lost		.50	.30			1.25	12
h 29¢ Millions of Women Join War Effort		.50	.30			1.25	12
i 29¢ Marines Land on Guadalcanal		.50	.30			1.25	12
j 29¢ Allies Land in North Africa		.50	.30			1.25	12
Literary Arts Issue, Dorothy Parker							
2698 29¢ Dorothy Parker	08/22/92	.50	.15	2.50	(4)	1.25	105
2699 29¢ Dr. Theodore von Karman	08/31/92	.50	.15	2.50	(4)	1.25	143
Minerals Issue							
2700 29¢ Azurite	09/17/92	.50	.15			1.25	37
2701 29¢ Copper	09/17/92	.50	.15			1.25	37
2702 29¢ Variscite	09/17/92	.50	.15			1.25	37
2703 29¢ Wulfenite	09/17/92	.50	.15			1.25	37
a Block of 4, #2700-03		2.00	1.75	2.50	(4)	2.75	
2704 29¢ Juan Rodriguez Cabrillo	09/28/92	.50	.15	2.50	(4)	1.25	85

Great for painting and as gems

The mineral azurite is found in many countries including France, Russia, Australia and the United States and is generally found with malachite since both are basic carbonates of copper. Blue pigment was made of azurite for ancient Eastern wall paintings as well as for some European paintings from the 15th to the middle of the 17th century. Another use for azurite is as a gemstone because it can be polished to a glassy shine. **(#2700)**

	Issues of 1992, Perf. 11		Un	U	PB	#	FDC	Q(M̄)
	Wild Animals Issue, Horizontal							
2705	29¢ Giraffe	10/01/92	.50	.15			1.25	80
2706	29¢ Giant Panda	10/01/92	.50	.15			1.25	80
2707	29¢ Flamingo	10/01/92	.50	.15			1.25	80
2708	29¢ King Penguins	10/01/92	.50	.15			1.25	80
2709	29¢ White Bengal Tiger	10/01/92	.50	.15			1.25	80
a	Booklet pane of 5, #2705-09		2.50	2.00			4.00	
	Christmas Issue, Perf. 11.5 x 11							
2710	29¢ Madonna and Child by Giovanni Bellini	10/22/92	.50	.15	2.50	(4)	1.25	300
a	Booklet pane of 10		5.25	—			7.25	349
2711	29¢ Horse and Rider	10/22/92	.50	.15			1.25	125
2712	29¢ Toy Train	10/22/92	.50	.15			1.25	125
2713	29¢ Toy Steamer	10/22/92	.50	.15			1.25	125
2714	29¢ Toy Ship	10/22/92	.50	.15			1.25	125
a	Block of 4, #2711-14		2.00	1.10	2.50	(4)	2.75	
	Perf. 11							
2715	29¢ Horse and Rider	10/22/92	.50	.15			1.25	102
2716	29¢ Toy Train	10/22/92	.50	.15			1.25	102
2717	29¢ Toy Steamer	10/22/92	.50	.15			1.25	102
2718	29¢ Toy Ship	10/22/92	.50	.15			1.25	102
a	Booklet pane of 4, #2715-18		2.25	—			2.75	
2719	29¢ Toy Train (self-adhesive)	10/22/92	.60	.15			1.25	22
a	Booklet pane of 18		11.00					
	Lunar New Year Issue							
2720	29¢ Year of the Rooster	12/30/92	.50	.15	2.00	(4)	1.50	

A toy train graces this self-adhesive sheet of 18 greeting stamps designed for use in Automated Teller Machines (ATMs). The sheet must be the same size and thickness as U.S. currency in order to be vended by ATMs. **(#2719a)**

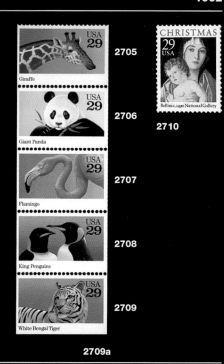

2705

2706

2707

2708

2709

2709a

2710

2711   2712

2713   2714   2714a

2715   2716

2719

2717   2718   2718a

2720

2721

2722

2723

2724   2725   2726   2727   2728

2729   2730

2731

2732

2733

2734

2735

2736

2737

2731

2737a

2737b

	Issues of 1993, Perf. 11		Un	U	PB	#	FDC	Q(M̄)
	Legends of American Music Series							
2721	29¢ Elvis Presley	01/08/93	.50	.15	2.50	(4)	1.50	517
	Perf. 10							
2722	29¢ *Oklahoma!*	03/30/93	.50	.15	2.50	(4)	1.25	150
2723	29¢ Hank Williams	06/09/93	.50	.15	2.50	(4)	1.25	152
	Legends of American Music Series, Rock & Roll/Rhythm & Blues Issue							
2724	29¢ Elvis Presley	06/16/93	.50	.15			1.25	14
2725	29¢ Bill Haley	06/16/93	.50	.15			1.25	14
2726	29¢ Clyde McPhatter	06/16/93	.50	.15			1.25	14
2727	29¢ Ritchie Valens	06/16/93	.50	.15			1.25	14
2728	29¢ Otis Redding	06/16/93	.50	.15			1.25	14
2729	29¢ Buddy Holly	06/16/93	.50	.15			1.25	14
2730	29¢ Dinah Washington	06/16/93	.50	.15			1.25	14
a	Vertical strip of 7, #2724-30		3.50	—	5.00	(10)	5.00	
	Perf. 11 Horizontal							
2731	29¢ Elvis Presley	06/16/93	.50	.15			1.25	99
2732	29¢ Bill Haley (2725)	06/16/93	.50	.15			1.25	33
2733	29¢ Clyde McPhatter (2726)	06/16/93	.50	.15			1.25	33
2734	29¢ Ritchie Valens (2727)	06/16/93	.50	.15			1.25	33
2735	29¢ Otis Redding	06/16/93	.50	.15			1.25	66
2736	29¢ Buddy Holly	06/16/93	.50	.15			1.25	66
2737	29¢ Dinah Washington	06/16/93	.50	.15			1.25	66
a	Booklet pane, 2 #2731, 1 each #2732-37		4.50	—			5.25	
b	Booklet pane of 4, #2731, 2735-37		2.50	—			2.75	
2738-40	Not assigned							

Oklahoma! remembered for catchy tunes

The sensational opening of *Oklahoma!* on March 31, 1943, at the St. James Theater in New York City was the first collaboration of Richard Rodgers, composer, and Oscar Hammerstein II, lyricist. It was acclaimed for its total integration and unity of the major elements of music, dance and drama. Based on an American folk play, its memorable songs, lively hoedowns and dramatic folk ballets bring to life a story of optimism and romance in the midwestern territory of the early 20th century. The entire score was recorded by the original

Broadway cast and rapidly spread across America, helping to make unforgettable classics of *Oh, What a Beautiful Morning*; *People Will Say We're in Love;* and the title song, *Oklahoma!*

(#2722)

Interesting Fact: Unprecedented for that time, Oklahoma! *ran for more than five years with over 2,200 performances.*

	Issues of 1993, Perf. 11		Un	U	PB	#	FDC	Q(M̄)
	Space Fantasy Issue, Perf. 11 Vertical on 1 or 2 sides							
2741	29¢ multicolored	01/25/93	.50	.15			1.25	140
2742	29¢ multicolored	01/25/93	.50	.15			1.25	140
2743	29¢ multicolored	01/25/93	.50	.15			1.25	140
2744	29¢ multicolored	01/25/93	.50	.15			1.25	140
2745	29¢ multicolored	01/25/93	.50	.15			1.25	140
a	Booklet pane of 5, #2741-45		2.50	2.00			3.25	
2746	29¢ Percy Lavon Julian	01/29/93	.50	.15	2.50	(4)	1.25	105
2747	29¢ Oregon Trail	02/12/93	.50	.15	2.50	(4)	1.25	110
2748	29¢ World University Games	02/25/93	.50	.15	2.50	(4)	1.25	110
2749	29¢ Grace Kelly	03/25/93	.50	.15	2.50	(4)	1.50	173
	Circus Issue, Perf. 11							
2750	29¢ Clown	04/06/93	.50	.15			1.25	66
2751	29¢ Ringmaster	04/06/93	.50	.15			1.25	66
2752	29¢ Trapeze Artist	04/06/93	.50	.15			1.25	66
2753	29¢ Elephant	04/06/93	.50	.15			1.25	66
a	Block of 4, #2750-53		2.00	1.75	3.50	(6)	2.75	
2754	29¢ Cherokee Strip	04/17/93	.50	.15	2.00	(4)	1.25	110
2755	29¢ Dean Acheson	04/21/93	.50	.15	2.50	(4)	1.25	116
b	As "a," black omitted		—					
	Sporting Horses Issue, Perf. 11 x 11.5							
2756	29¢ Steeplechase	05/01/93	.50	.15			1.25	40
2757	29¢ Thoroughbred Racing	05/01/93	.50	.15			1.25	40
2758	29¢ Harness Racing	05/01/93	.50	.15			1.25	40
2759	29¢ Polo	05/01/93	.50	.15			1.25	40
a	Block of 4, #2756-59		2.00	1.75	2.50	(4)	2.75	

CIRCUS

Send in the clowns

Typically, we think of clowns as buffoons who perform physical tricks, pratfalls and slapstick humor. However, clowns have been around since ancient times throughout the world, and not always as comic relief. Clowns have been considered to be sacred or ritual figures who take part in religious ceremonies; for example, clowns would act out to divert demonic attention from a ritual to keep the participants safe. **(#2750)**

Interesting Fact: The first female American circus clown, played by Amelia Butler, appeared in 1858 in a show called Nixon's Great American Circus and Kemp's Mammoth English Circus.

2741 2742 2743 2744 2745 2745a

2746

2747

2748

2749

2750 2751

2754

Dean Acheson
1893-1971
STATESMAN
USA 29

2755

2752 2753 2753a

2756 2757

2758 2759 2759a

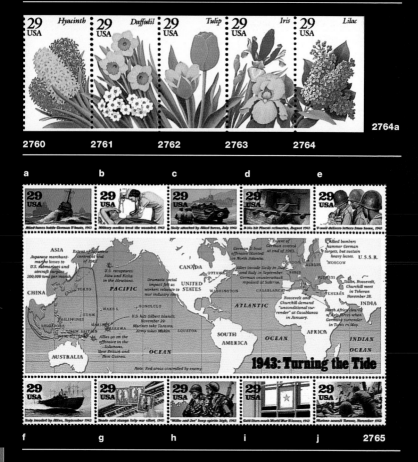

2764a

2760   2761   2762   2763   2764

a   b   c   d   e

1943: Turning the Tide

f   g   h   i   j   2765

2766

2767

2768

2769

2770

2770a

Issues of 1993			Un	U	PB	#	FDC	Q(M̄)
Garden Flowers Issue, Perf. 11 Vertical								
2760	29¢ Hyacinth	05/15/93	.50	.15			1.25	200
2761	29¢ Daffodil	05/15/93	.50	.15			1.25	200
2762	29¢ Tulip	05/15/93	.50	.15			1.25	200
2763	29¢ Iris	05/15/93	.50	.15			1.25	200
2764	29¢ Lilac	05/15/93	.50	.15			1.25	200
a	Booklet pane of 5, #2760-64		2.50	2.00			3.25	
b	As "a," black omitted		400.00					
c	As "a," imperf.		3,000.00					
World War II Issue, 1943: Turning The Tide, Miniature Sheet, Perf. 11								
2765	Sheet of 10 and central label	05/31/93	5.25	4.50			6.50	
a	29¢ Allied Forces Battle German U-boats		.50	.30			1.50	12
b	29¢ Military Medics Treat the Wounded		.50	.30			1.50	12
c	29¢ Sicily Attacked by Allied Forces		.50	.30			1.50	12
d	29¢ B-24s Hit Ploesti Refineries		.50	.30			1.50	12
e	29¢ V-Mail Delivers Letters from Home		.50	.30			1.50	12
f	29¢ Italy Invaded by Allies		.50	.30			1.50	12
g	29¢ Bonds and Stamps Help War Effort		.50	.30			1.50	12
h	29¢ "Willie and Joe" Keep Spirits High		.50	.30			1.50	12
i	29¢ Gold Stars Mark World War II Losses		.50	.30			1.50	12
j	29¢ Marines Assault Tarawa		.50	.30			1.50	12
2766	29¢ Joe Louis	06/22/93	.50	.15	2.50	(4)	1.50	160
Legends of American Music Series, Broadway Musicals Issue, Perf. 11 Horizontal								
2767	29¢ Show Boat	07/14/93	.50	.15			1.25	129
2768	29¢ Porgy & Bess	07/14/93	.50	.15			1.25	129
2769	29¢ Oklahoma!	07/14/93	.50	.15			1.25	129
2770	29¢ My Fair Lady	07/14/93	.50	.15			1.25	129
a	Booklet pane of 4, #2767-70		2.50	2.00			3.25	

Colorful tulip blossoms often signal springtime

The European love affair with the tulip is believed to have started in the mid-16th century when tulip bulbs were brought to Antwerp from Constantinople (now Istanbul). Between 1634 and 1637, what is known as a "tulip mania" took place in Holland where the price and demand for tulip bulbs were outrageously high. The Dutch government eventually took over the tulip-growing industry which it continues to lead today. Tulips are considered one of the most popular gardening flowers because of their beauty and relative ease with which they grow. **(#2762)**

Issues of 1993, Perf. 10			Un	U	PB	#	FDC	Q(M̄)
Legends of American Music Series, Country & Western Issue								
2771	29¢ Hank Williams (2775)	09/25/93	.50	.15			1.25	25
2772	29¢ Patsy Cline (2777)	09/25/93	.50	.15			1.25	25
2773	29¢ The Carter Family (2776)	09/25/93	.50	.15			1.25	25
2774	29¢ Bob Willis (2778)	09/25/93	.50	.15			1.25	25
a	Block or horiz. strip of 4, #2771-74		2.00	1.50	2.00	(4)	2.75	
Booklet Stamps, Perf. 11 Horizontal								
2775	29¢ Hank Williams	09/25/93	.50	.15			1.25	170
2776	29¢ The Carter Family	09/25/93	.50	.15			1.25	170
2777	29¢ Patsy Cline	09/25/93	.50	.15			1.25	170
2778	29¢ Bob Willis	09/25/93	.50	.15			1.25	170
a	Booklet pane of 4, #2775-78		2.50	2.00			2.75	
National Postal Museum Issue, Perf. 11								
2779	Independence Hall, Benjamin Franklin, Printing Press, Colonial Post Rider	07/30/93	.50	.15			1.25	38
2780	Pony Express Rider, Civil War Soldier, Concord Stagecoach	07/30/93	.50	.15			1.25	38
2781	Biplane, Charles Lindbergh, Railway Mail Car, 1931 Model A Ford Mail Truck	07/30/93	.50	.15			1.25	38
2782	California Gold Rush Miner's Letter, Barcode and Circular Date Stamp	07/30/93	.50	.15			1.25	38
a	Block or strip of 4, #2779-82		2.00	1.75	2.00	(4)	2.75	
American Sign Language Issue, Perf. 11.5								
2783	29¢ Recognizing Deafness	09/20/93	.50	.15			1.25	42
2784	29¢ American Sign Language	09/20/93	.50	.15			1.25	42
a	Pair, #2783-84		1.00	.65	2.00	(4)	2.00	
Classic Books Issues, Perf. 11								
2785	29¢ *Rebecca of Sunnybrook Farm*	10/23/93	.50	.15			1.25	38
2786	29¢ *Little House on the Prairie*	10/23/93	.50	.15			1.25	38
2787	29¢ *The Adventures of Huckleberry Finn*	10/23/93	.50	.15			1.25	38
2788	29¢ *Little Women*	10/23/93	.50	.15			1.25	38
a	Block or horiz. strip of 4, #2785-88		2.00	1.75	2.50	(4)	2.75	

Using aviation to change the world

Charles A. Lindbergh (1902-1974) is most famous for being the first aviator to fly nonstop between New York and Paris in 1927. Following the successful flight, Lindbergh went on a three-month tour of the U.S. promoting aviation and visiting 92 cities in 49 states. As famous as the transatlantic flight and follow-up tour made him, Lindbergh had other aeronautical accomplishments that helped him become known as one of the most famous pilots in history. These included another very important "first" just a year before his famous transatlantic flight: transporting mail between Chicago and St. Louis on the first-ever air mail flight. **(#2781)**

Interesting Fact: Twice during his days as an air mail pilot, Lindbergh had to parachute to safety from disabled mail planes.

2771   **2772**

2773   **2774**   **2774a**

2775

2776

2777

2778

2778a

2779   **2780**

2781   **2782**   **2782a**

2783   **2784**   **2784a**

2785   **2786**

2787   **2788**   **2788a**

2789

2791   **2792**

2793   **2794**

2795   **2796**

2797   **2798**

2790

2799   **2800**

2801   **2802**   **2802a**

2803

2804

2805

2806

2806a

	Issues of 1993, Perf. 11		Un	U	PB	#	FDC	Q(M̄)
	Christmas Issue							
2789	29¢ Madonna and Child	10/21/93	.50	.15	2.50	(4)	1.25	500
	Booklet Stamps, Perf. 11.5 x 11 on 2 or 3 sides							
2790	29¢ Madonna and Child (2789)	10/21/93	.50	.15			1.25	500
a	Booklet pane of 4		2.25	1.75			2.00	
	Perf. 11.5							
2791	29¢ Jack-in-the-Box	10/21/93	.50	.15			1.25	250
2792	29¢ Red-Nosed Reindeer	10/21/93	.50	.15			1.25	250
2793	29¢ Snowman	10/21/93	.50	.15			1.25	250
2794	29¢ Toy Soldier	10/21/93	.50	.15			1.25	250
a	Block or strip of 4, #2791-94		2.00	1.75	2.50	(4)	2.75	
	Booklet Stamps, Perf. 11 x 10 on 2 or 3 sides							
2795	29¢ Toy Soldier (2794)	10/21/93	.50	.15			1.25	200
2796	29¢ Snowman (2793)	10/21/93	.50	.15			1.25	200
2797	29¢ Red-Nosed Reindeer (2792)	10/21/93	.50	.15			1.25	200
2798	29¢ Jack-in-the-Box (2791)	10/21/93	.50	.15			1.25	200
a	Booklet pane, 3 each #2795-96, 2 each #2797-98		5.00	4.00			6.50	
b	Booklet pane, 3 each #2797-98, 2 each #2795-96		5.00	—			6.50	
	Self-Adhesive							
2799	29¢ Snowman	10/28/93	.50	.15			1.25	120
2800	29¢ Toy Soldier	10/28/93	.50	.15			1.25	120
2801	29¢ Jack-in-the-Box	10/28/93	.50	.15			1.25	120
2802	29¢ Red-Nosed Reindeer	10/28/93	.50	.15			1.25	120
a	Booklet pane, 3 each #2799-2802		7.00					
2803	29¢ Snowman	10/28/93	.50	.15			1.25	18
a	Booklet pane of 18		10.00					
	Perf. 11							
2804	29¢ Northern Mariana Islands	11/04/93	.50	.15	2.00	(4)	1.25	88
2805	29¢ Columbus Landing in Puerto Rico	11/19/93	.50	.15	2.50	(4)	1.25	105
2806	29¢ AIDS Awareness	12/01/93	.50	.15	2.50	(4)	1.25	100
a	Booklet version		.50	.15			1.25	250
b	Booklet pane of 5		2.50	2.00			3.25	

Examples of #2794a (marginal block of 10 with plate numbers, at left on top);
2802a (self-adhesive pane of 12, at left on bottom); self-adhesive coil
strip of 4 (top right); and 2798a and 2798b, booklet and booklet panes
(bottom right).

	Issues of 1994		Un	U	PB	#	FDC	Q(M)
	Winter Olympic Games Issue, Perf. 11.2							
2807	29¢ Slalom	01/06/94	.50	.15			1.25	36
2808	29¢ Luge	01/06/94	.50	.15			1.25	36
2809	29¢ Ice Dancing	01/06/94	.50	.15			1.25	36
2810	29¢ Cross-Country Skiing	01/06/94	.50	.15			1.25	36
2811	29¢ Ice Hockey	01/06/94	.50	.15			1.25	36
a	Strip of 5, #2807-11		2.50	2.25	5.00	(10)	3.00	36
2812	29¢ Edward R. Murrow	01/21/94	.50	.15	2.50	(4)	1.25	151
2813	29¢ Love Sunrise	01/27/94	.50	.15	6.00	(5)	1.25	358
a	Booklet of 18 (self-adhesive)		11.00					
	Perf. 10.9 x 11.1							
2814	29¢ Love Stamp	02/14/94	.50	.15			1.25	830
a	Booklet pane of 10		5.75	3.50			6.50	
	Perf. 11.1							
2814C	29¢ Love Stamp	06/11/94	.50	.15	2.50	(4)	1.25	300
	Perf. 11.2							
2815	52¢ Love Birds	02/14/94	1.00	.20	5.00	(4)	1.35	175
2816	29¢ Dr. Allison Davis	02/01/94	.50	.15	2.00	(4)	1.25	156
	Lunar New Year Issue							
2817	29¢ Year of the Dog	02/05/94	.50	.15	2.00	(4)	1.75	105
	Perf. 11.5 x 11.2							
2818	29¢ Buffalo Soldiers	04/22/94	.50	.15	2.00	(4)	1.50	186
	Stars of the Silent Screen Issue, Perf. 11.2							
2819	29¢ Rudolph Valentino	04/27/94	.50	.15			1.25	19
2820	29¢ Clara Bow	04/27/94	.50	.15			1.25	19
2821	29¢ Charlie Chaplin	04/27/94	.50	.15			1.25	19
2822	29¢ Lon Chaney	04/27/94	.50	.15			1.25	19
2823	29¢ John Gilbert	04/27/94	.50	.15			1.25	19
2824	29¢ Zasu Pitts	04/27/94	.50	.15			1.25	19
2825	29¢ Harold Lloyd	04/27/94	.50	.15			1.25	19
2826	29¢ Keystone Cops	04/27/94	.50	.15			1.25	19
2827	29¢ Theda Bara	04/27/94	.50	.15			1.25	19
2828	29¢ Buster Keaton	04/27/94	.50	.15			1.25	19
a	Block of 10 #2819-2828		5.00	4.00	5.00	(10)	6.50	19
b	As "a" black (litho.) omitted		—					
c	As "a" black (litho.) and red & brt. vio (engr.) omitted		—					

Customers could purchase this full pane, which contained 2 "miniature sheets" of 20, each containing 2 blocks of #2828a.

2807   2808   2809   2810   2811   2811a

2813   2814   2814C

2812

2815

2816   2817   2818

2819   2820   2821   2822   2823

2824   2825   2826   2827   2828

2828a

2829   2830   2831   2832   2833   2833a

2834   2835   2836

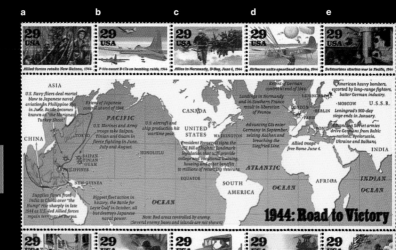

a   b   c   d   e

f   g   h   i   j   2838

Issues of 1994		Un	U	PB	#	FDC	Q(M̄)
Garden Flowers Booklet Issue, Perf. 10.9 Vertical							
2829	29¢ Lily	04/28/94	.50	.15			1.25	166
2830	29¢ Zinnia	04/28/94	.50	.15			1.25	166
2831	29¢ Gladiola	04/28/94	.50	.15			1.25	166
2832	29¢ Marigold	04/28/94	.50	.15			1.25	166
2833	29¢ Rose	04/28/94	.50	.15			1.25	166
a	Booklet pane of 5, #2829-2833		2.50	—			3.25	166
1994 World Cup Soccer Championships Issue, Perf. 11.1							
2834	29¢ Soccer Player	05/26/94	.50	.15	2.00	(4)	1.25	201
2835	40¢ Soccer Player	05/26/94	.80	.20	3.20	(4)	1.25	300
2836	50¢ Soccer Player	05/26/94	1.00	.20	4.00	(4)	1.35	269
2837	Souvenir Sheet of 3, #2834-2836	05/26/94	2.50	—			2.50	60
a	29¢ Soccer Player							
b	40¢ Soccer Player							
c	50¢ Soccer Player							
World War II Issue, 1944: Road to Victory Miniature, Sheet, Perf. 10.9							
2838	Sheet of 10 and central label	06/06/94	5.25	4.50			6.50	12
a	29¢ Allies Retake New Guinea		.50	.30			1.50	12
b	29¢ Bombing Raids		.50	.30			1.50	12
c	29¢ Allies in Normandy, D-Day		.50	.30			1.50	12
d	29¢ Airborne Units		.50	.30			1.50	12
e	29¢ Submarines Shorten War		.50	.30			1.50	12
f	29¢ Allies Free Rome, Paris		.50	.30			1.50	12
g	29¢ Troops Clear Siapan Bunkers		.50	.30			1.50	12
h	29¢ Red Ball Express		.50	.30			1.50	12
i	29¢ Battle for Leyte Gulf		.50	.30			1.50	12
j	29¢ Battle of the Bulge		.50	.30			1.50	12

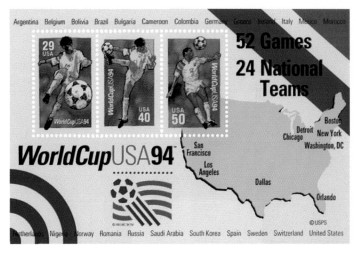

Example of #2837.

	Issues of 1994		Un	U	PB	#	FDC	Q(M̄)
	Norman Rockwell Issue, Perf. 10.9 x 11.1							
2839	29¢ Norman Rockwell	07/01/94	.50	.15	2.50	(4)	1.25	209
2840	Four Freedoms souvenir sheet	07/01/94	4.00	—			3.00	20
a	50¢ Freedom from Want		1.00	.65			1.35	20
b	50¢ Freedom from Fear		1.00	.65			1.35	20
c	50¢ Freedom of Speech		1.00	.65			1.35	20
d	50¢ Freedom of Worship		1.00	.65			1.35	20
	First Moon Landing Issue, Perf. 11.2 x 11.1							
2841	29¢ sheet of 12	07/20/94	7.50	—			6.50	13
a	Single stamp		.60	.60			1.25	155
	Perf. 10.7 x 11.1							
2842	$9.95 Moon Landing	07/20/94	17.50	7.50	70.00	(4)	15.00	101
	Locomotives Issue, Perf. 11 Horizontal							
2843	29¢ Hudson's General	07/28/94	.50	.15			1.25	159
2844	29¢ McQueen's Jupiter	07/28/94	.50	.15			1.25	159
2845	29¢ Eddy's No. 242	07/28/94	.50	.15			1.25	159
2846	29¢ Ely's No. 10	07/28/94	.50	.15			1.25	159
2847	29¢ Buchanan's No. 999	07/28/94	.50	.15			1.25	159
a	Booklet pane of 5, #2843-2847		2.50	2.00			3.25	159
	Perf. 11.1 x 11							
2848	29¢ George Meany	08/16/94	.50	.15	2.50	(4)	1.25	151
	Legends of American Music Series, Popular Singers Issue, Perf. 10.1 x 10.2							
2849	29¢ Al Jolson	09/01/94	.50	.15			1.25	35
2850	29¢ Bing Crosby	09/01/94	.50	.15			1.25	35
2851	29¢ Ethel Waters	09/01/94	.50	.15			1.25	35
2852	29¢ Nat "King" Cole	09/01/94	.50	.15			1.25	35
2853	29¢ Ethel Merman	09/01/94	.50	.15			1.25	35
a	Vert. strip of 5, #2849-2853		2.50	2.00			3.25	

First moon landing captivated television audiences in 1969

Astronaut Neil Armstrong became the first human to step foot on the Moon's surface during the Apollo 11 mission on July 20, 1969, when he and fellow astronaut, Edwin "Buzz" Aldrin, planted the U.S. flag onto the Moon's surface in front of an attentive television audience back home on Earth. This moon landing and return mission was preceded by 10 space flights—all part of the Apollo program which was announced in 1961 and was completed with the Apollo 17 mission in 1972. **(#2841a)**

2839

a b

c d

2840

2841a

2842

2843

2844

2845

2846

2847

2847a

2848

2849

2850

2851

2852

2853

2853a

1994

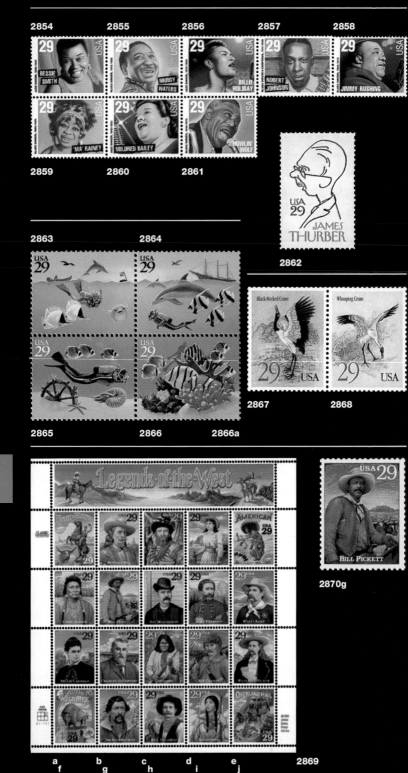

	Issues of 1994		Un	U	PB	#	FDC	Q(M̄)
	Legends of American Music Series, Jazz and Blues Singers Issue, Perf. 11 x 10.8							
2854	29¢ Bessie Smith	09/17/94	.50	.15			1.25	25
2855	29¢ Muddy Waters	09/17/94	.50	.15			1.25	25
2856	29¢ Billie Holiday	09/17/94	.50	.15			1.25	25
2857	29¢ Robert Johnson	09/17/94	.50	.15			1.25	20
2858	29¢ Jimmy Rushing	09/17/94	.50	.15			1.25	20
2859	29¢ "Ma" Rainey	09/17/94	.50	.15			1.25	20
2860	29¢ Mildred Bailey	09/17/94	.50	.15			1.25	20
2861	29¢ Howlin' Wolf	09/17/94	.50	.15			1.25	20
a	Block of 9, #2854-2861 + 1 additional stamp		4.50	3.50	5.00	(10)	6.00	
	Literary Arts Issue, James Thurber, Perf. 11							
2862	29¢ James Thurber	09/10/94	.50	.15	2.50	(4)	1.25	151
	Wonders of the Sea Issue, Perf. 11 x 10.9							
2863	29¢ Diver, Motorboat	10/03/94	.50	.15			1.25	56
2864	29¢ Diver, Ship	10/03/94	.50	.15			1.25	56
2865	29¢ Diver, Ship's Wheel	10/03/94	.50	.15			1.25	56
2866	29¢ Diver, Coral	10/03/94	.50	.15			1.25	56
a	Block of 4, #2963-2966		2.00	1.50	2.00	(4)	2.75	56
b	As "a" imperf.		2,500.00					
	Cranes Issue, Perf. 10.8 x 11							
2867	29¢ Black-Necked Crane	10/09/94	.50	.15			1.25	78
2868	29¢ Whooping Crane	10/09/94	.50	.15			1.25	78
a	Pair, #2867-2868		1.00	.65	2.00	(4)	2.00	78
b	Black and magenta (engr.) omitted		—					
	Legends of the West Issue, Perf. 10.1 x 10							
2869	Sheet of 20	10/18/94	12.00	—			13.00	20
a	29¢ Home on the Range		.60	.15			1.50	20
b	29¢ Buffalo Bill Cody		.60	.15			1.50	20
c	29¢ Jim Bridger		.60	.15			1.50	20
d	29¢ Annie Oakley		.60	.15			1.50	20
e	29¢ Native American Culture		.60	.15			1.50	20
f	29¢ Chief Joseph		.60	.15			1.50	20
g	29¢ Bill Pickett		.60	.15			1.50	20
h	29¢ Bat Masterson		.60	.15			1.50	20
i	29¢ John C. Fremont		.60	.15			1.50	20
j	29¢ Wyatt Earp		.60	.15			1.50	20
k	29¢ Nellie Cashman		.60	.15			1.50	20
l	29¢ Charles Goodnight		.60	.15			1.50	20
m	29¢ Geronimo		.60	.15			1.50	20
n	29¢ Kit Carson		.60	.15			1.50	20
o	29¢ Wild Bill Hickok		.60	.15			1.50	20
p	29¢ Western Wildlife		.60	.15			1.50	20
q	29¢ Jim Beckwourth		.60	.15			1.50	20
r	29¢ Bill Tilghman		.60	.15			1.50	20
s	29¢ Sacagawea		.60	.15			1.50	20
t	29¢ Overland Mail		.60	.15			1.50	20
2870	29¢ Sheet of 20 (recalled)	10/18/94	160.00	—				0.1

	Issues of 1994		Un	U	PB	#	FDC	Q(M̄)
	Christmas Issue, Perf. 11.1							
2871	29¢ Madonna and Child	10/20/94	.50	.15	2.50	(4)	1.25	
a	Perf. 9.8 x 10.8		.50	.15			1.25	
b	As "a," booklet pane of 10		5.25	3.50				50
c	As "a," Imperf.		—					
2872	29¢ Stocking	10/20/94	.50	.15	2.50	(4)	1.25	603
a	Booklet pane of 20		10.50	3.00				30
	Self-Adhesive							
2873	29¢ Santa Claus	10/20/94	.50	.15	6.00	(5)	1.25	240
a	Booklet pane of 12		6.25					20
2874	29¢ Cardinal in Snow	10/20/94	.50	.15			1.25	36
a	Booklet pane of 18		9.50					2
	Bureau of Engraving and Printing Issue, Perf.11							
2875	$2.00 Sheet of 4	11/03/94	15.00	—			12.00	5
a	Single stamp		3.00	1.25				20
	Lunar New Year Issue, Perf. 11.2 x 11.1							
2876	29¢ Year of the Boar	12/30/94	.50	.15	2.00	(4)	1.25	80
	Untagged, Perf. 11 x 10.8							
2877	(4¢) Dove Make-Up Rate	12/13/94	.15	.15	.30	(4)	1.25	
	Perf. 10.8 x 10.9							
2878	(4¢) Dove Make-Up Rate	12/13/94	.15	.15	.30	(4)	1.25	
	Tagged, Perf. 11.2 x 11.1							
2879	(20¢) Old Glory Postcard Rate	12/13/94	.40	.15	2.00	(4)	1.25	
	Perf. 11 x 10.9							
2880	(20¢) Old Glory Postcard Rate	12/13/94	.40	.15	2.00	(4)	1.25	
	Perf. 11.2 x 11.1							
2881	(32¢) "G" Old Glory	12/13/94	.60	.15	5.00	(4)	1.25	
a	Booklet pane of 10		6.00	—			7.50	
	Perf. 11 x 10.9							
2882	(32¢) "G" Old Glory	12/13/94	.60	.15	3.00	(4)	1.25	
	Booklet Stamps, Perf. 10 x 9.9 on 2 or 3 sides							
2883	(32¢) "G" Old Glory	12/13/94	.60	.15			1.25	
a	Booklet pane of 10		6.50	—			7.50	
	Perf. 10.9							
2884	(32¢) "G" Old Glory	12/13/94	.60	.15			1.25	
a	Booklet pane of 10		6.00	—			7.50	
	Perf. 11 x 10.9							
2885	(32¢) "G" Old Glory	12/13/94	.60	.15			1.25	
a	Booklet pane of 10		6.00	—			7.50	
	Self-Adhesive, Die Cut							
2886	(32¢) "G" Old Glory	12/13/94	.60	.15	5.75	(5)	1.25	
a	Booklet pane of 18		11.00					
2887	(32¢) "G" Old Glory	12/13/94	.60	.15			1.25	
a	Booklet pane of 18		11.00					
	Coil Stamps, Perf. 9.8 Vertical							
2888	(25¢) Old Glory First-Class Presort	12/13/94	.50	.15	5.50	(5)	1.25	
2889	(32¢) Black "G"	12/13/94	.60	.15	5.50	(5)	1.25	
2890	(32¢) Blue "G"	12/13/94	.60	.15	5.75	(5)	1.25	
2891	(32¢) Red "G"	12/13/94	.60	.15	5.75	(5)	1.25	
	Rouletted							
2892	(32¢) Red "G"	12/13/94	.60	.15	5.75	(5)	1.25	
	Issue of 1995, Perf. 9.8 Vertical							
2893	(5¢) Green	01/12/95	.15	.15				

2871

2873

2875

2872

2874

2876

2877

2878

2879

2880

2881

2882

2883

2884

2885

2886

2887

2888

2889

2890

2891

2892

2893

For details and illustrations of the new 1998 issues, see pages 20-43.

2897

2902

2903

2904

2905

2906

2907

2908

2909

2910

2911

2912

2913

2914

2915

2916

2919

2920

2921

2933

2934

2938

2940

2943

2948

2949

	Issues of 1995-97, Perf. 10.4		Un	U	PB	#	FDC	Q(M)
2897	32¢ Flag Over Porch	05/19/95	.60	.15	3.00	(4)	1.25	
	Coil Stamps, Perf. 9.8 Vertically							
2902	(5¢) Butte	03/10/95	.15	.15	1.50	(3)	1.25	
a	Imperf. pair		750.00					
2902B	Serpentine die-cut 11.5	06/15/96	.15	.15	1.50	(3)	1.25	550
2903	(5¢) Mountain, purple and multi	03/16/96	.20	.20	1.50	(3)	1.25	150
2904	(5¢) Mountain, blue and multi	03/16/96	.20	.20	1.50	(3)	1.25	150
2904A	Serpentine die-cut 11.2, self-adhesive	06/15/96	.20	.20	1.50	(3)	1.25	
2904B	Serpentine die-cut 9.8 vertical, self-adhesive	01/24/97	.20	.20	1.35	(3)	1.25	148
2905	(10¢) Automobile	03/10/95	.20	.20	2.25	(3)	1.25	
2906	(10¢) Automobile	06/15/96	.20	.20	2.25	(3)	1.25	450
2907	(10¢) Eagle and Shield	05/21/96	.20	.20	3.00	(3)	1.25	450
2908	(15¢) Auto Tail Fin, bureau printing	03/17/95	.30	.30	2.75	(3)	1.25	
2909	(15¢) Auto Tail Fin, private printing	03/17/95	.30	.30	2.75	(3)	1.25	
2910	(15¢) Auto Tail Fin	06/15/96	.30	.30	3.00	(3)	1.25	450
2911	(25¢) Juke Box, bureau printing	03/17/95	.50	.50	4.25	(3)	1.25	
2912	(25¢) Juke Box, private printing	03/17/95	.50	.50	4.25	(3)	1.25	
2912A	Serpentine die-cut 11.5	06/15/96	.50	.50				550
2912B	Serpentine die-cut 9.8 vertical, self-adhesive	01/24/97	.50	.50			1.25	200
	Perf. 9.9 Vertically							
2913	32¢ Flag Over Porch	05/19/95	.60	.15	5.00	(3)	1.25	
a	Imperf. pair		75.00					
2914	32¢ Flag Over Porch	05/19/95	.60	.15	4.75	(3)	1.25	
	Self-Adhesive, Serpentine Die-Cut Vertically							
2915	32¢ Flag Over Porch	04/18/95	.60	.30	4.75	(3)	1.25	
2915D	Serpentine die-cut 9.8 vertical, self-adhesive	01/24/97	.60	.15	4.00	(3)		300
	Booklet Stamps, Perf. 10.8 x 9.8							
2916	32¢ Flag Over Porch	05/19/95	.60	.15			1.25	
a	Booklet pane of 10		6.00				7.50	
b	As "a," imperf.		—					
	Self-Adhesive, Die-Cut							
2919	32¢ Flag Over Field	03/17/95	.60	.15			1.25	
a	Booklet pane of 18		11.00					
	Self-Adhesive, Serpentine Die-Cut 8.8							
2920	32¢ Flag Over Porch	04/18/95	.60	.15			1.25	
a	Booklet pane of 20 + label		12.00					
b	Small date		1.50	.15				
c	As "b," booklet pane of 20 + label		30.00					
d	Serpentine die-cut 11.3	01/20/96	.60	.15				789
	Coil Stamps, Serpentine Die-Cut Perf. 9.8 on 2 or 3 sides							
2921	32¢ Flag Over Porch	05/21/96	.60	.15			1.25	7,344
a	Booklet pane of 10		6.00					
	Great Americans Issue, Perf. 11.1							
2933	32¢ Milton S. Hershey	09/13/95	.60	.15	3.00	(4)	1.25	
2934	32¢ Cal Farley	04/26/96	.60	.15	3.00	(4)	1.25	150
2938	46¢ Ruth Benedict	10/20/95	.90	.15	4.50	(4)	1.35	
2940	55¢ Alice Hamilton, MD	07/11/95	1.10	.20	5.50	(4)	1.35	
2943	78¢ Alice Paul	08/18/95	1.60	.20	8.00	(4)	1.50	

	Issues of 1995, Perf. 11.2		Un	U	PB	#	FDC
	Love Issue, Perf. 11.2						
2948	32¢ Love, Cherub from Sistine Madonna, by Raphael	02/01/95	.60	.15	3.00	(4)	1.25
	Self-Adhesive, Die-Cut						
2949	32¢ Love, Cherub from Sistine Madonna, by Raphael	02/01/95	.60	.15			1.25
a	Booklet pane of 20 + label		12.00				
b	As "a," red (engr.) omitted		1,000.00				
	Perf. 11.1						
2950	32¢ Florida Statehood, 150th Anniversary	03/03/95	.60	.15	2.40	(4)	1.25
	Kids Care Earth Day Issue						
2951	32¢ Earth Clean-Up	04/20/95	.60	.15			1.25
2952	32¢ Solar Energy	04/20/95	.60	.15			1.25
2953	32¢ Tree Planting	04/20/95	.60	.15			1.25
2954	32¢ Beach Clean-Up	04/20/95	.60	.15			1.25
a	Block of 4, #2951-54		2.40	1.75	2.40	(4)	2.75
	Perf. 11.2						
2955	32¢ Richard Nixon	04/26/95	.60	.15	3.00	(4)	1.25
	Black Heritage Issue, Bessie Coleman						
2956	32¢ Bessie Coleman	04/27/95	.60	.15	3.00	(4)	1.25
	Love Issue						
2957	32¢ Love, Cherub from Sistine Madonna, by Raphael	05/12/95	.60	.15	3.00	(4)	1.25
2958	55¢ Love, Cherub from Sistine Madonna, by Raphael	05/12/95	1.10	.15	5.50	(4)	1.35
	Booklet Stamps, Perf. 9.8 x 10.8						
2959	32¢ Love, Cherub from Sistine Madonna, by Raphael	05/12/95	.60	.15			1.25
a	Booklet pane of 10		6.00				7.50
	Self-Adhesive, Die-Cut						
2960	55¢ Love, Cherub from Sistine Madonna, by Raphael	05/12/95	1.10	.15			1.35
a	Booklet pane of 20 + label		22.50				
	Recreational Sports Issue, Perf. 11.2						
2961	32¢ Volleyball	05/20/95	.60	.15			1.50
2962	32¢ Softball	05/20/95	.60	.15			1.50
2963	32¢ Bowling	05/20/95	.60	.15			1.50
2964	32¢ Tennis	05/20/95	.60	.15			1.50
2965	32¢ Golf	05/20/95	.60	.15			1.50
a	Vertical strip of 5, #2961-65		3.00	2.00	6.00	(10)	3.25
2966	32¢ Prisoners of War and Missing in Action	05/29/95	.60	.15	2.40	(4)	1.50
	Pane of 20		12.00	—			

Minimum value listed for a stamp is
15 cents; for a First Day Cover (FDC),
$1.00. This minimum represents a
fair-market price for having a dealer
locate and provide a single stamp or
cover from his or her stock. Dealers
may charge less per stamp or cover
for a group of such stamps or covers,
or less for a single stamp or cover.

2948

2949

2950

2951   2952

2954a

2953   2954

2961

2962

2963

2964

2955

2956

2965

2957

2958

2965a

2959

2960

2966

LEGENDS of HOLLYWOOD

Few other actresses personified the phrase "Hollywood movie star" as did Marilyn Monroe (1926-1962). Classically beautiful, Marilyn set the motion picture standard for glamour and sensuality in film favorites such as *Some Like It Hot, Gentlemen Prefer Blondes, Bus Stop,* and *The Seven Year Itch.*

2967a

2967

2968

2969   **2970**   **2971**   **2972**   **2973** **2973a**

Issues of 1995, Perf. 11.1		Un	U	PB	#	FDC
Legends of Hollywood Issue, Marilyn Monroe						
2967	32¢ Marilyn Monroe 06/01/95	.60	.15	2.40	(4)	1.50
a	Imperf., pair	600.00				
	Perf. 11.2					
2968	32¢ Texas Statehood 06/16/95	.60	.15	2.40	(4)	1.25
	Great Lakes Lighthouses Issue, Perf. 11.2 Vertically					
2969	32¢ Split Rock, Lake Superior 06/17/95	.60	.15			1.25
2970	32¢ St. Joseph, Lake Michigan 06/17/95	.60	.15			1.25
2971	32¢ Spectacle Reef, Lake Huron 06/17/95	.60	.15			1.25
2972	32¢ Marblehead, Lake Erie 06/17/95	.60	.15			1.25
2973	32¢ Thirty Mile Point,1.25 Lake Ontario 06/17/95	.60	.15			1.25
a	Booklet pane of 5, #2969-73	3.00	2.25			4.00

30-Mile Point Lighthouse found near the mouth of the Niagara River

This beautiful Lake Ontario lighthouse takes its name from its location, 30 miles east of the mouth of the Niagara River. Although decommissioned in the late 1950s, 30-Mile Point Lighthouse vigilantly warned vessels of nearby shoals and sandbars for more than 75 years with a beacon that could be seen 18 miles offshore. Today, its quaint keeper's dwelling, with 12-paned windows and peaked gables supported by decorative arches, holds a museum; the room that once housed its foghorn has been converted for recreational use; and its four-story tower offers a spectacular view of Lake Ontario and Gold Hill State Park, of which it is a part. **(#2973)**

Interesting Fact: Ten years after it was built in 1875, this became one of the first lighthouses ever to receive an electric lightbulb produced by Thomas Edison.

Issues of 1995, Perf. 11.2		Un	U	PB	#	FDC
2974	32¢ United Nations, 50th Anniversary					
	06/26/95	.60	.15	2.40	(4)	1.25
Civil War Issue, Perf. 10.1						
2975	Sheet of 20	06/29/95	12.00	—		13.00
a	32¢ *Monitor* and *Virginia*		.60	.15		1.50
b	32¢ Robert E. Lee		.60	.15		1.50
c	32¢ Clara Barton		.60	.15		1.50
d	32¢ Ulysses S. Grant		.60	.15		1.50
e	32¢ Battle of Shiloh		.60	.15		1.50
f	32¢ Jefferson Davis		.60	.15		1.50
g	32¢ David Farragut		.60	.15		1.50
h	32¢ Frederick Douglass		.60	.15		1.50
i	32¢ Raphael Semmes		.60	.15		1.50
j	32¢ Abraham Lincoln		.60	.15		1.50
k	32¢ Harriet Tubman		.60	.15		1.50
l	32¢ Stand Watie		.60	.15		1.50
m	32¢ Joseph E. Johnston		.60	.15		1.50
n	32¢ Winfield Hancock		.60	.15		1.50
o	32¢ Mary Chesnut		.60	.15		1.50
p	32¢ Battle of Chancellorsville		.60	.15		1.50
q	32¢ William T. Sherman		.60	.15		1.50
r	32¢ Phoebe Pember		.60	.15		1.50
s	32¢ "Stonewall" Jackson		.60	.15		1.50
t	32¢ Battle of Gettysburg		.60	.15		1.50

To receive your own souvenir edition, hardcover *Civil War* tabletop book featuring exciting stories, colorful illustrations and two full panes of these stamps, please call 1-800-STAMP24 or send $29.95 plus $4.20 for shipping and handling to:

Civil War Book Offer, U.S. Postal Service, Post Office Box 419219, Kansas City, MO 64141-6219

Please allow six weeks for delivery.

Offer expires July 1, 1996, or while supplies last. Offer valid only for orders delivered in the United States.

Shiloh
April 6-7, 1862

Confederates surprised Grant at Pittsburg Landing, TN, but lost General A.S. Johnston. Union counterattack at Shiloh Church forced Southerners to withdraw. Casualties: 13,050 Union, 10,700 Confederate.

Union Lt. General Ulysses S. Grant
1822-1885

Gained national fame with "unconditional surrender" victory at Fort Donelson. Crafted brilliant wins at Vicksburg, Chattanooga. Forced Lee's surrender. U.S. President 1869-77.

Union Nurse Clara Harlowe Barton
1821-1912

"Angel of the Battlefield" nursed the wounded at Antietam and at Virginia battlefields. Helped identify and mark graves at Andersonville prison. Founded American Red Cross.

Confederate General Robert Edward Lee
1807-1870

Army of Northern Virginia Commander. 1862-65. Won Seven Days' Campaign. 2nd Manassas, Chancellorsville. Repelled at Gettysburg. Surrendered April 9, 1865. Became college president.

Monitor & Virginia (Merrimack)
March 9, 1862

In the first clash of the ironclads, U.S.S. Monitor and C.S.S. Virginia battled to a stalemate, preserving U.S. blockade at Hampton Roads, VA. Virginia burned in May. Hatteras gale sank Monitor.

16th U.S. President Abraham Lincoln
1809-1865

Illinois "Rail-Splitter" pursued war vigorously to restore the Union "of . . . by . . . for the people." Urged "malice toward none." Assassinated five days after Lee's surrender.

Confederate Rear Admiral Raphael Semmes
1809-1877

Audacious commander of C.S.S. Sumter and Alabama plagued Union shipping, capturing or destroying more than 90 vessels. Professor, editor, lawyer. Wrote books of exploits.

Journalist-Orator Frederick Douglass
c1818-1895

"Wielding . . . pen . . . voice," ex-slave campaigned for rights for Blacks, women. Assisted runaways to Canada. Helped recruit Blacks for 54th Massachusetts Regiment. U.S. Minister to Haiti.

Union Vice Admiral David Glasgow Farragut
1801-1870

A midshipman at age 9. Electrified the North with daring naval assault to capture New Orleans. Yelled "Damn the torpedoes! Full speed ahead!" during the attack at Mobile Bay.

President of the Confederacy Jefferson Finis Davis
1808-1889

Ex-U.S. Senator from Mississippi, named provisional CSA head Feb 1861. Quarreled with military about war tactics and strategy but supported Lee. Captured May 1865 in GA, imprisoned two years.

Confederate Diarist Mary Boykin Miller Chesnut
1823-1886

Astute, articulate hostess. Wife of aide to Jefferson Davis. Wrote of daily life, events amid South's officialdom. Her plain-spoken journal published posthumously, sparkles with wit and irony.

Union Major General Winfield Scott Hancock
1824-1886

Brigade, Division, Corps Commander at Fredericksburg, Chancellorsville. Played major role in Union victory at Gettysburg, but was severely wounded. Presidential candidate 1880.

Confederate General Joseph Eggleston Johnston
1807-1891

Commander CSA forces Northern Virginia 1861-62. Wounded at Seven Pines. Master defensive strategist, bickered often with Davis. Led Army of Tennessee. Dalton to Atlanta.

Confederate Brig. General Stand Watie (De-ga-do-ga)
1806-1871

Known for guerrilla tactics tying down Union troops. Sole CSA Indian General raised Cherokee regiment, fought at Pea Ridge, captured federal steamboat. Last CSA General to surrender.

Abolitionist Harriet Ross Tubman
c1821-1913

Fugitive slave who fled to freedom. As "Moses of her people," led over 200 Blacks north via Underground Railroad. Served Union Army as cook, spy and scout.

Gettysburg
July 1-3, 1863

Lee invaded North 2nd time. Encounter led to carnage as Union Gen. George Meade elected "to stay and fight," repelling Pickett's Charge. Casualties: 23,050 Union, 28,075 Confederate.

Confederate Lt. General Thomas Jonathan Jackson
1824-1863

Nicknamed "Stonewall" at First Manassas. Brilliant tactician in Shenandoah Valley Campaign. Fatally wounded by own men after routing Union right flank at Chancellorsville.

Confederate Nurse Phoebe Yates Levy Pember
1823-1913

Directed care and dietary needs of over 10,000 soldiers at Richmond's Chimborazo, one of CSA's largest hospitals. Specialty: chicken soup. Criticized poor care in her A Southern Woman's Story.

Union Major General William Tecumseh Sherman
1820-1891

Blunt, grizzled strategist distinguished himself at Shiloh and Vicksburg. Captured Atlanta. Introduced total warfare in his March across GA and through the Carolinas. Negotiated lenient peace.

Chancellorsville
May 1-6, 1863

Greatly outnumbered, Lee boldly split forces, routed Hooker's Union army. Mortal wounding of Stonewall Jackson overshadowed Rebel victory. Casualties: 17,300 Union, 12,800 Confederate.

Gum side (back) of Civil War sheet

2974

a   b   c   d   e   **2975**
f   g   h   i   j
k   l   m   n   o
p   q   r   s   t

*Most stamps remain on sale from the U.S. Postal Service at least one year from date of issue, especially by mail order. Ask for them at your local post office, or request a free copy of the Stamps etc. mail-order catalog. To receive a catalog, call toll-free: **1-800-STAMP24.***

2976   2977

2980

2979a

2978   2979

a   b   c   d   e

1945: Victory at Last

Issues of 1995, Perf. 11		Un	U	PB	#	FDC
Carousel Horse Issue						
2976 32¢ Golden Horse with Roses	07/21/95	.60	.15			1.25
2977 32¢ Black Horse with Gold Bridle	07/21/95	.60	.15			1.25
2978 32¢ Horse with Armor	07/21/95	.60	.15			1.25
2979 32¢ Brown Horse with Green Bridle	07/21/95	.60	.15			1.25
a Block of 4, #2976-79		2.40	1.75	2.40	(4)	3.25
Perf. 11.1 x 11						
2980 32¢ Women's Suffrage	08/26/95	.60	.15	3.00	(4)	1.25
a Black (engr.) omitted		600.00				
World War II Issue, 1945: Victory at Last, Miniature Sheet , Perf. 11.1						
2981 Block of 10 and central label	09/02/95	6.00	4.50			6.50
a 32¢ Marines Raise Flag on Iwo Jima		.60	.30			1.25
b 32¢ Fierce Fighting Frees Manila by March 3, 1945		.60	.30			1.25
c 32¢ Soldiers Advancing: Okinawa, the Last Big Battle		.60	.30			1.25
d 32¢ Destroyed Bridge: U.S. and Soviets Link Up at Elbe River		.60	.30			1.25
e 32¢ Allies Liberate Holocaust Survivors		.60	.30			1.25
f 32¢ Germany Surrenders at Reims		.60	.30			1.25
g 32¢ Refugees: By 1945, World War II Has Uprooted Millions	1.25	.60	.30			1.25
h 32¢ Truman Announces Japan's Surrender		.60	.30			1.25
i 32¢ Sailor Kissing Nurse: News of Victory Hits Home	1.25	.60	.30			1.25
j 32¢ Hometowns Honor Their Returning Veterans		.60	.30			1.25

Who's that girl?

This popular stamp reproduces a photograph of a sailor kissing a nurse in New York City's Times Square on V-J Day, August 15, 1945, in celebration of the end of World War II. The photo of the nameless couple taken by Alfred Eisenstaedt (1898-1995) is his most famous even though he photographed celebrities like Sophia Loren and Marilyn Monroe. In 1980, a woman came forward claiming to be the nurse in the picture, and LIFE magazine ran an article about her and asked that the sailor in the photo identify himself. Twelve sailors and two more nurses have stepped forward to claim this particular place in history. However, only Eisenstaedt ever knew who he really shot for the photo, and his notes have vanished. **(#2981i)**

Interesting Fact: The first nurse and one of the sailors who came forward were brought together 50 years after the kiss, in 1995, for photography sessions and a spot on a late night talk show.

Issues of 1995, Perf. 11.1 x 11		Un	U	PB	#	FDC	Q(M̄)
	Legends of American Music Series						
2982	32¢ Louis Armstrong, white denomination 09/01/95	.60	.15	2.40	(4)	1.25	
2983	32¢ Coleman Hawkins 09/16/95	.60	.15			1.25	
2984	32¢ Louis Armstrong, black denomination 09/16/95	.60	.15			1.25	
2985	32¢ James W. Johnson 09/16/95	.60	.15			1.25	
2986	32¢ Jelly Roll Morton 09/16/95	.60	.15			1.25	
2987	32¢ Charlie Parker 09/16/95	.60	.15			1.25	
2988	32¢ Eubie Blake 09/16/95	.60	.15			1.25	
2989	32¢ Charles Mingus 09/16/95	.60	.15			1.25	
2990	32¢ Thelonious Monk 09/16/95	.60	.15			1.25	
2991	32¢ John Coltrane 09/16/95	.60	.15			1.25	
2992	32¢ Erroll Garner 09/16/95	.60	.15			1.25	
a	Vertical block of 10, #2983-92	6.00	—	6.00	(10)	6.50	
	Pane of 20	12.00	—				
	Garden Flowers Issue, Perf. 10.9 Vertically						
2993	32¢ Aster 09/19/95	.60	.15			1.25	800
2994	32¢ Chrysanthemum 09/19/95	.60	.15			1.25	800
2995	32¢ Dahlia 09/19/95	.60	.15			1.25	800
2996	32¢ Hydrangea 09/19/95	.60	.15			1.25	800
2997	32¢ Rudbeckia 09/19/95	.60	.15			1.25	800
a	Booklet pane of 5, #2993-97	3.00	2.25			4.00	
	Perf. 11.1						
2998	60¢ Eddie Rickenbacker, Aviator 09/25/95	1.25	.25	6.25	(4)	1.50	
2999	32¢ Republic of Palau 09/29/95	.60	.15	3.00	(4)	1.25	

Amateur gardeners will appreciate Rudbeckia's easy temperament

The Rudbeckia family of flowers found in North America consists of black-eyed susans, gloriosa daisies, golden glows and coneflowers. Because they grow well in ordinary or rich soil and in the sun or partial shade, Rudbeckia flowers are popular with gardeners. Their long blooming season often extends into the fall, making their bright blossoms blend well with the colorful changing tree leaves around them. **(#2997)**

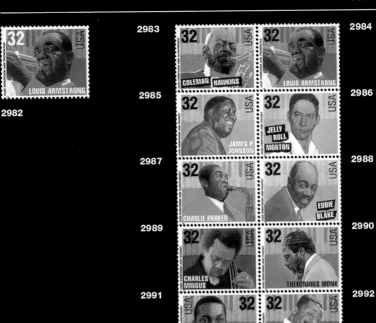

2982

2983
2984
2985
2986
2987
2988
2989
2990
2991
2992

2992a

2993 2994 2995 2996 2997 2997a

2998

2999

a   b   c   d   3000
e   f   g   h
i   j   k   l
m   n   o   p
q   r   s   t

3001

3002

Issues of 1995, Perf. 10.1		Un	U	PB	#	FDC
Comic Strip Classics Issue						
3000 Pane of 20	10/01/95	12.00	—			13.00
a 32¢ The Yellow Kid		.60	.15			1.25
b 32¢ Katzenjammer Kids		.60	.15			1.25
c 32¢ Little Nemo in Slumberland		.60	.15			1.25
d 32¢ Bringing Up Father		.60	.15			1.25
e 32¢ Krazy Kat		.60	.15			1.25
f 32¢ Rube Goldberg's Inventions		.60	.15			1.25
g 32¢ Toonerville Folks		.60	.15			1.25
h 32¢ Gasoline Alley		.60	.15			1.25
i 32¢ Barney Google		.60	.15			1.25
j 32¢ Little Orphan Annie		.60	.15			1.25
k 32¢ Popeye		.60	.15			1.25
l 32¢ Blondie		.60	.15			1.25
m 32¢ Dick Tracy		.60	.15			1.25
n 32¢ Alley Oop		.60	.15			1.25
o 32¢ Nancy		.60	.15			1.25
p 32¢ Flash Gordon		.60	.15			1.25
q 32¢ Li'l Abner		.60	.15			1.25
r 32¢ Terry and the Pirates		.60	.15			1.25
s 32¢ Prince Valiant		.60	.15			1.25
t 32¢ Brenda Starr, Reporter		.60	.15			1.25
Perf 10.9						
3001 32¢ U.S. Naval Academy, 150th Anniversary	10/10/95	.60	.15	2.40	(4)	1.25
Literary Arts Issue, Tennessee Williams, Perf 11.1						
3002 32¢ Tennessee Williams	10/13/95	.60	.15	2.40	(4)	1.25

To receive your own souvenir edition of the hardcover *American Comic Strip Classics* tabletop book featuring exciting stories, colorful illustrations, and two full sheets of these stamps, please call 1-800-STAMP 24 or send $29.95 plus $4.20 for shipping and handling to:

Comic Strips Book Offer
US Postal Service
Post Office Box 419219
Kansas City MO 64141-6219

Please allow six weeks for delivery. Offer expires October 1, 1996, or while supplies last. Offer valid only for orders delivered in the United States.

BRINGING UP FATHER
George McManus (1884-1954)
Also known as *Maggie & Jiggs*, this was the story of a *nouveau riche* Irish immigrant and his social-climbing wife Jiggs' habit of escaping from Maggie's fancy parties to eat corned beef and cabbage popularized this dish.
The strip began in 1913.
© 1995 King Features Syndicate, Inc.

LITTLE NEMO IN SLUMBERLAND
Winsor McCay (c.1867-1934)
Little Nemo was the first strip to be drawn realistically and to utilize quality color printing. Nemo's daydreams and nightmares were fantasies with dragons and monsters, travels to Mars, and slums that turned into gardens.
The strip ran 1905-11, 1924-27.

THE KATZENJAMMER KIDS
Rudolph Dirks (1877-1968)
The oldest comic strip still being produced, this comic stars the mischievous antics of Hans and Fritz. *The Katzenjammer Kids* was one of the first comics to use regular characters, sequential drawings, and cartoon symbols.
The strip started in 1897.
© 1995 King Features Syndicate, Inc.

THE YELLOW KID
R. F. Outcault (1863-1928)
The first popular newspaper color cartoon was *Hogan's Alley* starring the Yellow Kid. The tenement exploits of the Irish immigrant kid ignited public affection, when two New York papers fought over rival versions. "Yellow Journalism" was born.
The cartoon ran 1895-1898.

GASOLINE ALLEY
Frank King (1883-1969)
It began as a panel about men's interest in autos, but *Gasoline Alley* evolved to become a strip about the life and growth of average Americans. It was the first major strip where characters grew up in real time.
The strip began in 1919.
© Tribune Media Services, Inc.

TOONERVILLE FOLKS
Fontaine Fox (1884-1964)
"The Toonerville Trolley That Meets All Trains" began its run as a part of the colorful landscape of Toonerville in Fox's panel cartoons around 1910. The Skipper and his out-of-control car inspired toys, games, and movies.
The panel ran 1910-1955.

RUBE GOLDBERG'S INVENTIONS
Rube Goldberg (1883-1970)
Rube Goldberg was a cartoonist with an engineering degree. This combination led him to create a series of crazy inventions — in this case an automatic napkin — that amused readers for decades.
The panel ran 1914-1964.
© Rube Goldberg, Inc.

KRAZY KAT
George Herriman (1880-1944)
Krazy Kat was a surrealistic comic strip with changing backgrounds, poetic dialog, and strange props. While not widely popular in its own day, it's now generally considered to be a high mark of the art form.
The strip ran 1913-1944.
© 1995 King Features Syndicate, Inc.

BLONDIE
Chic Young (1901-1973)
Young once said that he found the magic formula for creating a comic strip with which millions could identify — he simply restricted his premises to: eating, sleeping, going to work, and raising a family.
The strip began in 1930.
© 1995 King Features Syndicate, Inc.

POPEYE
E. C. Segar (1894-1938)
Popeye was an overnight success when he made his debut on the stage of the *Thimble Theatre* comic strip in 1929. His adventures mixed thrills, satire, parody, and nonsense; his sayings ("I yam what I yam...") are part of our language.
The strip began in 1919.
© 1995 King Features Syndicate, Inc.

LITTLE ORPHAN ANNIE
Harold Gray (1894-1968)
During the Great Depression, Annie was as responsible as anyone for keeping up the nation's spirits. Gray's mounting tales of perseverance, independence, and courage helped make newspaper comics indispensable.
The strip began in 1924.
© Tribune Media Services, Inc.

BARNEY GOOGLE
Billy DeBeck (1890-1942)
The schemer Barney Google (with the goo-goo-googly eyes) as the popular song went) was the most prominent player in a marvelous parade of character types. Late the strip became a hillbilly saga starring Snuffy Smith.
The strip began in 1919.
© 1995 King Features Syndicate, Inc.

FLASH GORDON
Alex Raymond (1909-1956)
Cartoonist Alex Raymond steered the Sunday funnies toward Romanticism with exotic locales, memorable villains, and breathless action in this science-fiction classic.
The strip began in 1934.
© 1995 King Features Syndicate, Inc.

NANCY
Ernie Bushmiller (1905-1982)
Many of his fellow cartoonists admired Bushmiller for his ability to reduce gags and art to these simplest levels. In so doing, Nancy and her friend Sluggo became favorites of millions.
The strip began in 1938.
© United Feature Syndicate, Inc.

ALLEY OOP
V. T. Hamlin (1900-1993)
Hamlin's love of history and legend inspired him to create an epic strip filled with the strange and mysterious, leaving a legacy of impressive art and stories of time-travel, stone-age adventure, humor and romance.
The strip began in 1933.
© Newspaper Enterprise Association, Inc.

DICK TRACY
Chester Gould (1900-1985)
Although his Sunday pages utilized flat colors, Tracy's world was black-and-white, good vs. evil, right vs. wrong. The villains especially — from the Brow, Mumbles, Pruneface — were as ugly as their natures.
The strip began in 1931.
© Tribune Media Services, Inc.

BRENDA STARR
Dale Messick (1906-   )
This classic soap-opera strip was a pioneer — a comic featuring a strong female lead character created by a female cartoonist. Brenda's big-city newsroom assignments usually led to adventure and romance.
The strip began in 1940.
© Tribune Media Services, Inc.

PRINCE VALIANT
Harold R. Foster (1892-1982)
Prince Valiant was the last major strip to be created as a full-page, full-color picture-story. Foster's meticulous research for his Arthurian legend lent authenticity to battle scenes and domestic scenes alike.
The strip began in 1937.
© 1995 King Features Syndicate, Inc.

TERRY AND THE PIRATES
Milton Caniff (1907-1988)
Caniff's artwork looked photographic; his characters spoke realistic dialogue; and readers identified with their personalities. Mood, evocation, atmosphere were Caniff's trademarks.
The strip ran 1934-1973.
© Tribune Media Services, Inc.

LI'L ABNER
Al Capp (1909-1979)
Abner's town of Dogpatch was Capp's crossroads of the best and worst of the humanity he lampooned. His creations included the Shmoo, the Bald Iggle, Fearless Fosdick, and Sadie Hawkins' Day.
The strip ran 1934-1977.
© Capp Enterprises, Inc.

Dogwood
© 1995 King Features
Syndicate, Inc.

Gum side (back) of Comic Strip sheet

Issues of 1995, Perf. 11.2		Un	U	PB	#	FDC
Christmas Issue						
3003	32¢ Madonna and Child, by Giotto di Bondone 10/19/95	.60	.15	3.00	(4)	1.25
a	Perf. 9.8 x 10.8	.60	.15			1.25
b	As "a," booklet pane of 10	6.00	4.00			7.25
3004	32¢ Santa Claus Entering Chimney 09/30/95	.60	.15			1.25
3005	32¢ Child Holding Jumping Jack 09/30/95	.60	.15			1.25
3006	32¢ Child Holding Tree 09/30/95	.60	.15			1.25
3007	32¢ Santa Claus Working on Sled 09/30/95	.60	.15			1.25
a	Block of 4, #3004-07	2.40	1.25	3.00	(4)	3.25
b	Booklet pane of 10, 3 each #3004-05, 2 each 3006-07	6.00	4.00			7.25
c	Booklet pane of 10, 2 each #3004-05, 3 each 3006-07	6.00	4.00			7.25
d	As "a," imperf.	*900.00*				
Self-Adhesive, Photogravure, Serpentine Die-Cut						
3008	32¢ Santa Claus Working on Sled 09/30/95	.60	.15			1.25
3009	32¢ Child Holding Jumping Jack 09/30/95	.60	.15			1.25
3010	32¢ Santa Claus Entering Chimney 09/30/95	.60	.15			1.25
3011	32¢ Child Holding Tree 09/30/95	.60	.15			1.25
a	Booklet pane of 20, 5 each #3008-11 + label	12.00				
Self-Adhesive, Lithographed						
3012	32¢ Midnight Angel 10/19/95	.60	.15			1.25
a	Booklet pane of 20 + label	12.00				
Self-Adhesive, Photogravure						
3013	32¢ Children Sledding 10/19/95	.60	.15			1.25
a	Booklet pane of 18	11.00				
Self-Adhesive Coil Stamps, Serpentine Die-Cut Vertically						
3014	32¢ Santa Claus Working on Sled 09/30/95	.60	.30			1.25
3015	32¢ Child Holding Jumping Jack 09/30/95	.60	.30			1.25
3016	32¢ Santa Claus Entering Chimney 09/30/95	.60	.30			1.25
3017	32¢ Child Holding Tree 09/30/95	.60	.30			1.25
a	Block of 4, #3014-17			6.50	(8)	3.25
Self-Adhesive Coil Stamps, Lithographed						
3018	32¢ Midnight Angel 10/19/95	.60	.30	4.25	(3)	1.25

Picture postcards

This holiday postage stamp is from an illustration attributed to Ellen H. Clapsdale (1865-1934), a prolific and extremely popular American postcard artist during the first part of this century. This was the heyday of picture postcards. They were purchased not only for sending, but for collecting as well. Clapsdale had an extremely successful career, designing several thousand cards with varied subjects including animals, children and landscapes as well as seasonal and holiday themes. In the latter part of her life, she made a poor investment and died destitute. She is still popular among collectors, and her images of children for which she was especially well known, are highly sought after. **(#3018)**

3003

3004   3005

3007a

3006   3007

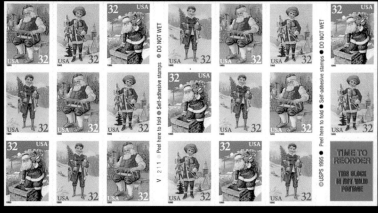

3011a   **3008**   **3009**   **3010**   **3011**

3012   **3013**

3019

3020

3021

3022

3023

3023a

3024

3025   3026   3027   3028   3029   3029a

3030   3032   3033   3044

3048   3049

Issues of 1995-1996, Perf. 11.1		Un	U	PB	#	FDC	Q(M)
	Antique Automobiles Issue						
3019	32¢ 1893 Duryea — 11/03/95	.60	.15			1.25	
3020	32¢ 1894 Haynes — 11/03/95	.60	.15			1.25	
3021	32¢ 1898 Columbia — 11/03/95	.60	.15			1.25	
3022	32¢ 1899 Winton — 11/03/95	.60	.15			1.25	
3023	32¢ 1901 White — 11/03/95	.60	.15			1.25	
a	Vertical or horizontal strip of 5, #3019-23	3.00	2.00			3.25	
3024	32¢ Utah Statehood — 01/04/96	.60	.15	3.00	(4)	1.25	
	Issues of 1996, Garden Flowers Issue, Perf 10.9 Vertically						
3025	32¢ Crocus — 01/19/96	.60	.15			1.25	
3026	32¢ Winter Sconite — 01/19/96	.60	.15			1.25	
3027	32¢ Pansy — 01/19/96	.60	.15			1.25	
3028	32¢ Snowdrop — 01/19/96	.60	.15			1.25	
3029	32¢ Anemone — 01/19/96	.60	.15			1.25	
a	Booklet pane of 5, #3025-3029	3.00	2.25			4.00	
	Love Issue, Serpentine Die Cut Perf. 11.3						
3030	32¢ Love Cherub from Sistine Madonna, by Raphael — 01/20/96	.60	.15			1.25	
	Flora and Fauna Issue, Perf. 11.1						
3032	2¢ Red-Headed Woodpecker — 02/02/96	.15	.15	.25	(4)	1.25	311
3033	3¢ Eastern Bluebird — 04/03/96	.15	.15	.25	(4)	1.25	317
3044	1¢ American Kestrel — 01/20/96	.15	.15	.50	(3)	1.25	
	Serpentine Die Cut 10.4 x 10.8 on 3						
3048	20¢ Blue Jay — 08/02/96	.40	.15			1.25	491
a	Booklet pane of 10	4.00					
	Serpentine Die Cut 11.3 x 11.7						
3049	32¢ Yellow Rose — 10/24/96	.60	.15			1.25	2,900
a	Booklet pane of 20 and label	12.00					
	Perf. 11.6 Vertically						
3053	20¢ Blue Jay — 08/02/96	.40	.15	2.75	(3)	1.25	330

Snowdrops get a head start on most other springtime garden flowers

The snowdrop flower is considered one of the earliest flowers to bloom in the springtime. Its fragrant blossoms compensate for the white snowdrop's lack of vibrant color. Well-known species include the common snowdrop which grows to about five inches in height and the giant snowdrop.

(#3028)

	Issues of 1996, Perf. 11.1		Un	U	PB	#	FDC	Q(M̄)
	Black Heritage Issue, Ernest E. Just							
3058	32¢ Ernest E. Just	02/01/96	.60	.15	2.40	(4)	1.25	92
3059	32¢ Smithsonian Institution	02/07/96	.60	.15	2.40	(4)	1.25	115
	Lunar New Year Issue							
3060	32¢ Year of the Rat	02/08/96	.60	.15	2.40	(4)	1.50	93
	Pioneers of Communication Issue, Perf. 11.1 x 11							
3061	32¢ Eadweard Muybridge	02/22/96	.60	.15			1.25	96
3062	32¢ Ottmar Mergenthaler	02/22/96	.60	.15			1.25	96
3063	32¢ Frederic E. Ives	02/22/96	.60	.15			1.25	96
3064	32¢ William Dickson	02/22/96	.60	.15			1.25	96
a	Block or strip of 4, #3061-3064		2.40	1.75	2.40	(4)	3.25	
	Perf. 11.1							
3065	32¢ Fulbright Scholarships	02/28/96	.60	.15	3.00	(4)	1.25	130
	Pioneers of Aviation Issue							
3066	50¢ Jacqueline Cochran	03/09/96	1.00	.20	5.00	(4)	1.35	314
3067	32¢ Marathon	04/11/96	.60	.15	2.40	(4)	1.25	209

History of the marathon

The term *marathon* takes its name from a plain in Greece where one of the most significant battles in antiquity was fought in 490 B.C. Inspired by a legend from that war, Olympic officials included a long-distance race from the plains of Marathon to the Olympic Stadium in Athens when they revived the games in 1896. Today, marathons are held in many cities around the world. Probably the most famous is the Boston Marathon which started in 1897 and has been run on an annual basis since that time. Special training to build strength and endurance is required by the participants whose major goals are to finish, to improve their time and, of course, to win. **(#3067)**

Interesting Fact: In 1908, the British Olympic Committee decided to start the Olympic race at Windsor Castle and finish it in front of the royal box in the stadium at London—a distance of 26 miles 385 yards. This became the standard distance for running the marathon.

3059

3060

3058

3063

3064

3064a

3061

3062

3066

3065

3067

Atlanta 1996
CENTENNIAL OLYMPIC GAMES

CLASSIC COLLECTIONS

32 x 20 $6.40

© 1996 United States Postal Service

PLATE POSITION

3068   a   b   c   d   e
    f   g   h   i   j
    k   l   m   n   o
    p   q   r   s   t

3069

3070

FANCY DANCE   BUTTERFLY DANCE   TRADITIONAL DANCE   RAVEN DANCE   HOOP DANCE

3072   3073   3074   3075   3076   3076a

	Issues of 1996, Perf. 11.1		Un	U	PB	#	FDC	Q(M̄)
	Summer Olympic Games Issue							
3068	Pane of 20	05/02/96	12.00	—			13.00	324
a	32¢ Decathlon		.60	.15			1.25	
b	32¢ Canoeing		.60	.15			1.25	
c	32¢ Women's running		.60	.15			1.25	
d	32¢ Women's diving		.60	.15			1.25	
e	32¢ Cycling		.60	.15			1.25	
f	32¢ Freestyle wrestling		.60	.15			1.25	
g	32¢ Women's gymnastic		.60	.15			1.25	
h	32¢ Women's sailboarding		.60	.15			1.25	
i	32¢ Shot put		.60	.15			1.25	
j	32¢ Women's soccer		.60	.15			1.25	
k	32¢ Beach volleyball		.60	.15			1.25	
l	32¢ Rowing		.60	.15			1.25	
m	32¢ Sprinting		.60	.15			1.25	
n	32¢ Women's swimming		.60	.15			1.25	
o	32¢ Women's softball		.60	.15			1.25	
p	32¢ Hurdles		.60	.15			1.25	
q	32¢ Swimming		.60	.15			1.25	
r	32¢ Gymnastics		.60	.15			1.25	
s	32¢ Equestrian		.60	.15			1.25	
t	32¢ Basketball		.60	.15			1.25	
	Perf. 11.6 x 11.4							
3069	32¢ Georgia O'Keefe	05/23/96	.60	.15	2.40	(4)	1.25	156
	Perf. 11.1							
3070	32¢ Tennessee Statehood	05/31/96	.60	.15	3.00	(4)	1.25	100
	Serpentine Die-Cut 9.9 x 10.8, Self-Adhesive							
3071	32¢ Tennessee Statehood	05/31/96	.60	.30			1.25	60
a	Booklet pane of 20		12.00					
	American Indian Dances Issue, Perf. 11.1							
3072	32¢ Fancy Dance	06/07/96	.60	.15			1.25	139
3073	32¢ Butterfly Dance	06/07/96	.60	.15			1.25	139
3074	32¢ Traditional Dance	06/07/96	.60	.15			1.25	139
3075	32¢ Raven Dance	06/07/96	.60	.15			1.25	139
3076	32¢ Hoop Dance	06/07/96	.60	.15			1.25	139
a	Strip of 5, #3072-3076		3.00	1.75	6.00	(10)	3.50	139

Native American hoop dance, a thrilling showstopper

HOOP DANCE

The hoop dance of the North American Indian, in its private, traditional form, is part of a healing ceremony, the hoop being a sacred symbol. In this century a public form has developed making it a highlight at powwows, gatherings of different tribes that place their emphasis on song and dance. Thrilling audiences, the hoop dance is often a favorite showstopper. The dancer manipulates more than a dozen hoops (sometimes as many as 50) over and around his arms and legs and even his whole body, creating a diversity of geometric shapes, eagles, butterflies, flowers and insects. Contests may be held with the judging based on precision, timing, showmanship, creativity and speed. **(#3076)**

	Issues of 1996, Perf. 11.1 x 11		Un	U	PB	#	FDC	Q(M̄)
	Prehistoric Animals Issue							
3077	32¢ Eohippus	06/08/96	.60	.15			1.25	150
3078	32¢ Woolly Mammoth	06/08/96	.60	.15			1.25	150
3079	32¢ Mastodon	06/08/96	.60	.15			1.25	150
3080	32¢ Saber-tooth cat	06/08/96	.60	.15			1.25	150
a	Block or strip of 4, #3077-3080		2.40	1.50	2.40	(4)	3.25	150
	Pane of 20		12.00					
	Perf. 11.1							
3081	32¢ Breast Cancer Awareness	06/15/96	.60	.15	2.40	(4)	1.25	96
	Legends of Hollywood Issue, Perf. 11.1							
3082	32¢ James Dean	06/24/96	.60	.15	2.40	(4)	1.50	300
	Pane of 20		12.00					
	Folks Heroes Issue, Perf. 11.1 x 11							
3083	32¢ Mighty Casey	07/11/96	.60	.15			1.25	113
3084	32¢ Paul Bunyan	07/11/96	.60	.15			1.25	113
3085	32¢ John Henry	07/11/96	.60	.15			1.25	113
3086	32¢ Pecos Bill	07/11/96	.60	.15			1.25	113
a	Block or strip of 4, #3083-3086		2.40	1.50	2.40	(4)	3.25	
	Centennial Olympic Games Issue, Perf. 11.1							
3087	32¢ Centennial Olympic Games	07/11/96	.60	.15	2.40	(4)	1.25	134
	Pane of 20		12.00					
3088	32¢ Iowa Statehood	08/01/96	.60	.15	3.00	(4)	1.25	103
	Booklet Stamp, Self-Adhesive Serpentine Die-Cut 11.6 x 11.4							
3089	32¢ Iowa Statehood	08/01/96	.60	.15			1.25	60
a	Booklet pane of 20		12.00					
	Perf. 11.2 x 11							
3090	32¢ Rural Free Delivery	08/07/96	.60	.15	2.40	(4)	1.25	134

Early postal improvement

Over one-half of America's 1890 population—76,000,000 people—lived in rural areas, but only about half of those had access to free postal delivery, as the city folks did. Rural farmers, feeling they were being left out, argued that the postal taxes they were paying helped fund city delivery for others, but not for themselves. Their protests were heard, and the U.S. Postal Department began Rural Free Delivery (RFD) on a limited basis in West Virginia in 1896. Three years later, RFD was established in 40 states and was acclaimed a great success.

(#3090)

Interesting Fact: Since the Postal Department could turn down proposed rural mail routes if the roads in the district were not good enough, one of the direct benefits of RFD was a much-needed incentive to improve the nation's highways.

Tell us about your stamp collecting!

The U.S. Postal Service received many responses to the reply card inserted in last year's Guide. We value your input, so keep it coming. Here are new elements of this year's Guide:

- **Expanded stamp listings**
- **Updated stamp prices**
- **Dozens of new illustrations**
- **More stamp stories than ever**
- **Expanded information on new issues**

Please answer these questions and return this postage-paid reply card so we can continue to provide a book that suits **your** *collecting needs.*

1. Are you ❏ male or ❏ female?

2. How old are you?
❏ Under 10 years   ❏ 11-15 years
❏ 16-20 years   ❏ 21-35 years
❏ 36-55 years   ❏ 56+ years

3. How long have you been collecting stamps?
❏ Less than 3 years ❏ 4-10 years
❏ 11-15 years   ❏ More than 15 years

4. Do you buy stamps or other related products from the Stamp Fulfillment Services (U.S. Postal Service Mail Order, Kansas City)?
❏ Yes   ❏ No

5. Have you used its toll-free number, 1-800-STAMP 24?
❏ Yes   ❏ No

6. How often do you buy this book?
❏ Every year   ❏ Every 2-3 years
❏ Every 4 or more years
❏ First time buyer

7. What do you like most about this book?
_____
_____

8. What do you like least about this book?
_____
_____

9. How could this book be improved to help you?
_____
_____

10. What types of stamps do you collect most?
❏ Stamps featuring people
❏ Stamps featuring animals
❏ Stamps featuring historic places
❏ Stamps featuring historical events
❏ Full-color stamps
❏ Single-color or engraved stamps
❏ All types
❏ Other_____

11. Would you be interested in an electronic version of the *Guide*?
❏ Yes   ❏ No

12. If so, in what format?
❏ On-line   ❏ CD-ROM

13. Would you be willing to pay more for a more deluxe binding?
❏ Yes   ❏ No

14. What type of binding option do you prefer?
❏ Conventional (similar to most paperbacks)
❏ Lay-flat (currently used on this book)
❏ Spiral   ❏ Loose-leaf
❏ Other_____

Comments:
_____
_____
_____
_____

Please detach at perforation.

UNITED STATES POSTAL SERVICE

PHILATELIC FULFILLMENT SERVICE CENTER
KANSAS CITY MO 64179-0997

Official Business

BUSINESS REPLY MAIL
FIRST CLASS MAIL   PERMIT NO 73026   WASHINGTON DC

POSTAGE WILL BE PAID BY THE ADDRESSEE

UNITED STATES POSTAL SERVICE
PHILATELIC FULFILLMENT SERVICE CENTER
CUSTOMER SERVICE
BOX 419424
KANSAS CITY MO 64179-1009

NO POSTAGE
NECESSARY
IF MAILED
IN THE
UNITED STATES

3077   3078

3079   3080   3080a

3083   3086a
                        3086

3081   3082

3085   3084

3090

3087   3088

3091 3092 3093 3094 3095 3095a

3091
ROBT. E. LEE
3092
SYLVAN DELL
3093
FAR WEST
3094
REBECCA EVERINGHAM
3095
BAILEY GATZERT

3096 3097
3098 3099 3099a

32 USA COUNT BASIE
32 USA TOMMY & JIMMY DORSEY
32 USA GLENN MILLER
32 USA BENNY GOODMAN

3100 3101
3102 3103 3103a

32 USA HAROLD ARLEN
32 USA JOHNNY MERCER
32 USA DOROTHY FIELDS
32 USA HOAGY CARMICHAEL

F. SCOTT FITZGERALD
23 USA

3104

*Most stamps remain on sale from the U.S. Postal Service at least one year from date of issue, especially by mail order. Ask for them at your local post office, or request a free copy of the Stamps etc. mail-order catalog. To receive a catalog, call toll-free: **1-800-STAMP24**.*

Issues of 1996		Un	U	PB	#	FDC	Q(M̄)
Riverboats Issue, Serpentine Die-Cut 11 x 11.1							
3091	32¢ Robert E. Lee	08/22/96	.60	.15			1.25	160
3092	32¢ Sylvan Dell	08/22/96	.60	.15			1.25	160
3093	32¢ Far West	08/22/96	.60	.15			1.25	160
3094	32¢ Rebecca Everingham	08/22/96	.60	.15			1.25	160
3095	32¢ Bailey Gatzert	08/22/96	.60	.15			1.25	160
a	Vertical strip of 5, #3091-3095		3.00		6.00	(10)	3.50	
American Music Series Issue, Perf. 11.1 x 11							
Big Band Leaders							
3096	32¢ Count Basie	09/11/96	.60	.15			1.25	92
3097	32¢ Tommy and Jimmy Dorsey	09/11/96	.60	.15			1.25	92
3098	32¢ Glenn Miller	09/11/96	.60	.15			1.25	92
3099	32¢ Benny Goodman	09/11/96	.60	.15			1.25	92
a	Block or strip of 4, #3096-3099		2.40	1.50	2.40	(4)	3.25	
Songwriters							
3100	32¢ Harold Arlen	09/11/96	.60	.15			1.25	92
3101	32¢ Johnny Mercer	09/11/96	.60	.15			1.25	92
3102	32¢ Dorothy Fields	09/11/96	.60	.15			1.25	92
3103	32¢ Hoagy Carmichael	09/11/96	.60	.15			1.25	92
a	Block or strip of 4, #3100-3103		2.40	1.50	2.40	(4)	3.25	
Literary Arts Issue, Perf. 11.1							
3104	32¢ F. Scott Fitzgerald	09/11/96	.45	.15	2.25	(4)	1.25	300

Rebecca Everingham steamboat part of water highway history

There was a time when America's most notable highways were made of water. Within 20 years of Robert Fulton's first steamboat run on the Hudson River in 1807, more than 200 steamboats were in use, hauling freight and passengers alike. Steamboating not only pre-dates railroads and automobiles, but was a lucrative industry in the U.S. for nearly 150 years. Because of many dangers and accidents, such as becoming grounded or having its hull punctured by a snag, the average life-span of a steamboat was only four to five years. In the late 19th and early 20th centuries, the advent of efficient automobiles and transcontinental railroads led to the decline of the steamboat era. The Rebecca Everingham was in service from 1880 to 1884. **(#3094)**

Interesting Fact: Rivalries between steamboat pilots led to races that had disastrous results. In the first 40 years of steamboats, it was estimated that 500 vessels and nearly 4,000 lives were lost.

1996

	Issues of 1996, Perf. 11.1 x 11		Un	U	PB	#	FDC	Q(M̄)
	Endangered Species Issue							
3105	Pane of 15	10/02/96	9.00	—			7.50	224
a	32¢ Black-footed ferret		.60	.15			1.25	
b	32¢ Thick-billed parrot		.60	.15			1.25	
c	32¢ Hawaiian monk seal		.60	.15			1.25	
d	32¢ American crocodile		.60	.15			1.25	
e	32¢ Ocelot		.60	.15			1.25	
f	32¢ Schaus swallowtail butterfly		.60	.15			1.25	
g	32¢ Wyoming toad		.60	.15			1.25	
h	32¢ Brown pelican		.60	.15			1.25	
i	32¢ California condor		.60	.15			1.25	
j	32¢ Gilatrout		.60	.15			1.25	
k	32¢ San Francisco garter snake		.60	.15			1.25	
l	32¢ Woodland caribou		.60	.15			1.25	
m	32¢ Florida panther		.60	.15			1.25	
n	32¢ Piping plover		.60	.15			1.25	
o	32¢ Florida manatee		.60	.15			1.25	
	Perf. 10.9 x 11.1							
3106	32¢ Computer Technology	10/08/96	.60	.15	3.00	(4)		94
	Christmas Issue, Perf. 11.1 x 11.2							
3107	32¢ Madonna and Child by Paolo de Mattels	10/08/96	.60	.15	3.00	(4)	1.25	848
	Perf. 11.3							
3108	32¢ Family at Fireplace	10/08/96	.60	.15			1.25	226
3109	32¢ Decorating Tree	10/08/96	.60	.15			1.25	226
3110	32¢ Dreaming of Santa Claus	10/08/96	.60	.15			1.25	226
3111	32¢ Holiday Shopping	10/08/96	.60	.15			1.25	226
a	Block or strip of 4, #3108-3111		2.40	1.50	3.00	(4)	3.25	
	Self-Adhesive Booklet Stamps, Serpentine Die-Cut 10 on 2, 3 or 4 sides							
3112	32¢ Madonna and Child by Paolo de Mattels	10/08/96	.60	.15			1.25	244
3113	32¢ Family at Fireplace	10/08/96	.60	.15			1.25	1,805
3114	32¢ Decorating Tree	10/08/96	.60	.15			1.25	1,805
3115	32¢ Dreaming of Santa Claus	10/08/96	.60	.15			1.25	1,805
3116	32¢ Holiday Shopping	10/08/96	.60	.15			1.25	1,805
a	Booklet pane, 5 ea #3113-3116		12.00					
	Die-Cut							
3117	32¢ Skaters	10/08/96	.60	.15			1.25	495
a	Booklet pane of 18		11.00					
	Serpentine Die-Cut 11.1							
3118	32¢ Hanukkah	10/22/96	.60	.15	2.40	(4)	1.25	104
	Cycling Issue, Perf. 11 x 11.1							
3119	32¢ Souvenier sheet of 2	11/01/96	2.00	2.00			2.50	
a	50¢ orange		1.00	1.00			1.50	
b	50¢ blue and green		1.00	1.00			1.50	

Minimum value listed for a stamp is 15 cents; for a First Day Cover (FDC), $1.00. This minimum represents a fair-market price for having a dealer locate and provide a single stamp or cover from his or her stock. Dealers may charge less per stamp or cover for a group of such stamps or covers, or less for a single stamp or cover.

Endangered Species

National Stamp Collecting Month 1996 highlights these 15 species to promote awareness of endangered wildlife. Each generation must work to protect the delicate balance of nature, so that future generations may share a sound and healthy planet.

3105

a b c

d e f

g h i

j k l

m n o

3106

3107

3108   3109
3113   3114

3117

3118

3110   3111
3115   3116

3119

3120

3121

3122

3123

3124

3125

3126

3127

3130

3131

3132

3133

3134

3135

Issues of 1997		Un	U	PB	#	FDC	Q(M)
Lunar New Year Issue, Perf. 11.2							
3120 32¢ Year of the Ox	01/05/97	.60	.15	2.40	(4)	1.25	106
Black Heritage Issue, Serpentine Die-Cut 11.4							
3121 32¢ Brig. Gen. Benjamin O. Davis Sr.	01/28/97	.60	.15	2.40	(4)	1.25	112
Self Adhesive Booklet Stamps, Serpentine Die-Cut 11 on 2, 3 or 4 sides							
3122 32¢ Statue of Liberty, Type of 1994	02/01/97	.60	.15			1.25	2,855
a Booklet panel of 20 + label		12.00					
b Booklet pane of 4		3.20					
c Booklet pane of 5 + label		3.00					
d Booklet pane of 6		3.60					
Self Adhesive, Serpentine Die-Cut 11.8 x 11.6 on 2, 3 or 4 sides							
3123 32¢ Love Swans	02/04/97	.60	.15			1.25	1,660
a Booklet pane of 20 + label		12.00					
Serpentine Die-Cut, Perf. 11.6 x 11.8 on 2, 3 or 4 sides							
3124 55¢ Love Swans	02/04/97	1.10	.15			1.50	814
a Booklet pane of 20 + label		22.00					
Self Adhesive, Serpentine Die-Cut, Perf. 11.6 x 11.7							
3125 32¢ Helping Children Learn	02/18/97	.60	.15	2.40	(4)	1.25	122
Merian Botanical Print Issues, Self Adhesive, Serpentine Die-Cut 10.9 x 10.2 on 2, 3 or 4 sides							
3126 32¢ Citron, Roth, Larvae, Pupa, Beetle	03/03/97	.60	.15			1.25	2,048
3127 32¢ Flowering Pineapple, Cockroaches	03/03/97	.60	.15			1.25	2,048
Serpentine Die-Cut 11.2 x 10.8 on 2 or 3 sides							
3128 32¢ Citron, Roth, Larvae, Pupa, Beetle	03/03/97	.60	.15			1.25	30
3129 32¢ Flowering Pineapple, Cockroaches	03/03/97	.60	.15			1.25	30
b Booklet pane of 5, 2 each #3128-29		3.00					
Pacific 97 Issues, Perf. 11.2							
3130 32¢ Sailing Ship	03/13/97	.60	.15			1.25	130
3131 32¢ Stagecoach	03/13/97	.60	.15			1.25	130
a Pair #3130-31		1.25	.30	2.50	(4)	1.75	
Self Adhesive Coil Stamps, Imperf.							
3132 25¢ Juke Box	03/14/97	.50	.50	3.50	(3)	1.25	24
Coil Stamps, Tagged, Serpentine Die-Cut 9.9 Vertically							
3133 32¢ Flag Over Porch	03/14/97	.60	.15	4.00	(3)	1.25	1
Literary Arts Issue, Perf. 11.1							
3134 32¢ Thornton Wilder	04/17/97	.60	.15	2.40	(4)	1.25	98
3135 32¢ Raoul Wallenberg	04/24/97	.60	.15	2.40	(4)	1.25	96

Issues of 1997			Un	U		FDC	Q(M)
The World of Dinosaurs Issue, Perf. 11 x 11.1							
3136	Sheet of 15	05/01/97	9.00	—		7.50	219
a	32¢ Ceratosaurus		.60	.15		1.25	
b	32¢ Camptosaurus		.60	.15		1.25	
c	32¢ Camarasaurus		.60	.15		1.25	
d	32¢ Brachiosaurus		.60	.15		1.25	
e	32¢ Goniopholis		.60	.15		1.25	
f	32¢ Stegosaurus		.60	.15		1.25	
g	32¢ Allosaurus		.60	.15		1.25	
h	32¢ Opisthias		.60	.15		1.25	
i	32¢ Edmontonia		.60	.15		1.25	
j	32¢ Einiosaurus		.60	.15		1.25	
k	32¢ Daspletosaurus		.60	.15		1.25	
l	32¢ Palaeosaniwa		.60	.15		1.25	
m	32¢ Corythosaurus		.60	.15		1.25	
n	32¢ Ornithominus		.60	.15		1.25	
o	32¢ Parasaurolophus		.60	.15		1.25	
Bugs Bunny Issue, Serpentine Die-Cut 11							
3137	Pane of 10	05/22/97	6.00				265
a	32¢ single		.60	.15		1.25	
b	Booklet pane of 9		5.40				
c	Booklet pane of 1		.60				
	Die-cutting on #3137b does not extend through the backing paper.						
3138	Pane of 10	05/22/97	250.00				
a	32¢ single		.60				
b	Booklet pane of 9		5.40				
c	Booklet pane of 1, imperf.		225.00				
	Die-cutting on #3138b extends through the backing paper.						

A jack(rabbit)-of-all-trades

Despite his advanced years (he's 58), Bugs Bunny has shot hoops with Michael Jordan in advertising and the movies, promoted the War Bond effort during World War II and generally has become one of America's most beloved cartoon characters. Today he serves as the "ambassador" for Stampers®, USPS' stamp-collecting program for kids. While Bugs and his signature line, "What's up, Doc?" have been universally renowned for generations, this is the first time he has appeared on a postage stamp anywhere in the world. **(#3137)**

Interesting Fact: The late comic actor/announcer Mel Blanc, Bugs' voice for decades, also supplied the voices for most of the Warner Bros. characters.

3137

3139

3140

3141

Issues of 1997		Un	U	PB	#	FDC	Q(M)
Pacific 97 Issue, Perf. 10.5 x 10.4							
Benjamin Franklin							
3139 Sheet of 12	05/29/97	12.00	—			12.00	56
a 50¢ single		1.00	.50			2.00	
George Washington							
3140 Sheet of 12	05/30/97	14.50	—			2.50	56
a 60¢ single		1.25	.60				
The Marshall Plan, 50th Anniversary Issue, Perf. 11.1							
3141 32¢ The Marshall Plan	06/04/97	.60	.15	2.40	(4)	1.25	45

George Washington, first president of the U.S.

The first two U.S. postal stamps issued in 1847 were of George Washington and Benjamin Franklin. These two stamps were re-engraved and re-issued in 1875 and re-engraved again in 1947. Once again these stamps were re-engraved with current denominations of 50¢ and 60¢ and re-issued in 1997 in souvenir sheets available for only 11 days. George Washington, one of the founding fathers of the United States of America, presided over the Constitutional Convention in 1786 and was unanimously elected the first president of the U.S. in 1789. **(#3140)**

Issues of 1997			Un	U		Q(M)
Classic American Aircraft Issue, Perf. 10.1						
3142	Pane of 20	07/19/97	12.00	—		161
a	32¢ Mustang		.60	.15		
b	32¢ Model B		.60	.15		
c	32¢ Cub		.60	.15		
d	32¢ Vega		.60	.15		
e	32¢ Alpha		.60	.15		
f	32¢ B-10		.60	.15		
g	32¢ Corsair		.60	.15		
h	32¢ Stratojet		.60	.15		
i	32¢ Gee Bee		.60	.15		
j	32¢ Staggerwing		.60	.15		
k	32¢ Flying Fortress		.60	.15		
l	32¢ Stearman		.60	.15		
m	32¢ Constellation		.60	.15		
n	32¢ Lightning		.60	.15		
o	32¢ Peashooter		.60	.15		
p	32¢ Tri-Motor		.60	.15		
q	32¢ DC-3		.60	.15		
r	32¢ 314 Clipper		.60	.15		
s	32¢ Jenny		.60	.15		
t	32¢ Wildcat		.60	.15		
Legendary Football Coaches Issue, Perf. 11.2						
3143	32¢ Bear Bryant	07/25/97	.60	.15		90
3144	32¢ Pop Warner	07/25/97	.60	.15		90
3145	32¢ Vince Lombardi	07/25/97	.60	.15		90
3146	32¢ George Halas	07/25/97	.60	.15		90
a	Block or strip of 4, #3143-3146		2.40	—		

"Pop" Warner, more than just a coach

The legendary Glenn "Pop" Warner, one of the most famous coaches in college football history, was an innovative strategist on the field and an inspiration for youngsters. The Junior Football Conference, which began in 1929 in Philadelphia as a way to provide organized recreation for young boys, was later renamed the Pop Warner Conference. In 1959 it became the Pop Warner Little Scholars, Inc., a national nonprofit organization dedicated to the pursuit of a good education as well as athletic competence. Open to both girls and boys of ages ranging from approximately 7 to 15, the program features cheerleading along with flag and tackle football programs. Participants must demonstrate satisfactory classroom achievement before they can compete. **(#3144)**

3142   a   b   c   d
        e   f   g   h
     i   j   k   l
    m   n   o   p
    q   r   s   t

3145   3146   3143   3144   3146a

3147

3148

3149

3150

CLASSIC
American Dolls

32
x15
$4.80

PLATE
POSITION

F11111

© 1996 USPS

"Alabama Baby" and Martha Chase   "The Columbian Doll"   Johnny Gruelle's "Raggedy Ann"   Martha Chase   "American Child"
"Baby Coos"   Plains Indian   Izannah Walker   "Babyland Flag"   "Scootles"
Ludwig Greiner   "Betsy McCall"   Percy Crosby's "Skippy"   "Maggie Mix-up"   Albert Schoenhut

The above names include doll makers, designers, trade names and common names.

3151   a   b   c   d   e
   f   g   h   i   j
   k   l   m   n   o

Issues of 1997			Un	U	Q(M)
Legendary Football Coaches Issue with Red Bar above Coach's Name, Perf. 11					
3147	32¢ Vince Lombardi	08/05/97	.60	.30	20
3148	32¢ Bear Bryant	08/07/97	.60	.30	20
3149	32¢ Pop Warner	08/08/97	.60	.30	10
3150	32¢ George Halas	08/16/97	.60	.30	10
Classic American Dolls Issue, Perf. 10.9 x 11.1					
3151	Pane of 15	07/28/97	9.00	—	105
a	32¢ "Alabama Baby," and doll by Martha Chase		.60	.15	
b	32¢ "Columbian Doll"		.60	.15	
c	32¢ Johnny Gruelle's "Raggedy Ann"		.60	.15	
d	32¢ Doll by Martha Chase		.60	.15	
e	32¢ "American Child"		.60	.15	
f	32¢ "Baby Coos"		.60	.15	
g	32¢ Plains Indian		.60	.15	
h	32¢ Doll by Izannah Walker		.60	.15	
i	32¢ "Babyland Rag"		.60	.15	
j	32¢ "Scootles"		.60	.15	
k	32¢ Doll by Ludwig Greiner		.60	.15	
l	32¢ "Betsy McCall"		.60	.15	
m	32¢ Percy Crosby's "Skippy"		.60	.15	
n	32¢ "Maggie Mix-up"		.60	.15	
o	32¢ Dolls by Albert Schoenhut		.60	.15	

German family brings doll-making art to America

Albert Schoenhut was part of a family of talented doll-makers from Germany. His wooden dolls, as shown in the Classic American Dolls series, were renowned for being "unbreakable" when they first appeared on the market in 1911. Innovative in their design, the dolls had movable joints which allowed them to move in human-like positions. In 1921, Schoenhut's doll design included movable wooden eyes. The weak U.S. economy negatively affected the Schoenhut doll business until the last doll was produced in 1924. The "American Girl" and "Scootles" doll are shown in this stamp. **(#3151o)**

Issues of 1997		Un	U	Q(M)
Legends of Hollywood Issue, Perf. 11.1				
3152	32¢ Humphrey Bogart 07/31/97	.60	.15	195
3153	32¢ "The Stars and Stripes Forever" 08/21/97	.60	.15	323
American Music Series Issue, Perf. 11				
Opera Singers				
3154	32¢ Lily Pons 09/10/97	.60	.15	86
3155	32¢ Richard Tucker 09/10/97	.60	.15	86
3156	32¢ Lawrence Tibbett 09/10/97	.60	.15	86
3157	32¢ Rosa Ponselle 09/10/97	.60	.15	86
a	Block or strip of 4, #3154-3157	2.40	—	

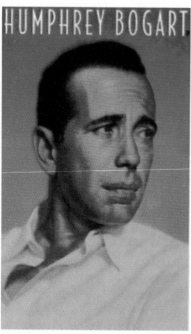

Humphrey Bogart, an American legend

The Oscar for best actor in 1951 was awarded to a scowling tough guy who was affectionately known as "Bogie." His role as Charlie Allnut in *The African Queen* was but one in a long list of unforgettable characters that would be forever associated with the name Humphrey Bogart including Rick Blaine in *Casablanca*, Captain Queeg in *The Caine Mutiny* and Sam Spade in *The Maltese Falcon*, to mention but a few. Born in 1899 in New York City, he was the son of well-to-do parents and led an upper-class life attending private schools until he enlisted in the Navy during World War I. After he returned from service, he began a career in acting in the New York theater. Lured by the early sound films, he went to Hollywood in the 1930s, making more than 75 films and becoming one of Hollywood's most famous leading men. **(#3152)**

Interesting Fact: The stiff-upper-lip speech pattern that was one of Bogart's trademarks was not an affectation but the result of a World War I injury to his upper lip.

3152

3153

3154   3155

3156   3157

3157a

3158 3159 3160 3161

3162 3163 3164 3165 3165a

3167

3166

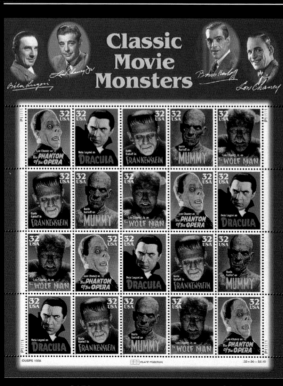

3169 3170 3171 3172 3168

Issues of 1997		Un	U	Q(M)
American Music Series Issue, Perf. 11				
Classical Composers & Conductors				
3158	32¢ Leopold Stokowski 09/12/97	.60	.15	86
3159	32¢ Arthur Fiedler 09/12/97	.60	.15	86
3160	32¢ George Szell 09/12/97	.60	.15	86
3161	32¢ Eugene Ormandy 09/12/97	.60	.15	86
3162	32¢ Samuel Barber 09/12/97	.60	.15	86
3163	32¢ Ferde Grofé 09/12/97	.60	.15	86
3164	32¢ Charles Ives 09/12/97	.60	.15	86
3165	32¢ Louis Moreau Gottschalk 09/12/97	.60	.15	86
a	Block of 8, #3158-3165	4.80	—	
	Perf. 11.2			
3166	32¢ Padre Félix Varela 09/15/97	.60	.15	2,855
Department of the Air Force, 50th Anniversary Issue, Perf. 11.2 x 11.1				
3167	32¢ Thunderbirds Aerial Demonstration Squadron 09/18/97	.60	.15	45
Classic Movie Monsters Series Issue, Perf. 10.2				
3168	32¢ Lon Chaney as The Phantom of the Opera 09/30/97	.60	.15	145
3169	32¢ Bela Lugosi as Dracula 09/30/97	.60	.15	145
3170	32¢ Boris Karloff as Frankenstein's Monster 09/30/97	.60	.15	145
3171	32¢ Boris Karloff as The Mummy 09/30/97	.60	.15	145
3172	32¢ Lon Chaney Jr. as The Wolf Man 09/30/97	.60	.15	145
a	Strip of 5, #3168-3172	3.00	—	

Beginning with No. 3167, a hidden 3-D design can be seen on some stamps when they are viewed with a special viewer sold by the post office.

Social Reformer

Padre Félix Varela

Social reformer spent more than 30 years helping poor minorities

The founder of New York's Parish of the Transfiguration, Padre Félix Varela, born in Cuba in 1788, was ordained a priest at age 23. An eminent educator, he was already famous for his political, religious and philosophical writings when he arrived in the United States in 1823. This devoted priest, dedicated to serving his fellow man, founded schools, an orphanage and a day nursery for children of the needy immigrants of his parish. During the deadly cholera epidemic of 1837, he ministered to the sick and dying day and night in nearby hospitals. He never returned to his native country but continued his work in the United States and died in Florida in 1853. **(#3166)**

Interesting Fact: His parish came to be known as "The Church of the Immigrants" because of its large Irish population, which later became predominately Italian and at the present time is almost 100% Chinese.

Issues of 1997		Un	U	Q(M)
Serpentine Die-Cut 11.4				
3173	32¢ First Supersonic Flight, 50th Anniversary 10/14/97	.60	.15	173
Perf. 11.1				
3174	32¢ Women in Military Service 10/18/97	.60	.15	
Self Adhesive, Serpentine Die-Cut 11				
3175	32¢ Kwanzaa 10/22/97	.60	.15	133
Holiday Traditional, Self Adhesive, Serpentine Die-Cut 9.9 on 2, 3 or 4 sides				
3176	32¢ Madonna and Child by Sano di Pietro 10/09/97	.60	.15	883
a	Booklet pane of 20 + label	12.00		
Holiday Contemporary, Serpentine Die-Cut 11.2 x 11.8 on 2, 3 or 4 sides				
3177	32¢ American Holly 10/30/97	.60	.15	180
a	Booklet pane of 20 + label	12.00		
b	Booklet pane of 4	2.50		
c	Booklet pane of 5 + label	3.00		
d	Booklet pane of 6	3.75		
Mars Pathfinder, Perf 11 x 11.1				
3178	$3 Mars Rover Sojourner 12/10/97	6.00	—	15

Madonna and child

Madonna and Child with Saints and Angels is the work of Sano di Pietro, a prolific and successful Sienese painter of the 15th century. Painted on a wood panel, the Madonna and Child are shown with St. Jerome and an adoring angel. Now in the permanent collection of the National Gallery of Art, it was acquired by the Samuel H. Kress foundation in 1937. Originally planning to create a private museum of Italian art in New York, Kress was persuaded instead to bestow his major collection to the National Gallery of Art in Washington, D.C., thus making it more accessible to the general public. **(#3176)**

Interesting Fact: Samuel Kress, one of the most important art collectors of the 20th century, made his fortune from a chain of five- and ten-cent stores that began with a small shop in Pennsylvania and eventually became a coast-to-coast operation offering a variety of simple, useful items under one roof.

3173

3174

3175

3176

3177

3178

918-1938

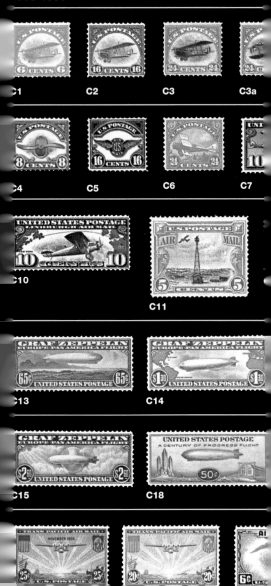

C1   C2   C3   C3a

C4   C5   C6   C7

C10   C11

C13   C14

C15   C18

	Issues of 1918, Perf. 11		Un	U	PB	#	FDC	Q(M̄)
	For prepayment of postage on all mailable matter sent by airmail. All unwatermarked.							
C1	6¢ Curtiss Jenny	12/10/18	75.00	30.00	800.00	(6)	32,500.00	3
	Double transfer		95.00	45.00				
C2	16¢ Curtiss Jenny	07/11/18	105.00	35.00	1,300.00	(6)	32,500.00	4
C3	24¢ Curtiss Jenny	05/13/18	105.00	35.00	500.00	(4)	27,500.00	2
a	Center Inverted		150,000.00		1,100,000.00	(4)		0.0001
	Issues of 1923							
C4	8¢ Airplane Radiator and Wooden Propeller	08/15/23	27.50	14.00	275.00	(6)	450.00	6
C5	16¢ Air Service Emblem	08/17/23	105.00	30.00	2,000.00	(6)	675.00	5
C6	24¢ De Havilland Biplane	08/21/23	120.00	30.00	2,600.00	(6)	825.00	5
	Issues of 1926-27							
C7	10¢ Map of U.S. and Two Mail Planes	02/13/26	3.00	.35	40.00	(6)	55.00	42
	Double transfer		5.75	1.10				
C8	15¢ olive brown (C7)	09/18/26	3.50	2.50	50.00	(6)	75.00	16
C9	20¢ yellow green (C7)	01/25/27	9.00	2.00	100.00	(6)	100.00	18
	Issue of 1927-28							
C10	10¢ Lindbergh's "Spirit of St. Louis"	06/18/27	8.50	2.50	125.00	(6)	20.00	20
a	Booklet pane of 3	05/26/28	85.00	65.00			825.00	
	Issue of 1928							
C11	5¢ Beacon on Rocky Mountains	07/25/28	5.25	.75	175.00	(8)	55.00	107
	Recut frame line at left		6.75	1.25				
	Issues of 1930							
C12	5¢ Winged Globe	02/10/30	11.00	.50	150.00	(6)	12.50	98
a	Horizontal pair, imperf. between		4,500.00					
	Graf Zeppelin Issue							
C13	65¢ Zeppelin over Atlantic Ocean	04/19/30	275.00	160.00	2,400.00	(6)	1,900.00	0.09
C14	$1.30 Zeppelin Between Continents	04/19/30	550.00	375.00	6,000.00	(6)	1,350.00	0.07
C15	$2.60 Zeppelin Passing Globe	04/19/30	850.00	575.00	8,750.00	(6)	1,600.00	0.06
	Issues of 1931-32, Perf. 10.5 x 11							
C16	5¢ violet (C12)	08/19/31	5.50	.60	80.00	(4)	175.00	57
C17	8¢ olive bister (C12)	09/26/32	2.50	.40	32.50	(4)	15.00	77
	Issue of 1933, Century of Progress Issue, Perf. 11							
C18	50¢ Zeppelin, Federal Building at Chicago Exposition and Hangar at Friedrichshafen	10/02/33	80.00	70.00	675.00	(6)	225.00	0.3
	Beginning with #C19, unused values are for never-hinged stamps.							
	Issue of 1934, Perf. 10.5 x 11							
C19	6¢ dull orange (C12)	06/30/34	3.50	.25	30.00	(4)	200.00	302
	Issues of 1935-37, Trans-Pacific Issue, Perf. 11							
C20	25¢ "China Clipper" over the Pacific	11/22/35	1.40	1.00	25.00	(6)	20.00	10
C21	20¢ "China Clipper" over the Pacific	02/15/37	11.00	1.75	120.00	(6)	20.00	13
C22	50¢ carmine (C21)	02/15/37	10.00	5.00	120.00	(6)	20.00	9
	Issue of 1938							
C23	6¢ Eagle Holding Shield, Olive Branch and Arrows	05/14/38	.50	.15	8.00	(4)	15.00	350
a	Vertical pair, imperf. horizontally		375.00					
b	Horizontal pair, imperf. vertically		12,500.00					
	6¢ ultramarine and carmine		150.00					

	Issue of 1939, Perf. 11		Un	U	PB/LP	#	FDC	Q(M̄)
	Transatlantic Issue							
C24	30¢ Winged Globe	05/16/39	10.50	1.50	165.00	(6)	45.00	20
	Issues of 1941-44, Perf. 11 x 10.5							
C25	6¢ Twin-Motor Transport	06/25/41	.15	.15	.70	(4)	2.25	4,477
a	Booklet pane of 3	03/18/43	5.00	1.50			25.00	
	Singles of #C25a are imperf. at sides or imperf. at sides and bottom.							
b	Horizontal pair, imperf. between		1,750.00					
C26	8¢ olive green (C25)	03/21/44	.20	.15	1.25	(4)	3.75	1,745
C27	10¢ violet (C25)	08/15/41	1.25	.20	8.00	(4)	8.00	67
C28	15¢ brn. carmine (C25)	08/19/41	2.75	.35	11.00	(4)	10.00	78
C29	20¢ bright green (C25)	08/27/41	2.25	.30	10.00	(4)	12.50	42
C30	30¢ blue (C25)	09/25/41	2.50	.35	11.00	(4)	20.00	60
C31	50¢ orange (C25)	10/29/41	11.00	3.00	80.00	(4)	40.00	11
	Issue of 1946							
C32	5¢ DC-4 Skymaster	09/25/46	.15	.15	.45	(4)	2.00	865
	Issues of 1947, Perf. 10.5 x 11							
C33	5¢ DC-4 Skymaster	03/26/47	.15	.15	.45	(4)	2.00	972
	Perf. 11 x 10.5							
C34	10¢ Pan American Union Bldg., Washington, D.C. and Martin 2-0-2	08/30/47	.25	.15	1.10	(4)	2.00	208
C35	15¢ Statue of Liberty, N.Y. Skyline and Lockheed Constellation	08/20/47	.35	.15	1.25	(4)	2.00	756
a	Horizontal pair, imperf. between		2,000.00					
b	Dry printing		.55	.15	2.50	(4)		
C36	25¢ San Francisco-Oakland Bay Bridge and Boeing Stratocruiser	07/30/47	.85	.15	3.50	(4)	2.75	133
	Issues of 1948, Coil Stamp, Perf. 10 Horizontally							
C37	5¢ carmine (C33)	01/15/48	1.00	.80	10.00	(2)	2.00	33
	Perf. 11 x 10.5							
C38	5¢ New York City	07/31/48	.15	.15	3.75	(4)	1.75	38
	Issues of 1949, Perf. 10.5 x 11							
C39	6¢ carmine (C33)	01/18/49	.15	.15	.50	(4)	1.50	5,070
a	Booklet pane of 6	11/18/49	10.00	5.00			9.00	
b	Dry printing		.50	.15	2.25	(4)		
c	As "a," dry printing		15.00	—				
	Perf. 11 x 10.5							
C40	6¢ Alexandria, Virginia	05/11/49	.15	.15	.50	(4)	1.25	75
	Coil Stamp, Perf. 10 Horizontally							
C41	6¢ carmine (C33)	08/25/49	3.00	.15	14.00	(2)	1.25	260
	Universal Postal Union Issue, Perf. 11 x 10.5							
C42	10¢ Post Office Dept. Bldg.	11/18/49	.20	.20	1.40	(4)	1.75	21
C43	15¢ Globe and Doves Carrying Messages	10/07/49	.30	.25	1.25	(4)	2.25	37
C44	25¢ Boeing Stratocruiser and Globe	11/30/49	.50	.40	5.75	(4)	3.00	16
C45	6¢ Wright Brothers	12/17/49	.15	.15	.65	(4)	3.50	80
	Issue of 1952							
C46	80¢ Diamond Head, Honolulu, Hawaii	03/26/52	5.00	1.25	25.00	(4)	20.00	19
	Issue of 1953							
C47	6¢ Powered Flight	05/29/53	.15	.15	.55	(4)	1.50	78
	Issue of 1954							
C48	4¢ Eagle in Flight	09/03/54	.15	.15	1.40	(4)	1.00	50

C24

C25

C32

C33

C34

C35

C36

C38

C40

C42

C43

C44

C45

C46

C47

C48

C49

C51

C53

C54

C55

C56

C57

C58

C59

C61

C62

C63

C64

C66

C67

C68

C69

	Issue of 1957, Perf. 11 x 10.5		Un	U	PB/LP	#	FDC	Q(M̄)
C49	6¢ Air Force	08/01/57	.15	.15	.75	(4)	2.00	63
	Issues of 1958							
C50	5¢ rose red (C48)	07/31/58	.15	.15	1.40	(4)	1.00	72
	Perf. 10.5 x 11							
C51	7¢ Jet Airliner	07/31/58	.15	.15	.60	(4)	1.00	1,327
a	Booklet pane of 6		14.00	*7.00*			9.50	221
	Coil Stamp, Perf. 10 Horizontally							
C52	7¢ blue (C51)	07/31/58	2.25	.15	15.00	(2)	1.00	157
	Issues of 1959, Perf. 11 x 10.5							
C53	7¢ Alaska Statehood	01/03/59	.15	.15	.60	(4)	1.00	90
	Perf. 11							
C54	7¢ Balloon Jupiter	08/17/59	.15	.15	.60	(4)	1.10	79
	Perf. 11 x 10.5							
C55	7¢ Hawaii Statehood	08/21/59	.15	.15	.60	(4)	1.00	85
	Perf. 11							
C56	10¢ Pan American Games	08/27/59	.25	.25	1.25	(4)	1.00	39
	Issues of 1959-66							
C57	10¢ Liberty Bell	06/10/60	1.25	.70	5.50	(4)	1.25	40
C58	15¢ Statue of Liberty	11/20/59	.35	.20	1.50	(4)	1.25	98
C59	25¢ Abraham Lincoln	04/22/60	.50	.15	2.00	(4)	1.75	
a	Tagged	12/29/66	.60	.30	2.50	(4)	15.00	
	Issues of 1960, Perf. 10.5 x 11							
C60	7¢ carmine (C61)	08/12/60	.15	.15	.60	(4)	1.00	1,289
	Pair with full horizontal gutter between		—					
a	Booklet pane of 6	08/19/60	17.50	*8.00*			9.50	
	Coil Stamp, Perf. 10 Horizontally							
C61	7¢ Jet Airliner	10//22/60	4.25	.25	35.00	(2)	1.00	87
	Issues of 1961-67, Perf. 11							
C62	13¢ Liberty Bell	06/28/61	.40	.15	1.65	(4)	1.00	
a	Tagged	02/15/67	.75	.50	5.00	(4)	10.00	
C63	15¢ Statue of Liberty	01/13/61	.30	.15	1.25	(4)	1.00	
a	Tagged	01/11/67	.35	.20	1.50	(4)	15.00	
b	As "a," horiz. pair, imperf. vertically		*15,000.00*					
	#C63 has a gutter between the two parts of the design; C58 does not.							
	Issues of 1962-65, Perf. 10.5 x 11							
C64	8¢ Jetliner over Capitol	12/05/62	.15	.15	.65	(4)	1.00	
a	Tagged	08/01/63	.15	.15	.65	(4)	3.00	
b	Bklt. pane of 5 + label		7.00	*3.00*			3.00	
c	As "b," tagged	1964	2.00	*.75*				
	Coil Stamp, Perf. 10 Horizontally							
C65	8¢ carmine (C64)	12/05/62	.40	.15	3.75	(2)	1.00	
a	Tagged	01/14/65	.35	.15	1.50	(2)	—	
	Issue of 1963, Perf. 11							
C66	15¢ Montgomery Blair	05/03/63	.60	.55	2.75	(4)	1.10	42
	Issues of 1963-67, Perf. 11 x 10.5							
C67	6¢ Bald Eagle	07/12/63	.15	.15	1.80	(4)	1.00	
a	Tagged	02/15/67	3.00	2.50	35.00	(4)	15.00	
	1963 continued, Perf. 11							
C68	8¢ Amelia Earhart	07/24/63	.20	.15	1.00	(4)	2.00	64
	Issue of 1964							
C69	8¢ Robert H. Goddard	10/05/64	.40	.15	1.75	(4)	2.00	62

1967-1976

	Issues of 1967, Perf. 11		Un	U	PB/LP	#	FDC	Q(M̄)
C70	8¢ Alaska Purchase	03/30/67	.25	.15	1.40	(4)	1.00	56
C71	20¢ "Columbia Jays," by Audubon, (See also #1241)	04/26/67	.80	.15	3.50	(4)	2.00	165
	Issues of 1968, Unwmk., Perf. 11 x 10.5							
C72	10¢ 50-Star Runway	01/05/68	.20	.15	.90	(4)	1.00	
b	Booklet pane of 8		2.00	.75			3.50	
c	Booklet pane of 5 + label	01/06/68	3.75	.75			125.00	
	Coil Stamp, Perf. 10 Vertically							
C73	10¢ carmine (C72)	01/05/68	.30	.15	1.70	(2)	1.00	
a	Imperf. pair		600.00		900.00	(2)		
	Perf. 11							
C74	10¢ U.S. Air Mail Service	05/15/68	.25	.15	2.00	(4)	1.50	
a	Red (tail stripe) omitted			—				
C75	20¢ USA and Jet	11/22/68	.35	.15	1.75	(4)	1.10	
	Issue of 1969							
C76	10¢ Moon Landing	09/09/69	.25	.15	.95	(4)	5.00	152
a	Rose red omitted		500.00	—				
	Issues of 1971-73, Perf. 10.5 x 11							
C77	9¢ Delta Wing Plane	05/15/71	.20	.15	.90	(4)	1.00	
	Perf. 11 x 10.5							
C78	11¢ Silhouette of Jet	05/07/71	.20	.15	.90	(4)	1.00	
a	Booklet pane of 4 + 2 labels		1.25	.75			1.75	
C79	13¢ Winged Airmail Envelope	11/16/73	.25	.15	1.10	(4)	1.00	
a	Booklet pane of 5 + label	12/27/73	1.50	.75			1.75	
b	Untagged (Bureau precanceled)			.30				
	Perf. 11							
C80	17¢ Statue of Liberty	07/13/71	.30	.15	1.40	(4)	1.00	
C81	21¢ USA and Jet	05/21/71	.35	.15	1.65	(4)	1.00	
	Coil Stamps, Perf. 10 Vertically							
C82	11¢ carmine (C78)	05/07/71	.25	.15	.80	(2)	1.00	
a	Imperf. pair		250.00		375.00	(2)		
C83	13¢ carmine (C79)	12/27/73	.30	.15	1.00	(2)	1.00	
a	Imperf. pair		80.00		125.00	(2)		
	Issues of 1972, National Parks Centennial Issue, Perf. 11 (See also #1448-54)							
C84	11¢ Kii Statue and Temple at City of Refuge Historical National Park, Honaunau, Hawaii	05/03/72	.20	.15	.90	(4)	1.00	78
a	Blue and green omitted		1,100.00					
	Olympic Games Issue, Perf. 11 x 10.5 (See also #1460-62)							
C85	11¢ Skiers and Olympic Rings	08/17/72	.20	.15	2.25	(10)	1.00	96
	Issues of 1973, Progress in Electronics Issue, Perf. 11 (See also #1500-02)							
C86	11¢ DeForest Audions	07/10/73	.20	.15	.95	(4)	1.00	59
a	Vermilion and green omitted		1,400.00					
	Issues of 1974							
C87	18¢ Statue of Liberty	01/11/74	.35	.25	1.50	(4)	1.00	
C88	26¢ Mount Rushmore National Memorial	01/02/74	.50	.15	2.25	(4)	1.25	
	Issues of 1976							
C89	25¢ Plane and Globes	01/02/76	.45	.15	2.10	(4)	1.25	
C90	31¢ Plane, Globes and Flag	01/02/76	.50	.15	2.25	(4)	1.25	

C70

C71

C72

C74

C75

C76

C77

C78

C79

C80

C81

C84

C85

C86

C87

C88

C89

C90

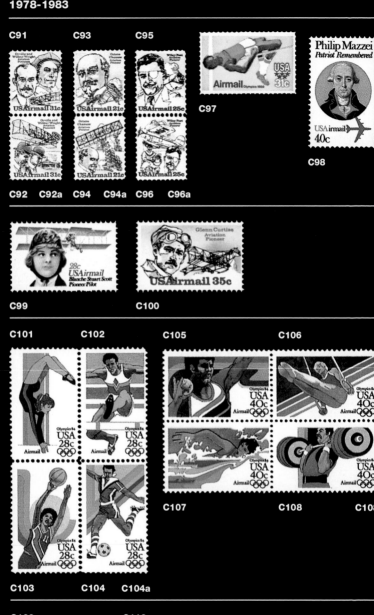

C91 C93 C95

C97

C98

C92 C92a C94 C94a C96 C96a

C99 C100

C101 C102

C105 C106

C107 C108 C108

C103 C104 C104a

C109 C110

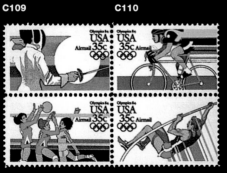

C111 C112 C112a

	Issues of 1978, Perf. 11		Un	U	PB	#	FDC	Q(M̄)
	Aviation Pioneers Issue, Wright Brothers (See also #C93-96)							
C91	31¢ Wright Brothers, Flyer A	09/23/78	.60	.30			3.00	157
C92	31¢ Wright Brothers, Flyer A and Shed	09/23/78	.60	.30			3.00	157
a	Vert. pair, #C91-92		1.20	1.10	2.75	(4)	4.00	
b	As "a," ultramarine and black omitted		800.00					
c	As "a," black omitted		—					
d	As "a," black, yellow, magenta, blue and brown omitted		2,250.00					
	Issues of 1979, Aviation Pioneers Issue, Octave Chanute							
C93	21¢ Chanute and Biplane Hang-Glider	03/29/79	.70	.30			3.00	29
C94	21¢ Biplane Hang-Glider and Chanute	03/29/79	.70	.30			3.00	29
a	Attached pair, #C93-94		1.40	1.10	3.25	(4)	4.00	
b	As "a," ultramarine and black omitted		4,500.00					
	Aviation Pioneers Issue, Wiley Post (See also #C99-100)							
C95	25¢ Wiley Post and "Winnie Mae"	11/20/79	1.10	.35			3.00	32
C96	25¢ NR-105-W, Post in Pressurized Suit and Portrait	11/20/79	1.10	.35			3.00	32
a	Attached pair, #C95-96		2.25	1.25	8.00	(4)	4.00	
	Olympic Summer Games Issue (See also #1790-94)							
C97	31¢ High Jumper	11/01/79	.65	.30	9.50	(12)	1.25	47
	Issues of 1980-82							
C98	40¢ Philip Mazzei	10/13/80	.75	.15	9.50	(12)	1.35	81
a	Perf. 10.5 x 11	1982	4.50	—	90.00	(12)		
b	Imperf. pair		3,500.00					
	Issues of 1980, Aviation Pioneers Issues, Blanche Stuart Scott							
C99	28¢ Portrait of Scott and Biplane	12/30/80	.55	.15	6.75	(12)	1.25	20
	Glenn Curtiss (See also #C113-14)							
C100	35¢ Portrait of Curtiss and "Pusher" Biplane	12/30/80	.60	.15	8.00	(12)	1.25	23
	Issues of 1983, Olympic Summer Games Issue (See also #2048-51 and 2082-85)							
C101	28¢ Gymnast	06/17/83	1.00	.30			1.25	43
C102	28¢ Hurdler	06/17/83	1.00	.30			1.25	43
C103	28¢ Basketball Player	06/17/83	1.00	.30			1.25	43
C104	28¢ Soccer Player	06/17/83	1.00	.30			1.25	43
a	Block of 4, #C101-04		4.50	2.00	6.75	(4)	3.75	
	Olympic Summer Games Issue (See also #2048-51 and 2082-85)							
C105	40¢ Shotputter	04/08/83	.90	.40			1.35	67
C106	40¢ Gymnast	04/08/83	.90	.40			1.35	67
C107	40¢ Swimmer	04/08/83	.90	.40			1.35	67
C108	40¢ Weightlifter	04/08/83	.90	.40			1.35	67
a	Block of 4, #C105-08		4.25	2.50	4.75	(4)	5.00	
b	As "a," imperf.		1,350.00					
	Olympic Summer Games Issue (See also #2048-51 and 2082-85)							
C109	35¢ Fencer	11/04/83	.90	.50			1.25	43
C110	35¢ Bicyclist	11/04/83	.90	.50			1.25	43
C111	35¢ Volleyball Players	11/04/83	.90	.50			1.25	43
C112	35¢ Pole Vaulter	11/04/83	.90	.50			1.25	43
a	Block of 4, #C109-12		4.00	3.00	6.75	(4)	4.50	

	Issues of 1985, Perf. 11		Un	U	PB	#	FDC	Q(M)
	Aviation Pioneers Issues, Alfred Verville							
C113	33¢ Portrait of Verville and Airplane Diagram	02/13/85	.60	.20	3.00	(4)	1.25	168
a	Imperf. pair		1,000.00					
	Lawrence and Elmer Sperry (See also #C118-19)							
C114	39¢ Portrait of Sperrys and Seaplane	02/13/85	.70	.25	3.25	(4)	1.35	168
a	Imperf. pair		1,400.00					
C115	44¢ Transpacific Airmail	02/15/85	.80	.25	3.75	(4)	1.35	209
a	Imperf. pair		1,000.00					
C116	44¢ Junipero Serra	08/22/85	.90	.30	8.00	(4)	1.50	164
a	Imperf. pair		1,600.00					
	Issues of 1988							
C117	44¢ New Sweden	03/29/88	1.00	.25	7.00	(4)	1.35	137
	Aviation Pioneers Issues, Langley and Sikorsky (See also #C128-29)							
C118	45¢ Samuel P. Langley	05/14/88	.85	.20	4.00	(4)	1.40	406
C119	36¢ Igor Sikorsky	06/23/88	.65	.20	3.10	(4)	2.50	179
	Issues of 1989, Perf. 11.5 x 11							
C120	45¢ French Revolution	07/14/89	.85	.20	4.50	(4)	1.40	38
	America/PUAS Issue, Perf. 11 (See also #2426)							
C121	45¢ Southeast Carved Wood Figure, Key Marco Cat (A.D. 700-1450), Emblem of the Postal Union of the Americas and Spain	10/12/89	.85	.20	5.25	(4)	1.40	39
	20th UPU Congress Issue, Future Mail Transportation (See also #2434-38)							
C122	45¢ Hypersonic Airliner	11/27/89	1.00	.40			1.40	27
C123	45¢ Air-Cushion Vehicle	11/27/89	1.00	.40			1.40	27
C124	45¢ Surface Rover	11/27/89	1.00	.40			1.40	27
C125	45¢ Shuttle	11/27/89	1.00	.40			1.40	27
a	Block of 4, #C122-25		4.00	3.00	5.00	(4)	5.00	
b	As "a," light blue omitted		1,350.00					

Key Marco Cat artifact

This ceremonial carved wooden figure, now known as the Key Marco Cat, is one of several pre-Colombian Indian artifacts uncovered at Key Marco, Florida, in 1896. They are among the few known remains of the ancient Calusa culture, which once thrived along Florida's southwest coast and outlying keys. The Calusa were hard workers and fierce fighters, with tools and weapons fashioned from seashells and fishbones. A maritime people, they were also accomplished seamen, paddling dugout canoes not only around much of the Florida coast but journeying to Cuba and other Caribbean islands to trade fish, skins and amber. Their disappearance during the 18th century remains an unsolved mystery. **(#C121)**

Interesting Fact: While one theory has the Calusa emigrating to Cuba, the Seminole maintain that the Calusa remained in Florida and accompanied them west when the tribe relocated to Oklahoma.

C113

C114

C115

C116

C117

C118

C119

C120

C121

C122   C123

C124   C125   C125a

20th Universal Postal Congress

A glimpse at several potential mail delivery methods of the future is the theme of these four stamps issued by the U.S. in commemoration of the convening of the 20th Universal Postal Congress in Washington, D.C. from November 13 through December 14, 1989. The United States, as host nation to the Congress for the first time in ninety-two years, welcomed more than 1,000 delegates from most of the member nations of the Universal Postal Union to the major international event.

C126

C127

C128

C129

C130

C131

CE1

CE2

E1

E3

E4

Issues of 1989, Imperf.		Un	U	PB	#	FDC	Q(M)
20th UPU Congress Issue Souvenir Sheet							
C126 Designs of #C122-25	11/24/89	4.25	3.25			3.00	2
a-d Single stamp from sheet		.90	.50				
Issue of 1990, America/PUAS Issue, Perf. 11 (See also #2512)							
C127 45¢ Tropical Coast	10/12/90	.85	.20	5.25	(4)	1.40	39
Issues of 1991, Aviation Pioneers Issues, Harriet Quimby							
C128 50¢ Portrait of Quimby and Early Plane	04/27/91	.90	.25	4.50	(4)	1.35	
b 50¢ Portrait of Quimby (C128)	04/27/91	.90	.25	4.50	(4)		
William T. Piper							
C129 40¢ Portrait of Piper and Piper Cub Airplane	05/17/91	.80	.20	4.00	(4)	1.25	
C130 50¢ Antarctic Treaty	06/21/91	.90	.25	4.50	(4)	1.35	113
Issues of 1991-93, America/PUAS Issue							
C131 50¢ Eskimo and Bering Land Bridge	10/12/91	.90	.25	4.75	(4)	1.35	15
C132 40¢ Portrait of Piper	1993	.80	.20	4.00	(4)		
Airmail Special Delivery Stamps							
Issues of 1934							
CE1 16¢ Great Seal of the United States	08/30/34	.60	.65	15.00	(6)	25.00	
For imperforate variety see #771.							
Issue of 1936							
CE2 16¢ red and blue	02/10/36	.40	.25	6.50	(4)	17.50	
a Horizontal pair, imperf. vertically		4,000.00					
Special Delivery Stamps							
Issue of 1885, Perf. 12, Unwmkd.							
E1 10¢ Messenger Running	10/01/85	275.00	40.00	11,000.00	(8)	8,000.00	
Issue of 1888							
E2 10¢ blue Messenger Running (E3)	09/06/88	250.00	15.00	10,000.00	(8)		
Issue of 1893							
E3 10¢ Messenger Running	01/24/93	165.00	20.00	6,000.00	(8)		
Issue of 1894, Line under "Ten Cents"							
E4 10¢ Messenger Running	10/10/94	600.00	25.00	12,000.00	(6)		

"The First Americans Crossed Over From Asia"

These words explain the history of the Eskimo people. The Bering Land "Bridge," which is believed to be a continent-sized land mass connecting Asia to North America, now lies at the bottom of the Bering Sea, dividing Alaska and Siberia. The discovery of this land at the bottom of the sea answered the question of how man arrived in North America and why the present day people of the Arctic region of Alaska and Siberia, known as Eskimos or Inuit, are considered an Asian people. The Arctic people in Alaska generally prefer the name Eskimo, while those in Canada and Greenland are believed to prefer Inuit. **(#C131)**

	Issue of 1895		Un	U	PB	#	FDC
	Perf. 12, Wmkd. (191)						
E5	10¢ bl. Messenger Running (E4)	08/16/95	140.00	3.25	*4,000.00*	(6)	
	Double transfer		—	15.00			
	Line of color through "POSTAL DELIVERY"		175.00	10.50			
	Dots in curved frame above messenger		160.00	7.50			
	Issue of 1902						
E6	10¢ Messenger on Bicycle	12/09/02	90.00	3.00	*2,250.00*	(6)	
	Damaged transfer under "N" of "CENTS"		110.00	3.50			
	Issue of 1908						
E7	10¢ Mercury Helmet and Olive Branch	12/12/08	55.00	30.00	*850.00*	(6)	
	Issue of 1911, Wmkd. (190)						
E8	10¢ ultramarine Messenger on Bicycle (E6)	01/11	90.00	5.00	*2,000.00*	(6)	
	Top frame line missing		110.00	6.00			
	Issue of 1914, Perf. 10						
E9	10¢ ultramarine Messenger on Bicycle (E6)	09/14	160.00	6.00	*3,500.00*	(6)	
	Issue of 1916, Unwmkd.						
E10	10¢ ultramarine Messenger on Bicycle (E6)	10/19/16	265.00	25.00	*4,750.00*	(6)	
	Issue of 1917, Perf. 11						
E11	10¢ ultramarine Messenger on Bicycle (E6)	05/02/17	16.50	.50	200.00	(6)	
c	Blue		45.00	2.50			
d	Perf. 10 at left		—				
	Issue of 1922						
E12	10¢ Postman and Motorcycle	07/12/22	27.50	.40	350.00	(6)	400.00
a	10¢ deep ultramarine		32.50	.50			
	Double transfer		42.50	1.25			
	Issues of 1925						
E13	15¢ Postman and Motorcycle	04/11/25	25.00	.90	250.00	(6)	225.00
E14	20¢ Post Office Truck	04/25/25	1.75	1.40	30.00	(6)	90.00
	Issue of 1927, Perf. 11 x 10.5						
E15	10¢ gray violet Postman and Motorcycle (E12)	11/29/27	.60	.15	4.00	(4)	90.00
c	Horizontal pair, imperf. between		300.00				
	Cracked plate		35.00				
	Issue of 1931						
E16	15¢ or. Postman and Motorcycle (E13)	08/13/31	.70	.15	3.75	(4)	125.00
	Beginning with #E17, unused values are for never-hinged stamps.						
	Issues of 1944						
E17	13¢ Postman and Motorcycle	10/30/44	.60	.15	3.00	(4)	12.00
E18	17¢ Postman and Motorcycle	10/30/44	2.75	1.75	22.50	(4)	12.00
	Issue of 1951						
E19	20¢ blk. Post Office Truck (E14)	11/30/51	1.25	.15	5.50	(4)	5.00
	Issues of 1954-57						
E20	20¢ Delivery of Letter	10/13/54	.40	.15	2.00	(4)	3.00
E21	30¢ Delivery of Letter	09/03/57	.50	.15	2.40	(4)	2.25
	Issues of 1969-71, Perf. 11						
E22	45¢ Arrows	11/21/69	1.25	.25	5.50	(4)	3.50
E23	60¢ Arrows	05/10/71	1.25	.20	5.50	(4)	3.50

E6

E7

E12

E13

E14

E18

E20

E21

E22

E23

Registration, Certified Mail and Postage Due Stamps

1879-1959

F1

FA1

J2   J19   J25   J33

J69   J78

J88   J98

J101

	Issue of 1911		Un	U	PB	#	FDC	Q(M̄)
	Perf. 12, Wmkd. (190)							
	Registration Stamp Issued for the prepayment of registry; not usable for postage. Sale discontinued May 28, 1913.							
F1	10¢ Bald Eagle	12/01/11	75.00	6.00	*1,500.00*	(6)	*8,000.00*	
	Certified Mail Stamp For use on First-Class mail for which no indemnity value was claimed, but for which proof of mailing and proof of delivery were available at less cost than registered mail.							
	Issue of 1955, Perf. 10.5 x 11							
FA1	15¢ Letter Carrier	06/06/55	.40	.25	4.50	(4)	3.25	54
	Postage Due Stamps For affixing by a postal clerk to any mail to denote amount to be collected from addressee because of insufficient prepayment of postage.							
	Issues of 1879, Printed by American Bank Note Co., Design of #J2, Perf. 12, Unwmkd.							
J1	1¢ brown		45.00	8.50				
J2	2¢ Figure of Value		300.00	7.50				
J3	3¢ brown		40.00	4.50				
J4	5¢ brown		500.00	45.00				
J5	10¢ brown	09/19/79	525.00	25.00				
a	Imperf. pair		*1,600.00*					
J6	30¢ brown	09/19/79	250.00	50.00				
J7	50¢ brown	09/19/79	350.00	60.00				
	Special Printing, Soft, Porous Paper							
J8	1¢ deep brown		*6,250.00*					
J9	2¢ deep brown		*4,250.00*					
J10	3¢ deep brown		*3,750.00*					
J11	5¢ deep brown		*3,500.00*					
J12	10¢ deep brown		*2,250.00*					
J13	30¢ deep brown		*2,400.00*					
J14	50¢ deep brown		*2,500.00*					
	Issues of 1884, Design of #J19							
J15	1¢ red brown		45.00	4.50				
J16	2¢ red brown		55.00	4.50				
J17	3¢ red brown		825.00	175.00				
J18	5¢ red brown		385.00	25.00				
J19	10¢ Figure of Value		385.00	17.50				
J20	30¢ red brown		175.00	50.00				
J21	50¢ red brown		1,500.00	175.00				
	Issues of 1891, Design of #J25							
J22	1¢ bright claret		20.00	1.00				
J23	2¢ bright claret		25.00	1.00				
J24	3¢ bright claret		50.00	8.00				
J25	5¢ Figure of Value		60.00	8.00				
J26	10¢ bright claret		100.00	17.50				
J27	30¢ bright claret		350.00	150.00				
J28	50¢ bright claret		375.00	150.00				
	Issues of 1894, Printed by the Bureau of Engraving and Printing, Design of #J33, Perf. 12							
J29	1¢ vermilion		1,300.00	325.00	8,500.00	(6)		
J30	2¢ vermilion		550.00	125.00	4,250.00	(6)		
	Issues of 1894-95, Design of #J33, Unwmkd., Perf. 12							
J31	1¢ deep claret	08/14/94	37.50	6.00	525.00	(6)		
J32	2¢ deep claret	07/20/94	35.00	4.00	475.00	(6)		
J33	3¢ Figure of Value	04/27/95	140.00	30.00	1,350.00	(6)		

	Issues of 1894-95		Un	U	PB	#
	Design of #J33, Unwmkd., Perf. 12					
J34	5¢ deep claret	04/27/95	200.00	35.00	1,500.00	(6)
J35	10¢ deep claret	09/24/94	200.00	25.00	1,650.00	(6)
J36	30¢ deep claret	04/27/95	350.00	90.00		
b	30¢ pale rose		290.00	85.00	2,750.00	(6)
J37	50¢ deep claret	04/27/95	925.00	250.00		
a	50¢ pale rose		875.00	250.00	7,000.00	(6)
	Issues of 1895-97, Design of #J33, Wmkd. (191)					
J38	1¢ deep claret	08/29/95	7.50	.75	225.00	(6)
J39	2¢ deep claret	09/14/95	7.50	.70	225.00	(6)
J40	3¢ deep claret	10/30/95	47.50	1.75	550.00	(6)
J41	5¢ deep claret	10/15/95	50.00	1.75	600.00	(6)
J42	10¢ deep claret	09/14/95	52.50	3.50	650.00	(6)
J43	30¢ deep claret	08/21/97	450.00	50.00	4,750.00	(6)
J44	50¢ deep claret	03/17/96	275.00	37.50	3,000.00	(6)
	Issues of 1910-12, Design of #J33, Wmkd. (190)					
J45	1¢ deep claret	08/30/10	27.50	3.00		
a	1¢ rose carmine		25.00	3.00	450.00	(6)
J46	2¢ deep claret	11/25/10	27.50	1.00		
a	2¢ rose carmine		25.00	1.00	425.00	(6)
J47	3¢ deep claret	08/31/10	450.00	30.00	4,500.00	(6)
J48	5¢ deep claret	08/31/10	75.00	6.50		
a	5¢ rose carmine		—	—	750.00	(6)
J49	10¢ deep claret	08/31/10	95.00	12.50	1,300.00	(6)
J50	50¢ deep claret	09/23/12	750.00	120.00	8,000.00	(6)
	Issues of 1914, Design of #J33, Perf. 10					
J52	1¢ carmine lake		50.00	11.00	550.00	(6)
J53	2¢ carmine lake		40.00	.40	450.00	(6)
J54	3¢ carmine lake		750.00	37.50	6,500.00	(6)
J55	5¢ carmine lake		32.50	2.50	325.00	(6)
	5¢ deep claret		—	—		
J56	10¢ carmine lake		50.00	2.00	650.00	(6)
J57	30¢ carmine lake		200.00	17.50	2,500.00	(6)
J58	50¢ carmine lake		8,250.00	650.00	57,500.00	(6)
	Issues of 1916, Design of #J33, Unwmkd.					
J59	1¢ rose		2,000.00	300.00	13,000.00	(6)
	Experimental Bureau precancel, New Orleans			200.00		
J60	2¢ rose		150.00	20.00	1,250.00	(6)
	Issues of 1917-25, Design of #J33, Perf. 11					
J61	1¢ carmine rose		2.50	.25	45.00	(6)
J62	2¢ carmine rose		2.25	.25	40.00	(6)
J63	3¢ carmine rose		10.00	.25	100.00	(6)
J64	5¢ carmine		10.00	.25	100.00	(6)
J65	10¢ carmine rose		15.00	.30	160.00	(6)
	Double transfer		—	—		
J66	30¢ carmine rose		80.00	.75	675.00	(6)
J67	50¢ carmine rose		100.00	.30	900.00	(6)
J68	1/2¢ dull red	04/13/25	1.00	.25	12.50	(6)

	Issue of 1930-31		Un	U	PB	#
	Design of #J69, Perf. 11					
J69	1/2¢ Figure of Value		4.50	1.40	42.50	(6)
J70	1¢ carmine		3.00	.25	30.00	(6)
J71	2¢ carmine		4.00	.25	45.00	(6)
J72	3¢ carmine		21.00	1.75	275.00	(6)
J73	5¢ carmine		19.00	2.50	250.00	(6)
J74	10¢ carmine		40.00	1.00	450.00	(6)
J75	30¢ carmine		110.00	2.00	1,100.00	(6)
J76	50¢ carmine		140.00	.75	1,400.00	(6)
	Design of #J78					
J77	$1 carmine		30.00	.25		
a	$1 scarlet		25.00	.25	275.00	(6)
J78	$5 "FIVE" on $		37.50	.25		
a	$5 scarlet		32.50	.25		
b	As "a," wet printing		35.00	.25	375.00	(6)
	Issues of 1931-56, Design of #J69, Perf. 11 x 10.5					
J79	1/2¢ dull carmine		.90	.15	22.50	(4)
J80	1¢ dull carmine		.20	.15	1.75	(4)
J81	2¢ dull carmine		.20	.15	1.75	(4)
J82	3¢ dull carmine		.25	.15	2.50	(4)
b	Scarlet, wet printing		.30	.15		
J83	5¢ dull carmine		.40	.15	3.25	(4)
J84	10¢ dull carmine		1.10	.15	6.75	(4)
b	Scarlet, wet printing		1.25	.15		
J85	30¢ dull carmine		7.50	.25	35.00	(4)
J86	50¢ dull carmine		10.00	.25	52.50	(4)
	Design of J78, Perf. 10.5 x 11					
J87	$1 scarlet		35.00	.25	210.00	(4)
	Beginning with #J88, unused values are for never-hinged stamps.					
	Issues of 1959, Designs of #J88, J98 and J101, Perf. 11 x 10.5					
J88	1/2¢ Figure of Value	06/19/59	1.50	1.10	180.00	(4)
J89	1¢ carmine rose	06/19/59	.15	.15	.35	(4)
a	"1 CENT" omitted		300.00			
b	Pair, one without "1 CENT"		450.00			
J90	2¢ carmine rose	06/19/59	.15	.15	.45	(4)
J91	3¢ carmine rose	06/19/59	.15	.15	.50	(4)
J92	4¢ carmine rose	06/19/59	.15	.15	.60	(4)
J93	5¢ carmine rose	06/19/59	.15	.15	.65	(4)
J94	6¢ carmine rose	06/19/59	.15	.15	.70	(4)
a	Pair, one without "6 CENTS"		800.00			
J95	7¢ carmine rose	06/19/59	.20	.15	.80	(4)
J96	8¢ carmine rose	06/19/59	.20	.15	.90	(4)
J97	10¢ carmine rose	06/19/59	.20	.15	1.00	(4)
J98	30¢ Figure of Value	06/19/59	.65	.15	2.75	(4)
J99	50¢ carmine rose	06/19/59	1.10	.15	5.00	(4)
	Design of #J101					
J100	$1 carmine rose	06/19/59	2.00	.15	8.75	(4)
J101	$5 Outline Figure of Value	06/19/59	9.00	.20	45.00	(4)
	Issues of 1978-85, Designs of #J98					
J102	11¢ carmine rose	01/02/78	.25	.20	2.00	(4)
J103	13¢ carmine rose	01/02/78	.25	.20	2.00	(4)
J104	17¢ carmine rose	06/10/85	.40	.35	25.00	(4)

Official and Penalty Mail Stamps

1873-1995

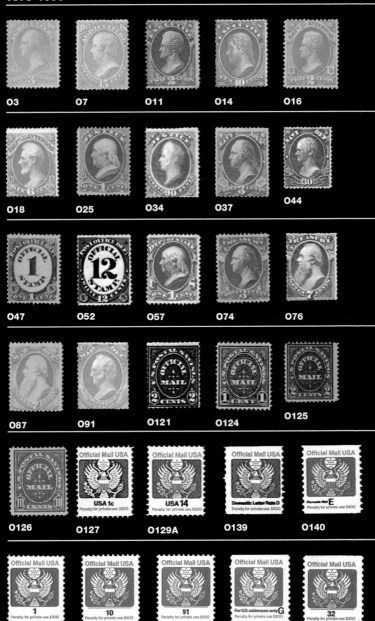

O3 O7 O11 O14 O16

O18 O25 O34 O37 O44

O47 O52 O57 O74 O76

O87 O91 O121 O124 O125

O126 O127 O129A O139 O140

O143 O146A O151 O152 O153

O154 O155 O156

Issues of 1873	Un	U
Thin, Hard Paper, Perf. 12, Unwmkd.		

Official Stamps

The franking privilege having been abolished as of July 1, 1873, these stamps were provided for each of the departments of government for the prepayment on official matter. These stamps were supplanted on May 1, 1879, by penalty envelopes and on July 5, 1884, were declared obsolete.

Department of Agriculture Issue: Yellow

		Un	U
O1	1¢ Franklin	150.00	110.00
	Ribbed paper	150.00	120.00
O2	2¢ Jackson	125.00	45.00
O3	3¢ Washington	110.00	8.50
	Double transfer	—	—
O4	6¢ Lincoln	120.00	35.00
O5	10¢ Jefferson	240.00	140.00
	10¢ golden yellow	240.00	145.00
	10¢ olive yellow	250.00	150.00
O6	12¢ Clay	325.00	175.00
	12¢ golden yellow	325.00	180.00
O7	15¢ Webster	275.00	160.00
	15¢ olive yellow	270.00	170.00
O8	24¢ Scott	275.00	140.00
	24¢ golden yellow	275.00	145.00
O9	30¢ Hamilton	350.00	200.00
	30¢ olive yellow	360.00	210.00

Executive Dept. Issue: Carmine

O10	1¢ Franklin	525.00	300.00
O11	2¢ Jackson	350.00	150.00
	Double transfer	—	—
O12	3¢ Washington	425.00	150.00
O13	6¢ Lincoln	625.00	375.00
O14	10¢ Jefferson	575.00	450.00

Dept. of the Interior Issue: Vermilion

O15	1¢ Franklin	32.50	7.50
	Ribbed paper	35.00	9.00
O16	2¢ Jackson	27.50	5.00
O17	3¢ Washington	45.00	4.50
O18	6¢ Lincoln	32.50	4.50
O19	10¢ Jefferson	32.50	9.00
O20	12¢ Clay	47.50	7.00
O21	15¢ Webster	80.00	15.00
	Double transfer of left side	125.00	22.50
O22	24¢ Scott	57.50	12.50
O23	30¢ Hamilton	80.00	12.50
O24	90¢ Perry	180.00	32.50

Dept. of Justice Issue: Purple

O25	1¢ Franklin	100.00	70.00
O26	2¢ Jackson	165.00	75.00
O27	3¢ Washington	165.00	15.00
O28	6¢ Lincoln	150.00	22.50

Issues of 1873, Perf. 12	Un	U
Dept. of Justice Issue (continued): Purple		

O29	10¢ Jefferson	170.00	50.00
	Double transfer	—	—
O30	12¢ Clay	135.00	32.50
O31	15¢ Webster	260.00	110.00
O32	24¢ Scott	650.00	250.00
O33	30¢ Hamilton	550.00	150.00
	Double transfer at top	550.00	160.00
O34	90¢ Perry	825.00	375.00

Navy Dept. Issue: Ultramarine

O35	1¢ Franklin	70.00	32.50
a	1¢ dull blue	80.00	35.00
O36	2¢ Jackson	55.00	15.00
a	2¢ dull blue	65.00	10.00
	2¢ gray blue	52.50	15.00
O37	3¢ Washington	55.00	7.50
a	3¢ dull blue	65.00	10.00
O38	6¢ Lincoln	55.00	12.50
a	6¢ dull blue	65.00	13.00
	Vertical line through "N" of "NAVY"	85.00	17.50
O39	7¢ Stanton	350.00	130.00
a	7¢ dull blue	400.00	140.00
O40	10¢ Jefferson	75.00	25.00
a	10¢ dull blue	80.00	25.00
	Cracked plate	*150.00*	—
O41	12¢ Clay	90.00	22.50
	Double transfer of left side	140.00	40.00
O42	15¢ Webster	165.00	45.00
O43	24¢ Scott	165.00	50.00
a	24¢ dull blue	190.00	—
O44	30¢ Hamilton	135.00	25.00
O45	90¢ Perry	650.00	160.00
a	Double impression		*3,750.00*

Post Office Dept. Issue: Black

O47	1¢ Figure of Value	12.00	5.00
O48	2¢ Figure of Value	15.00	4.00
a	Double impression	300.00	
O49	3¢ Figure of Value	5.00	1.25
	Cracked plate	—	—
O50	6¢ Figure of Value	15.00	3.00
	Vertical ribbed paper	—	9.00
O51	10¢ Figure of Value	65.00	30.00
O52	12¢ Figure of Value	32.50	7.50
O53	15¢ Figure of Value	45.00	12.50
	Double transfer	—	—
O54	24¢ Figure of Value	55.00	15.00
O55	30¢ Figure of Value	55.00	15.00
O56	90¢ Figure of Value	85.00	12.50

1873-1879

Dept. of State Issue: Green

		Un	U
O57	1¢ Franklin	100.00	35.00
O58	2¢ Jackson	200.00	55.00
O59	3¢ Washington	80.00	15.00
	Double paper	—	—
O60	6¢ Lincoln	75.00	17.50
O61	7¢ Stanton	150.00	35.00
	Ribbed paper	160.00	40.00
O62	10¢ Jefferson	120.00	25.00
	Short transfer	140.00	37.50
O63	12¢ Clay	185.00	75.00
O64	15¢ Webster	200.00	50.00
O65	24¢ Scott	400.00	130.00
O66	30¢ Hamilton	375.00	100.00
O67	90¢ Perry	700.00	225.00
O68	$2 Seward	850.00	600.00
O69	$5 Seward	6,000.00	3,000.00
O70	$10 Seward	4,000.00	2,000.00
O71	$20 Seward	3,250.00	1,500.00

Treasury Dept. Issue: Brown

		Un	U
O72	1¢ Franklin	35.00	4.00
	Double transfer	37.50	5.50
O73	2¢ Jackson	45.00	4.00
	Double transfer	—	7.00
	Cracked plate	55.00	—
O74	3¢ Washington	30.00	1.50
	Shaded circle outside right frame line	—	—
O75	6¢ Lincoln	40.00	3.50
	Worn plate	35.00	4.75
O76	7¢ Stanton	85.00	20.00
O77	10¢ Jefferson	85.00	7.00
O78	12¢ Clay	85.00	5.50
O79	15¢ Webster	80.00	7.00
O80	24¢ Scott	400.00	57.50
O81	30¢ Hamilton	135.00	8.00
	Short transfer top right	—	—
O82	90¢ Perry	140.00	9.00

War Dept. Issue: Rose

		Un	U
O83	1¢ Franklin	130.00	6.50
O84	2¢ Jackson	120.00	8.50
	Ribbed paper	110.00	10.00
O85	3¢ Washington	125.00	2.50
O86	6¢ Lincoln	400.00	5.50
O87	7¢ Stanton	120.00	65.00
O88	10¢ Jefferson	40.00	10.00

War Dept. Issue (continued): Rose

		Un	U
O89	12¢ Clay	135.00	8.00
	Ribbed paper	140.00	9.00
O90	15¢ Webster	35.00	10.00
	Ribbed paper	35.00	12.50
O91	24¢ Scott	35.00	6.00
O92	30¢ Hamilton	37.50	6.00
O93	90¢ Perry	85.00	35.00

Issues of 1879, Soft, Porous Paper
Dept. of Agriculture: Yellow

		Un	U
O94	1¢ Franklin, issued without gum	2,100.00	
O95	3¢ Washington	275.00	50.00

Dept. of the Interior Issue: Vermilion

		Un	U
O96	1¢ Franklin	200.00	175.00
O97	2¢ Jackson	3.75	1.50
O98	3¢ Washington	3.25	1.00
O99	6¢ Lincoln	5.00	5.00
O100	10¢ Jefferson	60.00	50.00
O101	12¢ Clay	120.00	80.00
O102	15¢ Webster	275.00	200.00
	Double transfer	300.00	—
O103	24¢ Scott	2,600.00	
O104-05	Not assigned		

Dept. of Justice Issue: Bluish Purple

		Un	U
O106	3¢ Washington	80.00	50.00
O107	6¢ Lincoln	175.00	140.00

Post Office Dept. Issue: Black

		Un	U
O108	3¢ Figure of Value	14.00	4.50

Treasury Dept. Issue: Brown

		Un	U
O109	3¢ Washington	42.50	6.00
O110	6¢ Lincoln	80.00	30.00
O111	10¢ Jefferson	120.00	35.00
O112	30¢ Hamilton	1,200.00	250.00
O113	90¢ Perry	1,650.00	250.00

War Dept. Issue: Rose Red

		Un	U
O114	1¢ Franklin	3.25	2.50
O115	2¢ Jackson	4.75	2.75
O116	3¢ Washington	4.75	1.40
b	Double impression	750.00	
	Double transfer	7.50	4.75
O117	6¢ Lincoln	4.25	1.30
O118	10¢ Jefferson	35.00	32.50
O119	12¢ Clay	27.50	9.00
O120	30¢ Hamilton	75.00	60.00

Issues of 1910-11	Un	U

Perf. 12

Official Postal Savings Mail

These stamps were used to prepay postage on official correspondence of the Postal Savings Division of the Post Office Department. Discontinued Sept. 23, 1914.

		Un	U
O121	2¢ Postal Savings	13.00	1.50
	Double transfer	17.50	2.50
O122	50¢ dark green	130.00	40.00
O123	$1 ultramarine	120.00	11.00

Wmkd. (190)

O124	1¢ dark violet	7.00	1.50
O125	2¢ Postal Savings (O121)	40.00	5.50
O126	10¢ carmine	15.00	1.60

Penalty Mail Stamps

Stamps for use by government departments were reinstituted in 1983. Now known as Penalty Mail stamps, they help provide a better accounting of actual mail costs for official departments and agencies, etc.

Beginning with #O127, unused values are for never-hinged stamps.

Issues of 1983-91, Unwmkd., Perf. 11 x 10.5, O129A is Perf. 11

O127	1¢, Jan. 12, 1983	.15	.15
O128	4¢, Jan. 12, 1983	.15	.25
O129	13¢, Jan. 12, 1983	.40	.75
O129A	14¢, May 15, 1985	.40	.50
O130	17¢, Jan. 12, 1983	.45	.40

Issues of 1983-91	Un	U

Perf. 11 x 10.5

O131, O134, O137, O142 Not assigned			
O132	$1, Jan. 12, 1983	2.00	1.00
O133	$5, Jan. 12, 1983	9.00	5.00

Coil Stamps, Perf. 10 Vertically

O135	20¢, Jan. 12, 1983	1.75	2.00
a	Imperf. pair	2,000.00	
O136	22¢, May 15, 1985	.70	2.00

Perf. 11

O138	"D" postcard rate (14¢) Feb. 4, 1985	4.50	5.00

Coil Stamps, Perf. 10 Vertically

O138A	15¢, June 11, 1988	.40	.50
O138B	20¢, May 19, 1988	.45	.30
O139	"D" (22¢), Feb. 4, 1985	4.50	3.00
O140	"E" (25¢), Mar. 22, 1988	.75	2.00
O141	25¢, June 11, 1988	.65	.50

Perf. 11

O143	1¢, July 5, 1989	.15	.15

Perf. 10

O144	"F" (29¢), Jan. 22, 1991	.75	.50
O145	29¢, May 24, 1991	.65	.30

Perf. 11

O146	4¢, Apr. 6, 1991	.15	.30
O146A	10¢, Apr. 6, 1991	.25	.30
O147	19¢, May 24, 1991	.40	.50
O148	23¢, May 24, 1991	.45	.30
O151	$1, Sept., 1993	2.00	.75
O152	(32¢), Dec. 13, 1994	.65	—
O153	32¢, May 9, 1995	.65	—
O154	1¢, May 9, 1995	.15	—
O155	20¢, May 9, 1995	.40	—
O156	23¢, May 9, 1995	.45	—

Variable Rate Coil Stamps

Date of Issue:
August 20, 1992
Printing: Intaglio

Date of Issue:
January 26, 1996
Printing: Gravure

Date of Issue:
February 19, 1994
Printing: Gravure

These are coil postage stamps printed without denominations. The denomination is imprinted by the dispensing equipment called a Postage and Mailing Center (PMC). Denominations can be set between 1¢ and $99.99. In 1993, the minimum denomination was adjusted to 19¢ (the postcard rate at the time).

Parcel Post and
Special Handling Stamps

1913-1955

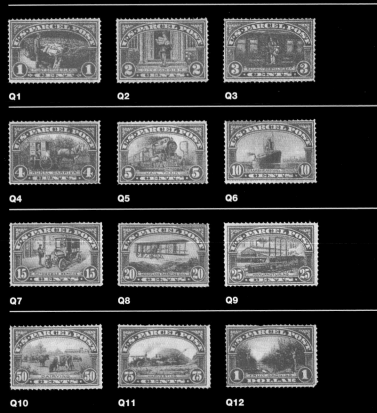

Q1   Q2   Q3

Q4   Q5   Q6

Q7   Q8   Q9

Q10   Q11   Q12

QE1   QE2   QE3

QE4   JQ1   JQ5

Issues of 1913		Un	U	PB	#	FDC
	Wmkd. (190), Perf. 12					

Parcel Post Stamps

Issued for the prepayment of postage on parcel post packages only. Beginning July 1, 1913 these stamps were valid for all postal purposes.

			Un	U	PB	#	FDC
Q1	1¢ Post Office Clerk	07/01/13	4.75	1.30	37.50	(4)	1,500.00
	Double transfer		7.00	3.50			
Q2	2¢ City Carrier	07/01/13	6.00	1.00	42.50	(4)	1,500.00
	2¢ lake		—				
	Double transfer		—	—			
Q3	3¢ Railway Postal Clerk	04/05/13	10.00	5.25	85.00	(4)	3,250.00
	Retouched at lower right corner		20.00	13.00			
	Double transfer		20.00	13.00			
Q4	4¢ Rural Carrier	07/01/13	30.00	2.50	325.00	(4)	3,250.00
	Double transfer		—	—			
Q5	5¢ Mail Train	07/01/13	25.00	2.00	300.00	(4)	3,250.00
	Double transfer		37.50	5.50			
Q6	10¢ Steamship and Mail Tender		45.00	2.50	400.00	(4)	
	Double transfer		—	—			
Q7	15¢ Automobile Service	07/01/13	60.00	10.00	625.00	(4)	
Q8	20¢ Aeroplane Carrying Mail		120.00	20.00	1,300.00	(4)	
Q9	25¢ Manufacturing		60.00	6.00	2,750.00	(6)	
Q10	50¢ Dairying	03/15/13	250.00	37.50	2,000.00	(4)	
Q11	75¢ Harvesting		80.00	30.00	3,100.00	(6)	
Q12	$1 Fruit Growing	01/03/13	325.00	25.00	20,000.00	(6)	

Special Handling Stamps

Issued for use on parcel post packages to secure the same expeditious handling accorded first class mail matter.

	Issues of 1925, 1928-29, 1955, Unwmkd., Perf. 11,		Un	U	PB	#	FDC
QE1	10¢ Special Handling	1955	1.40	1.00	19.00	(6)	
a	Wet printing	06/25/28	3.00	1.00			45.00
QE2	15¢ Special Handling	1955	1.50	.90	27.50	(6)	
a	Wet printing	06/25/28	3.00	.90			45.00
QE3	20¢ Special Handling	1955	2.25	1.50	30.00	(6)	
a	Wet printing	06/25/28	3.25	1.50			45.00
QE4	25¢ Special Handling	1929	19.00	7.50	250.00	(6)	
a	25¢ deep grn.	04/11/25	27.50	5.50	325.00	(6)	225.00
	"A" and "T" of "STATES" joined at top		45.00	22.50			
	"T" and "A" of "POSTAGE" joined at top		45.00	45.00			

Parcel Post Postage Due Stamps

Issued for affixing by a postal clerk to any parcel post package to denote the amount to be collected from the addressee because of insufficient prepayment of postage. Beginning July 1, 1913 these stamps were valid for use as regular postage due stamps.

	Issues of 1913, Wmkd. (190), Perf. 12		Un	U	PB	#	FDC
JQ1	1¢ Figure of Value	11/27/13	9.00	4.00	600.00	(6)	
JQ2	2¢ dark green	12/09/13	70.00	16.00	4,250.00	(6)	
JQ3	5¢ dark green	11/27/13	12.50	5.25	700.00	(6)	
JQ4	10¢ dark green	12/12/13	150.00	40.00	10,500.00	(6)	
JQ5	25¢ Figure of Value	12/16/13	85.00	4.75	4,750.00	(6)	

Migratory Bird Hunting & Conservation Stamps

1934-1949

RW1

RW3

RW10

RW13

RW15

RW16

Issues of 1934-1955		Un	U	PB	#	Q(M̄)
Department of Agriculture Duck Stamps						
RW1 $1 Mallards Alighting	1934	675.00	115.00	8,750.00	(6)	0.6
a	Imperf. pair	—				
b	Vert. pair, imperf. horiz.	—				
RW2 $1 Canvasbacks	1935	650.00	130.00	8,000.00	(6)	0.4
RW3 $1 Canada Geese	1936	325.00	65.00	2,750.00	(6)	0.6
RW4 $1 Scaup Ducks	1937	275.00	47.50	2,100.00	(6)	0.8
RW5 $1 Pintail Drake and Hen Alighting	1938	350.00	47.50	2,500.00	(6)	1
Department of the Interior Duck Stamps						
RW6 $1 Green-winged Teal	1939	200.00	40.00	1,500.00	(6)	1
RW7 $1 Black Mallards	1940	200.00	40.00	1,500.00	(6)	1
RW8 $1 Ruddy Ducks	1941	200.00	40.00	1,500.00	(6)	1
RW9 $1 Baldpates	1942	200.00	40.00	1,500.00	(6)	1
RW10 $1 Wood Ducks	1943	75.00	35.00	525.00	(6)	1
RW11 $1 White-fronted Geese	1944	85.00	25.00	625.00	(6)	1
RW12 $1 Shoveller Ducks	1945	60.00	22.50	400.00	(6)	2
RW13 $1 Redhead Ducks	1946	45.00	13.00	300.00	(6)	2
RW14 $1 Snow Geese	1947	45.00	13.00	300.00	(6)	2
RW15 $1 Buffleheads in Flight	1948	50.00	13.00	325.00	(6)	2
RW16 $2 Goldeneye Ducks	1949	55.00	13.00	325.00	(6)	2
RW17 $2 Trumpeter Swans	1950	72.50	10.00	450.00	(6)	2
RW18 $2 Gadwall Ducks	1951	72.50	10.00	475.00	(6)	2
RW19 $2 Harlequin Ducks	1952	72.50	10.00	475.00	(6)	2
RW20 $2 Blue-winged Teal	1953	75.00	10.00	475.00	(6)	2
RW21 $2 Ring-necked Ducks	1954	75.00	9.00	475.00	(6)	2
RW22 $2 Blue Geese	1955	75.00	9.00	475.00	(6)	2

Migratory Bird Hunting and Conservation Stamps (popularly known as "Duck Stamps") are sold as hunting permits. While they are sold through many post offices, they are not usable for postage.

Issues of 1956-1982			Un	U	PB	#	Q(M̄)
Department of the Interior Duck Stamps (continued)							
RW23	$2 American Merganser	1956	75.00	9.00	475.00	(6)	2
RW24	$2 American Eider	1957	75.00	9.00	475.00	(6)	2
RW25	$2 Canada Geese	1958	72.50	9.00	475.00	(6)	2
RW26	$3 Labrador Retriever Carrying Mallard Drake	1959	92.50	9.00	425.00	(4)	2
RW27	$3 Redhead Ducks	1960	80.00	9.00	375.00	(4)	2
RW28	$3 Mallard Hen and Ducklings	1961	82.50	9.00	375.00	(4)	1
RW29	$3 Pintail Drakes	1962	95.00	9.00	425.00	(4)	1
RW30	$3 Pair of Brant Landing	1963	95.00	9.00	425.00	(4)	1
RW31	$3 Hawaiian Nene Geese	1964	95.00	9.00	2,100.00	(6)	2
RW32	$3 Three Canvasback Drakes	1965	92.50	9.00	425.00	(4)	2
RW33	$3 Whistling Swans	1966	95.00	9.00	425.00	(4)	2
RW34	$3 Old Squaw Ducks	1967	100.00	9.00	450.00	(4)	2
RW35	$3 Hooded Mergansers	1968	57.50	8.00	275.00	(4)	2
RW36	$3 White-winged Scoters	1969	57.50	7.00	250.00	(4)	2
RW37	$3 Ross's Geese	1970	57.50	6.50	260.00	(4)	2
RW38	$3 Three Cinnamon Teal	1971	40.00	6.50	175.00	(4)	2
RW39	$5 Emperor Geese	1972	25.00	6.50	140.00	(4)	2
RW40	$5 Steller's Eiders	1973	21.00	6.00	100.00	(4)	2
RW41	$5 Wood Ducks	1974	20.00	6.00	85.00	(4)	2
RW42	$5 Canvasbacks Decoy, 3 Flying Canvasbacks	1975	15.00	5.50	65.00	(4)	2
RW43	$5 Canada Geese	1976	14.00	5.50	57.50	(4)	2
RW44	$5 Pair of Ross's Geese	1977	15.00	5.50	65.00	(4)	2
RW45	$5 Hooded Merganser Drake	1978	12.50	5.50	55.00	(4)	2
RW46	$7.50 Green-winged Teal	1979	14.00	6.00	55.00	(4)	2
RW47	$7.50 Mallards	1980	14.00	6.00	55.00	(4)	2
RW48	$7.50 Ruddy Ducks	1981	14.00	6.00	55.00	(4)	2
RW49	$7.50 Canvasbacks	1982	14.00	6.00	55.00	(4)	2

RW26-34

RW37-53

RW57

RW58-present

Gum side (back) of duck stamps.

RW23

RW26

RW33

RW36

RW38

RW39

RW46

RW49

RW54

RW57

RW58

RW59

RW60

RW61

RW62

RW63

1998 Barrow's Goldeneye

Issues of 1983-1998		Un	U	PB	#	Q(M̄)
Department of the Interior Duck Stamps (continued)						
RW50 $7.50 Pintails	1983	15.00	6.00	65.00	(4)	2
RW51 $7.50 Widgeons	1984	15.00	6.00	65.00	(4)	2
RW52 $7.50 Cinnamon Teal	1985	14.00	6.00	65.00	(4)	2
RW53 $7.50 Fulvous Whistling Duck	1986	15.00	6.00	65.00	(4)	2
a Black omitted		3,750.00				
RW54 $10 Redheads	1987	15.00	8.00	65.00	(4)	2
RW55 $10 Snow Goose	1988	16.00	8.00	65.00	(4)	1
RW56 $12.50 Lesser Scaup	1989	19.00	9.00	77.50	(4)	1
RW57 $12.50 Black Bellied Whistling Duck	1990	19.00	9.00	77.50	(4)	1
RW58 $15 King Eiders	1991	22.50	9.00	90.00	(4)	1
RW59 $15 Spectacled Eider	1992	22.50	9.00	90.00	(4)	1
RW60 $15 Canvasbacks	1993	22.50	9.00	90.00	(4)	1
RW61 $15 Red-breasted Merganser	1994	21.00	9.00	90.00	(4)	1
RW62 $15 Mallards	1995	21.00	9.00	90.00	(4)	
RW63 $15 Surf Scoters	1996	21.00	9.00	100.00	(4)	
RW64 $15 Canada Goose	1997	21.00	9.00			
— $15 Barrow's Goldeneye	1998	—	—	—		

What's threatening the existence of these birds?

Named for the distinctive white patches around the eyes of males, the spectacled eider is a threatened species whose population has decreased more than 90% in the past 30 to 40 years. Biologists who are studying this large-bodied sea duck have had difficulties until just a few years ago because the eiders' wintering grounds had been undiscovered. Finally, in March 1995, nearly 150,000 of the birds (approximately the full estimated population) were discovered living in holes in the ice out in the Bering Sea. The eiders pack themselves, body against body, in these ice holes to keep them from freezing over for the winter. The cause of the decline in population of the spectacled eider is still unknown, but now that biologists can study them year-round, the chance of finding and correcting any problems is much greater. **(#RW59)**

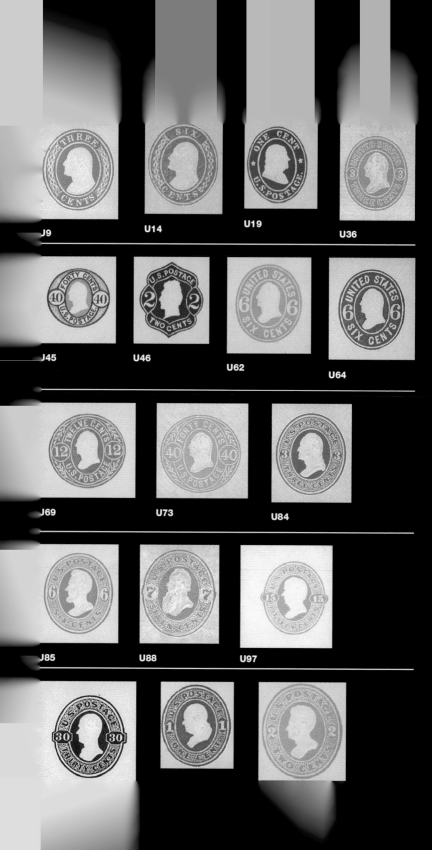

J9

U14

U19

U36

J45

U46

U62

U64

J69

U73

U84

J85

U88

U97

Issues of 1853-65		Un	U

Represented below is only a partial listing of stamped envelopes. At least one example is listed for most die types; most die types exist on several colors of envelope paper. Values are for cut squares; prices for entire envelopes are higher. Color in italic is the color of the envelope paper; when no color is specified, envelope paper is white. "W" with catalog number indicates wrapper instead of envelope.

U1	3¢ red Washington (top label 13mm wide), *buff*	240.00	20.00
U4	3¢ red Washington (top label 15mm wide) *buff*	250.00	20.00
U5	3¢ red (label has octagonal ends)	4,500.00	375.00
U7	3¢ red (label 20mm wide)	700.00	85.00
U9	3¢ red (label 14½mm)	25.00	3.00
U12	6¢ red Washington, *buff*	125.00	55.00
U14	6¢ green Washington, *buff*	185.00	80.00
U15	10¢ green Washington (label 15½mm wide)	200.00	70.00
U17	10¢ green (label 20mm)	250.00	100.00
a	10¢ pale green	225.00	100.00
U19	1¢ blue Franklin (period after "POSTAGE"), *buff*	30.00	15.00
U23	1¢ blue (bust touches inner frame line), *orange*	450.00	350.00
U24	1¢ blue (no period after "POSTAGE"), *buff*	225.00	90.00
U27	3¢ red, no label, *buff*	20.00	12.50
U28	3¢ + 1¢ (U12 and U9)	325.00	240.00
U30	6¢ red Wash., no label	2,400.00	1,250.00
U33	10¢ green, no label, *buff*	1,100.00	250.00
U34	3¢ pink Washington (outline lettering)	20.00	5.50
U36	3¢ pink, *blue* (letter sheet)	75.00	50.00
U39	6¢ pink Washington, *buff*	65.00	60.00
U40	10¢ yellow green Wash.	32.50	30.00
U42	12¢ red, brn. Wash., *buff*	180.00	160.00
U44	24¢ Washington, *buff*	200.00	175.00
U45	40¢ blk., red Wash., *buff*	300.00	300.00
U46	2¢ black Jackson ("U.S. POSTAGE" downstroke, tail of "2" unite near point)	35.00	17.50
U49	2¢ black ("POSTAGE" downstroke and tail of "2" touch but do not merge), *orange*	1,200.00	
U50	2¢ blk. Jack. ("U.S. POST." stamp 24-25mm wide), *buff*	12.50	9.00
W51	2¢ blk. Jack. ("U.S. POST." stamp 24-25mm wide), buff	160.00	150.00
U54	2¢ blk. Jack. ("U.S. POST." stp. 25½-26½mm), *buff*	12.50	9.00
W55	2¢ blk. Jack. ("U.S. POST." stp. 25½-26½mm), *buff*	75.00	55.00
U58	3¢ pink Washington (solid lettering)	7.00	1.50
U60	3¢ brown Washington	42.50	27.50
U62	6¢ pink Washington	60.00	27.50

Issues of 1863-86		Un	U
U64	6¢ purple Washington	45.00	27.50
U66	9¢ lemon Washington, *buff*	400.00	240.00
U67	9¢ orange Washington, *buff*	100.00	80.00
U68	12¢ brn. Wash., *buff*	350.00	225.00
U69	12¢ red brown Wash., *buff*	85.00	55.00
U70	18¢ red Washington, *buff*	90.00	90.00
U71	24¢ bl. Washington, *buff*	95.00	80.00
U72	30¢ green Washington, *buff*	65.00	60.00
U73	40¢ rose Washington, *buff*	90.00	*225.00*
U75	1¢ blue Franklin (bust points to end of "N" of "ONE"), *amber*	32.50	27.50
U78	2¢ brown Jackson (bust narrow at back; small, thick numerals)	37.50	15.00
U84	3¢ grn. Washington ("ponytail" projects below bust), *cream*	8.50	4.00
U85	6¢ dark red Lincoln (neck very long at back)	20.00	16.00
a	6¢ vermilion	15.00	16.00
U88	7¢ verm. Stanton (figures 7 normal), *amber*	45.00	*180.00*
U89	10¢ olive blk. Jefferson	475.00	425.00
U92	10¢ brown Jefferson, *amber*	70.00	50.00
U93	12¢ plum Clay (chin prominent)	110.00	82.50
U97	15¢ red orange Webster (has side whiskers), *amber*	140.00	180.00
U99	24¢ purple Scott (locks of hair project, top of head)	120.00	120.00
U103	30¢ black Hamilton (back of bust very narrow), *amber*	190.00	250.00
U105	90¢ carmine Perry (front of bust very narrow, pointed)	140.00	225.00
U113	1¢ lt. blue Frank. (lower part of bust points to end of "E" in "ONE")	1.50	.75
a	1¢ dark blue	7.50	7.50
U114	1¢ lt. blue (lower part of bust points to end of "E" in "Postage"), *amber*	4.00	4.00
U122	2¢ brown Jackson (bust narrow at back; numerals thin)	90.00	37.50
U128	2¢ brown Jackson (numerals in long ovals)	42.50	32.50
U132	2¢ brown, die 3 (left numeral touches oval)	60.00	27.50
U134	2¢ brown Jackson (similar to U128-31 but "O" of "TWO" has center netted instead of plain)	575.00	135.00
U139	2¢ brown (bust broad; numerals short, thick)	40.00	32.50
U142	2¢ verm. Jackson (U139)	5.50	2.75

Issues of 1874-86	Un	U
U149	2¢ verm. Jackson (similar to U139-48 but circles around ovals much heavier)	45.00	30.00
W155	2¢ verm. Jackson (like U149 but middle stroke of "N" as thin as verticals), *manila*	19.00	9.50
U156	2¢ verm. Jackson (bottom of bust cut almost semi-circularly)	600.00	130.00
U159	3¢ grn. Wash. (thin letters, long numerals)	22.50	6.50
U163	3¢ grn. Wash. (thick letters, "ponytail" does not project below bust)	1.25	.25
U169	3¢ grn. (top of head egg-shaped; "ponytail" knot projects as point), *amber*	225.00	100.00
U172	5¢ Taylor, die 1 (numerals have thick, curved tops)	10.00	8.00
U177	5¢ blue, die 2 (numerals have long, thin tops)	7.50	6.50
U183	6¢ red Lincoln (neck short at back), *cream*	20.00	12.50
U186	7¢ verm. Stanton (figures turned up at ends), *amber*	95.00	60.00
U187	10¢ brown Jefferson (very large head)	32.50	20.00
U190	10¢ choc. Jeff. (knot of "ponytail" stands out) *amb.*	8.50	7.50
U195	12¢ plum Clay (chin receding)	175.00	85.00
U198	15¢ orange Webster (no side whiskers)	45.00	37.50
U201	24¢ purple Scott (hair does not project)	150.00	125.00
U204	30¢ blk. Hamilton (back of bust rather broad)	60.00	27.50
U212	90¢ carm. Perry (front of bust broad, sloping), *amber*	160.00	225.00
U218	3¢ red Post Rider, Train (1 line under "POSTAGE")	50.00	25.00
U225	5¢ brown Garfield, *blue*	60.00	35.00
U228	2¢ red Washington, *amber*	4.50	2.75
U234	2¢ red, four wavy lines in oval (wavy lines fine, clear), *fawn*	5.50	4.50
U236	2¢ red (wavy lines thick, blurred)	7.50	4.00
U240	2¢ red Washington (3½ links over left "2")	65.00	40.00
U244	2¢ red Wash. (2 links below right "2"), *amber*	160.00	75.00
U249	2¢ red Washington (round "O" in "TWO"), *fawn*	600.00	375.00
U250	4¢ green Jackson, die 1 (left numeral 2¾mm wide)	3.50	3.50

Issues of 1883-93	Un	U
U256	4¢ green, die 2 (left numeral 3¼mm wide)	5.00	5.00
U259	4¢, die 2, *amber manila*	10.00	7.50
U262	2¢ brn. Wash. (U234), *blue*	12.00	9.50
U267	2¢ brn. Wash. (U236)	12.00	6.00
U270	2¢ brown Washington (2 links below right "2")	85.00	37.50
U274	2¢ brown Wash. (round "O" in "TWO"), *amber*	200.00	80.00
U277	2¢ brn. Washington (extremity of bust below "ponytail" forms point)	.45	.15
U288	2¢ brn. Wash. (extremity of bust is rounded)	150.00	35.00
U294	1¢ blue Franklin, no wavy lines	.50	.20
U302	1¢ dark blue, *manila*	22.50	10.00
U307	2¢ grn. Washington ("G" of "POSTAGE" has no bar), *oriental buff*	75.00	30.00
U314	2¢ green ("G" has bar, ear indicated by 1 heavy line), *blue*	.60	.30
U320	2¢ green (like U314 but ear indicated by 2 curved lines), *oriental buff*	155.00	40.00
U327	4¢ carmine Jackson, *blue*	4.50	4.00
U331	5¢ blue Grant (space between beard and collar), *amber*	4.00	2.25
U335	5¢ blue (collar touches beard), *amber*	10.00	5.50
U340	30¢ red brown Hamilton (U204), *manila*	42.50	42.50
U344	90¢ pur. Perry (U212), *oriental buff*	75.00	80.00
U348	1¢ Columbus and Liberty	2.00	1.10
U351	10¢ slate brown	30.00	25.00
U355	1¢ grn. Frank. (U294), *bl.*	11.00	7.50
U358	2¢ carm. Washington (bust points to first notch of inner oval)	2.75	1.75
U362	2¢ carmine (bust points to middle of second notch of inner oval, "ponytail")	.30	.20
U368	2¢ carm. (same as U362 but hair flowing; no ribbon "ponytail"), *amber*	8.00	6.75
U371	4¢ brown Lincoln (bust pointed, undraped)	15.00	11.00
U374	4¢ brown (head larger; inner oval has no notches)	10.00	8.00
U377	5¢ blue Grant (like U331, U335 but smaller)	9.50	9.50

W155

U159

U172

U190

U204

U218

U250

U294

U314

U348

U351

U358

U368

U374

U377

U379

U386

U390

U393

U398

U400

U406

U416

U429

U447

U468

W485

U522

U523

U524

Issues of 1899-1906	Un	U
U379 1¢ green Franklin, horizontal oval	.60	.20
U386 2¢ carm. Wash. (1 short, 2 long vertical lines at right of "CENTS"), *amber*	1.50	.20
U390 4¢ chocolate Grant	18.00	11.00
U393 5¢ blue Lincoln	17.50	12.50
U398 2¢ carm. Washington, recut die (lines at end of "TWO CENTS" all short), *blue*	3.25	.90
U400 1¢ grn. Frank., oval, die 1 (wide "D" in "UNITED")	.25	.15
U401a 1¢ grn. Frank., die 2 (narrow "D"), *amber*	.85	.70
U402b 1¢, grn. die 3 (wide "S" in "STATES"), *oriental buff*	6.00	1.50
U403c 1¢, die 4 (sharp angle at back of bust, "N," "E" of "ONE" are parallel), *blue*	3.75	1.25
U406 2¢ brn. red Wash., die 1 (oval "O" in "TWO" and "C" in "CENTS")	.70	.15
U407a 2¢ die 2 (like die 1, but hair recut in 2 distinct locks, top of head), *amb.*	100.00	45.00
U408b 2¢, die 3 (round "O" in "TWO" and "C" in "CENTS," coarse letters), *or. buff*	6.00	2.50
U411c 2¢ carmine, die 4 (like die 3 but lettering, hair lines fine, clear)	.35	.20
U412d 2¢ carmine Wash., die 5 (all S's wide), *amber*	.55	.35
U413e 2¢ carm., die 6 (like die 1 but front of bust narrow), *oriental buff*	.50	.35
U414f 2¢ carm., die 7 (like die 6 but upper corner of front of bust cut away), *blue*	12.50	7.50
g 2¢ carm., die 8 (like die 7 but lower stroke of "S" in "CENTS" straight line; hair as in die 2), *blue*	12.50	7.50
U416 4¢ blk. Wash., die 2 ("F" is 1 3/4mm from left "4")	3.50	2.25
a 4¢, die 1 ("F" is 1mm from left "4")	4.25	3.00
U420 1¢ grn. Frank., round, die 1 ("UNITED" nearer inner circle than outer circle)	.15	.15
U421a 1¢, die 2 (large "U"; "NT" closely spaced), *amber*	300.00	175.00
U423a 1¢ grn. die 3 (knob of hair at back of neck; large "NT" widely spaced), *blue*	.75	.45
b 1¢, die 4 ("UNITED" nearer outer circle than inner)	1.25	.65
c 1¢, die 5 (narrow, oval "C")	.65	.35

Issues of 1907-32	Un	U
U429 2¢ carmine Washington, die 1 (letters broad, numerals vertical, "E" closer than "N" to inner circle)	.15	.15
a 2¢, die 2 (like die 1 but "U" far from left circle), *amber*	9.00	6.00
b 2¢, die 3 (like die 2 but inner circles very thin)	30.00	25.00
U430b 2¢, die 4 (like die 1 but "C" very close to left circle), *amber*	20.00	10.00
c 2¢, die 5 (small head, 8 3/4mm from tip of nose to back of neck; "TS" of "CENTS" close at bottom)	1.10	.35
U431d 2¢, die 6 (like die 6 but "TS" of "CENTS" far apart at bottom; left numeral slopes right), *oriental buff*	3.00	2.00
e 2¢, die 7 (large head, both numerals slope right, T's have short top strokes)	2.75	1.75
U432h 2¢, die 8 (like die 7 but all T's have long top strokes), *blue*	.60	.25
i 2¢, die 9 (narrow, oval "C")	.90	.30
U436 3¢ dk. violet Washington, die 1 (as 2¢)	.50	.20
U440 4¢ black Washington	1.00	.60
U447 2¢ on 3¢ dark violet, rose surcharge	7.00	6.50
U458 Same as U447, black surcharge, bars 2mm apart	.45	.35
U468 Same as U458, bars 1 1/2mm apart	.70	.45
U481 1 1/2¢ brown Washington, die 1 (as U429)	.15	.15
W485 1 1/2¢ brown, *manila*	.75	.15
U490 1 1/2¢ on 1¢ grn. Franklin, black surcharge	3.75	3.50
U499 1 1/2¢ on 1¢, *manila*	11.00	6.00
U510 1 1/2¢ on 1¢ grn., outline numeral in surcharge	2.00	1.25
U522 2¢ carmine Liberty Bell	1.10	.50
a 2¢, center bar of "E" of "Postage" same length as top bar	6.00	3.75
U523 1¢ ol. grn. Mount Vernon	.90	.80
U524 1 1/2¢ choc. Mount Vernon	1.75	1.50

Issues of 1916-62	Un	U
U525 2¢ carmine Mount Vernon	.40	.20
a 2¢, die 2 "S" of "POSTAGE" raised	70.00	16.00
U526 3¢ violet Mount Vernon	1.75	.35
U527 4¢ black Mount Vernon	18.00	16.00
U528 5¢ dark blue Mount Vernon	3.75	3.50
U529 6¢ orange Washington	5.50	4.00
U530 6¢ orange Wash., *amber*	11.00	8.00
U531 6¢ or. Washington, *blue*	11.00	10.00
U532 1¢ green Franklin	5.00	1.75
U533 2¢ carmine Wash. (oval)	.75	.25
U534 3¢ dk. violet Washington, die 4 (short N in UNITED, thin crossbar in A of STATES)	.40	.20
U535 1½¢ brown Washington	5.00	3.50
U536 4¢ red violet Franklin	.75	.20
U537 2¢ + 2¢ Wash. (U429)	3.00	1.50
U538 2¢ + 2¢ Washington (U533)	.75	.20
U539 3¢ + 1¢ purple, die 1 (4½mm tall, thick "3")	15.00	11.00
U540 3¢ + 1¢ purple, die 3 (4mm tall, thin "3")	.50	.15
a Die 2 (4½mm tall, thin "3" in medium circle), entire	1,000.00	—
U541 1¼¢ turquoise Franklin	.70	.50
a Die 2 ("4" 3½mm high), precanceled		2.00
U542 2½¢ dull blue Washington	.80	.50
U543 4¢ brn. Pony Express Rider	.60	.30
U544 5¢ dark blue Lincoln	.80	.20
c With albino impression of 4¢ (U536)	50.00	—
U545 4¢ + 1¢, type 1 (U536)	1.40	.50
U546 5¢ New York World's Fair	.60	.40
U547 1¼¢ brown Liberty Bell		.15
U548 1⁴⁄₁₀¢ brown Liberty Bell		.15
U548A 1⁶⁄₁₀¢ orange Liberty Bell		.15
U549 4¢ blue Old Ironsides	.75	.15
U550 5¢ purple Eagle	.75	.15
a Tagged	1.25	.15
U551 6¢ green Statue of Liberty	.70	.15
U552 4¢ + 2¢ brt. bl. (U549)	3.75	2.00
U553 5¢ + 1¢ brt. pur. (U550)	3.50	2.50
U554 6¢ lt. blue Herman Melville	.50	.15
U555 6¢ Youth Conference	.75	.15
U556 1⁷⁄₁₀¢ lilac Liberty Bell		.15
U557 8¢ ultramarine Eagle	.40	.15
U561 6¢ + (2¢) lt. grn.	1.00	.30
U562 6¢ + (2¢) lt. blue	2.00	1.60
U563 8¢ rose red Bowling	.50	.15
U564 8¢ Aging Conference	.50	.15
U565 8¢ Transpo '72	.50	.15
U566 8¢ + 2¢ brt. ultra.	.40	.15
U567 10¢ emerald Liberty Bell	.40	.15
U568 1⁸⁄₁₀¢ Volunteer Yourself		.15

Issues of 1962-78	Un	U
U569 10¢ Tennis Centenary	.30	.20
U571 10¢ Compass Rose	.30	.15
a Brown "10¢/USA" omitted, entire	125.00	
U572 13¢ Quilt Pattern	.35	.15
U573 13¢ Sheaf of Wheat	.35	.15
U574 13¢ Mortar and Pestle	.35	.15
U575 13¢ Tools	.35	.15
U576 13¢ Liberty Tree	.30	.15
U577 2¢ red Nonprofit		.15
U578 2.1¢ yel. green Nonprofit		.15
U579 2.7¢ green Nonprofit		.15
U580 15¢ orange Eagle, A	.40	.15
U581 15¢ red Uncle Sam	.40	.15
U582 13¢ emerald Centennial	.35	.15
U583 13¢ Golf	.45	.20
U584 13¢ Energy Conservation	.40	.15
d Blk, red omitted, ent.	475.00	
U585 13¢ Energy Development	.40	.15
U586 15¢ on 16¢ blue USA	.35	.15
U587 15¢ Auto Racing	.35	.15
a Black omitted, entire	140.00	
U588 15¢ on 13¢ (U576)	.35	.15
U589 3.1¢ ultramarine nonprofit		.15
U590 3.5¢ purple Violins		.15
U591 5.9¢ Auth Nonprofit Org		.15
U592 18¢ violet Eagle, B	.45	.20
U593 18¢ dark blue Star	.45	.20
U594 20¢ brown Eagle, C	.45	.15
U595 15¢ Veterinary Medicine	.35	.15
U596 15¢ Summer Oly. Games	.60	.15
a Red, grn. omitted, ent.	225.00	
U597 15¢ Highwheeler Bicycle	.40	.15
a Blue "15¢ USA" omitted, entire	100.00	
U598 15¢ America's Cup	.40	.15
U599 Brown 15¢ Honeybee	.35	.15
a Brown "15¢ USA" omitted, entire	140.00	
U600 18¢ Blind Veterans	.45	.20
U601 20¢ Capitol Dome	.45	.15
U602 20¢ Great Seal of U.S.	.45	.15
U603 20¢ Purple Heart	.45	.15
U604 5.2¢ Auth Nonprofit Org		.15
U605 20¢ Paralyzed Veterans	.45	.15
U606 20¢ Small Business	.50	.15
U607 22¢ Eagle, D	.55	.15
U608 22¢ Bison	.55	.15
U609 6¢ USS Constitution		.15
U610 8.5¢ Mayflower		.15
U611 25¢ Stars	.60	.15
U612 8.4¢ USF Constellation		.15
U613 25¢ Snowflake	.60	.25
U614 25¢ USA, Stars (Philatelic Mail)	.50	.25

U530

U531

U541

U542

U543

U569

U576

U581

U587

U601

U609

U610

U611

U614

447

U616

U617

U632

U631

U637

U635

U636

U639

U640

U641

Issues of 1978-85		Un	U
U615	25¢ Stars (lined paper)	.50	.25
U616	25¢ Love	.50	.25
U617	25¢ Space hologram	.60	.30
U618	25¢ Football hologram	.50	.25
U619	29¢ Star	.60	.30
U620	11.1¢ Birds		.20
U621	29¢ Love	.60	.30
U622	29¢ Magazine Industry	.60	.30
U623	29¢ Star and Bars	.60	.30
U624	29¢ Country Geese	.60	.60
U625	29¢ Space Shuttle	.60	.25
U626	29¢ Western Americana	.60	.30
U627	29¢ Protect the Environment	.60	.30
U628	19.8¢ Bulk Rate precanceled		.40

Issues of 1978-96		Un	U
U629	29¢ Disabled Americans	.60	.30
U630	29¢ Kitten	.60	.30
U631	29¢ Football	.60	.30
U632	32¢ Liberty Bell	.65	.32
U634	32¢ Old Glory	.65	.30
U635	5¢ Nonprofit		.15
U636	10¢ Graphic Eagle		.15
U637	32¢ Spiral Heart	.65	.30
U639	32¢ Space Shuttle	.65	.35
U640	32¢ Save Our Environment	.60	.30
U641	32¢ 1996 Paralympic Games	.60	.30

Cracked Liberty Bell rings no longer in Philadelphia

The Liberty Bell, which today is on display about 100 yards from Independence Hall in Philadelphia, Pennsylvania, was commissioned by the Pennsylvania Provincial Assembly in 1751 to represent freedom in America. It first hung in the Pennsylvania State House (now Independence Hall) in June 1753 and was rung on July 8, 1776, in honor of the reading of the Declaration of Independence in public. The bell cracked irreparably in 1846 when it was rung on the anniversary of George Washington's birth and has never tolled since. **(#U632)**

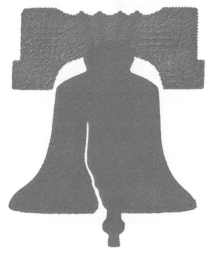

Bela Lugosi as

DRACULA

Airmail Envelopes and Aerogrammes

1929-1973

UC1

UC3

UC7

UC8

UC14

UC21

UC25

UC26

UC30

UC39

UC46

	Issues of 1929-46	Un	U
UC1	5¢ blue Airplane, die 1 (vertical rudder is not semicircular)	3.50	2.00
	1933 wmk., entire	*700.00*	*700.00*
	1937 wmk., entire	—	*2,000.00*
	Bicolored border omitted, entire	600.00	
UC2	5¢ blue, die 2 (vertical rudder is semicircular)	11.00	5.00
	1929 wmk., entire	—	*1,500.00*
	1933 wmk., entire	*600.00*	—
UC3	6¢ orange Airplane, die 2a ("6" is 6½mm wide)	1.45	.40
a	With #U436a added impression	*3,000.00*	
UC4	6¢ orange, die 2b ("6" is 6mm wide)	2.75	2.00
UC5	6¢ orange, die 2c ("6" is 5½mm wide)	.75	.30
UC6	6¢ orange, die 3 (vertical rudder leans forward)	1.00	.35
a	6¢ orange, *blue*, entire	*3,500.00*	*2,400.00*
UC7	8¢ olive green Airplane	13.00	3.50
UC8	6¢ on 2¢ carm. Washington (U429)	1.25	.65
a	6¢ on 1¢ green (U420)	*1,750.00*	
c	6¢ on 3¢ purple (U437a)	*3,000.00*	
UC9	6¢ on 2¢ Wash. (U525)	75.00	40.00
UC10	5¢ on 6¢ orange (UC3)	2.75	1.50
a	Double surcharge	60.00	
	Issues of 1946-58		
UC11	5¢ on 6¢ orange (UC4)	9.00	5.50
UC13	5¢ on 6¢ orange (UC6)	.80	.60
a	Double surcharge	60.00	
UC14	5¢ carm. DC-4, die 1 (end of wing on right is smooth curve)	.75	.20
UC16	10¢ red, DC-4 2-line back inscription, entire, *pale blue*	7.50	6.00
a	"Air Letter" on face, 4-line back inscription	16.00	14.00
	Die-cutting reversed	275.00	
b	10¢ chocolate	400.00	
c	"Air Letter" and "Aerogramme" on face	45.00	12.50
d	3-line back inscription	8.00	8.00

	Issues of 1946-58	Un	U
UC17	5¢ Postage Centenary	.40	.25
UC18	6¢ carm. Airplane (UC14), type I (6's lean right)	.35	.15
a	Type II (6's upright)	.75	.25
UC20	6¢ on 5¢ (UC15)	.80	.50
a	6¢ on 6¢ carmine, entire	1,500.00	
b	Double surcharge	*250.00*	—
UC21	6¢ on 5¢ (UC14)	27.50	17.50
UC22	6¢ on 5¢ (UC14)	3.50	2.50
a	Double surcharge	75.00	
UC23	6¢ on 5¢ (UC17)	*1,750.00*	
UC25	6¢ red Eagle	.75	.50
UC26	7¢ blue (UC14)	.65	.50
	Issues of 1958-73		
UC27	6¢ + 1¢ orange (UC3)	250.00	225.00
UC28	6¢ + 1¢ orange (UC4)	65.00	75.00
UC29	6¢ + 1¢ orange (UC5)	37.50	50.00
UC30	6¢ + 1¢ (UC5)	1.00	.50
UC32	10¢ Jet Airliner, back inscription in 2 lines	6.00	5.00
a	Type 1, entire	10.00	5.00
UC33	7¢ blue Jet Silhouette	.60	.25
UC34	7¢ carmine (UC33)	.60	.25
UC35	11¢ Jet, Globe, entire	2.75	1.50
a	Red omitted	*875.00*	
	Die-cutting reversed	35.00	
UC36	8¢ red Jet Airliner	.55	.15
UC37	8¢ red Jet in Triangle	.35	.15
a	Tagged	1.25	.30
UC39	13¢ John Kennedy, entire	3.00	1.50
a	Red omitted	*500.00*	
UC40	10¢ Jet in Triangle	.50	.15
UC41	8¢ + 2¢ (UC37)	.65	.15
UC42	13¢ Human Rights, entire	8.00	4.00
	Die-cutting reversed	75.00	
UC43	11¢ Jet in Circle	.50	.15
UC44	15¢ gray, red, white and blue Birds in Flight	1.50	1.10
UC45	10¢ + (1¢) (UC40)	1.50	.20
UC46	15¢ red, white, bl.	.75	.40

Issues of 1973-91		Un	U
UC47	13¢ red Bird in Flight	.30	.15
UC48	18¢ USA, entire	.90	.30
UC50	22¢ red and bl. USA, entire	.90	.40
UC51	22¢ blue USA, entire	.70	.25
	Die-cutting reversed	25.00	
UC52	22¢ Summer Olympic Games	1.50	.25
UC53	30¢ blue, red, brn. Tour the United States, entire	.65	.30
a	Red "30" omitted	75.00	
UC54	30¢ *yellow, magenta, blue and black* (UC53), entire	.65	.30
	Die-cutting reversed	20.00	
UC55	30¢ Made in USA, entire	.65	.30
UC56	30¢ World Communications Year, entire	.65	.30
	Die-cutting reversed	25.00	
UC57	30¢ Olympic Games, entire	.65	.30
UC58	36¢ Landsat, entire	.70	.35
UC59	36¢ Tourism Week, entire	.70	.35
UC60	36¢ Mark Twain/ Halley's Comet, entire	.70	.35
UC61	39¢ Envelope	.80	.40
UC62	39¢ Montgomery Blair	.80	.40
UC63	45¢ Eagle, entire, *blue*	.90	.45
a	White paper	.90	.45

Issues of 1873-75		Un	U
Official Envelopes			
Post Office Department			
Numeral 9¹/₂mm high			
UO1	2¢ black, *lemon*	15.00	8.00
Numeral 10¹/₂mm high			
UO5	2¢ black, *lemon*	6.00	4.00
UO9	3¢ black, *amber*	45.00	35.00
Postal Service			
UO16	blue, *amber*	45.00	30.00
War Department			
UO20	3¢ dk. red Washington	60.00	40.00
UO26	12¢ dark red Clay	110.00	50.00
UO39	10¢ vermilion Jefferson	200.00	
UO48	2¢ red Jackson, *amber*	25.00	14.00
UO55	3¢ red Washington, *fawn*	4.50	2.75
Issues of 1983-95 (Enteres), Penalty Mail Envelopes			
UO73	20¢ blue Great Seal	1.00	*30.00*
UO74	22¢ (seal embossed)	.65	*5.00*
UO75	22¢ (seal typographed)	.65	*20.00*
UO76	"E" (25¢) Great Seal	.65	*20.00*
UO77	25¢ black, blue Great Seal (seal embossed)	.65	*5.00*
UO78	25¢ (seal typographed)	.65	*25.00*
UO79	45¢ (stars illegible)	1.25	—
UO80	65¢ (stars illegible)	1.50	—
UO81	45¢ (stars clear)	1.25	—
UO82	65¢ (stars clear)	1.50	—
UO83	"F" (29¢) Great Seal	1.00	*20.00*
UO84	29¢ black, blue, entire	.70	*2.00*
UO88	32¢ Official Mail	.75	*5.00*

A favorite symbol worldwide

Although this postage, created for an embossed stamped envelope, depicts a stylized version of the eagle, the majestic birds of prey have been the favorite emblem of kings, emperors and nations for many centuries. Today's national seal of Mexico shows an eagle devouring a serpent, symbolizing the triumph of good over evil; other nations, such as Egypt and Persia (now Iran) have used the eagle as a battle standard. While eagles cannot be tamed or trained as falcons can, they can gradually shed their fear of man to the extent of catching and accepting food tossed to them in mid-air. With its fearsome gaze and soaring flights, the eagle continues to be the symbol of choice for kings and nations to this day. **(#U073)**

Interesting Fact: For all their power, eagles are widely over-rated for their ability to lift prey off the ground and carry it away. Several have actually been found drowned, unable to extricate their talons from fish that proved too heavy to handle.

UC48

UC52

UC53

UC56

UC57

UC59

UC63

UO1

UO16

UO20

UO73

UO84

UO88

455

UX5

UX6

UX11

UX14

UX16

UX18

UX25

UX27

UX28

UX37

UX43

UX44

UX45

UX46

UX48

UX50

Issues of 1873-1917	Un	U

Represented below is only a partial listing of postal cards. Values are for entire cards. Color in italic is color of card. Cards preprinted with written address or message usually sell for much less.

		Un	U
UX1	1¢ brown Liberty, wmkd. (90 x 60mm)	325.00	15.00
UX3	1¢ brown Liberty, wmkd. (53 x 36mm)	70.00	2.25
UX4	1¢ blk. Liberty, wmkd., USPOD in monogram	1,900.00	300.00
UX5	1¢ blk. Liberty, unwmkd.	60.00	.40
UX6	2¢ blue Liberty, *buff*	25.00	17.50
a	2¢ dark blue, *buff*	30.00	19.00
UX7	1¢ (UX5), inscribed "Nothing But The Address"	55.00	.35
a	23 teeth below "One Cent"	500.00	30.00
b	Printed on both sides	*575.00*	*400.00*
UX8	1¢ brown Jefferson, large "one-cent" wreath	45.00	1.25
c	1¢ chocolate	85.00	6.00
UX9	1¢ blk. Jefferson, *buff*	15.00	.55
a	1¢ blk., *dark buff*	20.00	1.25
UX10	1¢ black Grant	30.00	1.40
UX11	1¢ blue Grant	12.50	2.50
UX12	1¢ black Jefferson, wreath smaller than UX14	35.00	.40
UX13	2¢ blue Liberty, *cream*	125.00	75.00
UX14	1¢ Jefferson	25.00	.40
UX15	1¢ black John Adams	40.00	15.00
UX16	2¢ black Liberty	10.00	9.00
UX17	1¢ black McKinley	*4,500.00*	*2,500.00*
UX18	1¢ black McKinley, facing left	10.00	.30
UX19	1¢ black McKinley, triangles in top corners	35.00	.50
UX20	1¢ (UX19), correspondence space at left	45.00	4.00
UX21	1¢ blue McKinley, shaded background	90.00	6.50
a	1¢ bronze blue, *bluish*	165.00	12.50
UX22	1¢ blue McKinley, white background	13.00	.25
UX23	1¢ red Lincoln, solid background	8.00	5.50
UX24	1¢ red McKinley	9.00	.25
UX25	2¢ red Grant	1.25	8.50
UX26	1¢ green Lincoln, solid background	10.00	6.00
UX27	1¢ Jefferson, *buff*	.25	.25
a	1¢ green, *cream*	3.50	.60
UX27C	1¢ green Jefferson, *gray*, die I	2,000.00	150.00
UX28	1¢ green Lincoln, *cream*	.60	.30
a	1¢ green, *buff*	1.50	.60
UX29	2¢ red Jefferson, *buff*	37.50	2.00
a	2¢ lake, *cream*	47.50	2.50
c	2¢ vermilion, *buff*	275.00	60.00

Issues of 1918-68	Un	U

		Un	U
UX30	2¢ red Jefferson, *cream*	25.00	1.50
	Surcharged in one line by canceling machine.		
UX31	1¢ on 2¢ red Jefferson	*3,500.00*	*3,500.00*
	Surcharged in two lines by canceling machine.		
UX32	1¢ on 2¢ red Jeff., *buff*	50.00	12.50
a	1¢ on 2¢ vermilion	*95.00*	60.00
b	Double surcharge	—	*82.50*
UX33	1¢ on 2¢ red Jefferson, *cream*	11.00	1.75
a	Inverted surcharge	55.00	
b	Double surcharge	55.00	35.00
d	Triple surcharge	350.00	
	Surcharged in two lines by press printing.		
UX34	1¢ on 2¢ red (UX29)	500.00	45.00
UX35	1¢ on 2¢ red Jefferson, *cream*	200.00	30.00
UX36	1¢ on 2¢ red (UX25)		*28,500.00*
UX37	3¢ red McKinley, *buff*	4.00	*9.00*
UX38	2¢ carmine rose Franklin	.35	.25
a	Double impression	200.00	
	Surcharged by canceling machine in light green.		
UX39	2¢ on 1¢ green Jefferson, *buff*	.50	.35
b	Double surcharge	17.50	20.00
UX40	2¢ on 1¢ green (UX28)	.65	.45
	Surcharged typographically in dark green.		
UX41	2¢ on 1¢ green Jefferson, *buff*	4.50	1.50
a	Inverted surcharge lower left	75.00	125.00
UX42	2¢ on 1¢ green (UX29)	5.00	2.00
b	Surcharged on back	80.00	
UX43	2¢ carmine Lincoln	.30	*1.00*
UX44	2¢ FIPEX	.25	*1.00*
b	Dk. vio. blue omitted	450.00	225.00
UX45	4¢ Statue of Liberty	1.50	*40.00*
UX46	3¢ purple Statue of Liberty	.50	.20
a	"N GOD WE TRUST"	15.00	25.00
UX47	2¢ + 1¢ carmine rose Franklin	175.00	250.00
UX48	4¢ red violet Lincoln	.25	.20
UX49	7¢ World Vacationland	3.75	*35.00*
UX50	4¢ U.S. Customs	.50	*1.00*
a	Blue omitted	450.00	
UX51	4¢ Social Security	.40	*1.00*
b	Blue omitted	*700.00*	
UX52	4¢ blue & red Coast Guard	.30	*1.00*
UX53	4¢ Bureau of the Census	.30	*1.00*
UX54	8¢ blue & red (UX49)	3.75	*35.00*
UX55	5¢ emerald Lincoln	.30	*.50*
UX56	5¢ Women Marines	.35	*1.00*

1970-1990

	Issues of 1970-83	Un	U
UX57	5¢ Weather Services	.30	1.00
a	Yellow, black omitted	700.00	
b	Blue omitted	650.00	
c	Black omitted	600.00	
UX58	6¢ brown Paul Revere	.30	1.00
a	Double impression	300.00	
UX59	10¢ blue & red (UX49)	4.00	35.00
UX60	6¢ America's Hospitals	.30	1.00
a	Blue, yellow omitted	700.00	
UX61	6¢ USF *Constellation*	.85	3.00
a	Address side blank	300.00	
UX62	6¢ black Monument Valley	.40	3.00
UX63	6¢ Gloucester, MA	.40	3.00
UX64	6¢ blue John Hanson	.25	1.00
UX65	6¢ magenta Liberty	.25	1.00
UX66	8¢ orange Samuel Adams	.25	1.00
UX67	12¢ Visit USA/ Ship's Figurehead	.35	30.00
UX68	7¢ Charles Thomson	.30	5.00
UX69	9¢ John Witherspoon	.25	1.00
UX70	9¢ blue Caesar Rodney	.25	1.00
UX71	9¢ Federal Court House	.25	1.00
UX72	9¢ green Nathan Hale	.25	1.00
UX73	10¢ Cincinnati Music Hall	.30	1.00
UX74	10¢ John Hancock	.30	1.00
UX75	10¢ John Hancock	.30	.15
UX76	14¢ Coast Guard Eagle	.40	15.00
UX77	10¢ Molly Pitcher	.30	1.00
UX78	10¢ George Rogers Clark	.30	1.00
UX79	10¢ Casimir Pulaski	.30	1.00
UX80	10¢ Olympic Sprinter	.60	1.00
UX81	10¢ Iolani Palace	.30	1.00
UX82	14¢ Olympic Games	.60	10.00
UX83	10¢ Salt Lake Temple	.25	1.00
UX84	10¢ Landing of Rochambeau	.25	1.00
UX85	10¢ Battle of Kings Mtn.	.25	1.00
UX86	19¢ Drake's Golden Hinde	.65	10.00
UX87	10¢ Battle of Cowpens	.25	2.50
UX88	12¢ violet Eagle, nondenominated	.30	.50
UX89	12¢ lt. bl. Isaiah Thomas	.30	.50
UX90	12¢ Nathanael Greene	.30	1.00
UX91	12¢ Lewis and Clark	.30	3.00
UX92	13¢ buff Robert Morris	.30	.50
UX93	13¢ buff Robert Morris	.30	.50
UX94	13¢ "Swamp Fox" Francis Marion	.30	.75
UX95	13¢ LaSalle Claims Louisiana	.30	.75
UX96	13¢ Academy of Music	.30	.75
UX97	13¢ Old Post Office, St. Louis, Missouri	.30	.75
UX100	13¢ Olympic Yachting	.30	.75

	Issues of 1984-90	Un	U
UX101	13¢ *Ark* and *Dove,* Maryland	.30	.75
UX102	13¢ Olympic Torch	.30	.75
UX103	13¢ Frederic Baraga	.30	.75
UX104	13¢ Dominguez Adobe	.30	.75
UX105	14¢ Charles Carroll	.30	.50
UX106	14¢ green Charles Carroll	.45	.25
UX107	25¢ Clipper *Flying Cloud*	.70	5.00
UX108	14¢ brt. grn. George Wythe	.30	.50
UX109	14¢ Settlement of Connecticut	.30	.75
UX110	14¢ Stamp Collecting	.30	.75
UX111	14¢ Francis Vigo	.30	.75
UX112	14¢ Settling of Rhode Island	.30	.75
UX113	14¢ Wisconsin Territory	.30	.75
UX114	14¢ National Guard	.30	.75
UX115	14¢ Self-Scouring Plow	.30	.50
UX116	14¢ Constitutional Convention	.30	.50
UX117	14¢ Stars and Stripes	.30	.50
UX118	14¢ Take Pride in America	.30	.50
UX119	14¢ Timberline Lodge	.30	.50
UX120	15¢ Bison and Prairie	.30	.50
UX121	15¢ Blair House	.30	.50
UX122	28¢ *Yorkshire*	.60	3.00
UX123	15¢ Iowa Territory	.30	.50
UX124	15¢ Ohio, Northwest Terr.	.30	.50
UX125	15¢ Hearst Castle	.30	.50
UX126	15¢ The Federalist Papers	.30	.50
UX127	15¢ Hawk and Desert	.30	.50
UX128	15¢ Healy Hall	.30	.50
UX129	15¢ Blue Heron and Marsh	.30	.50
UX130	15¢ Settling of Oklahoma	.30	.50
UX131	21¢ Geese and Mountains	.40	3.00
UX132	15¢ Seagull and Seashore	.30	.50
UX133	15¢ Deer and Waterfall	.30	.50
UX134	15¢ Hull House, Chicago	.30	.50
UX135	15¢ Ind. Hall, Philadelphia	.30	.50
UX136	15¢ Inner Harbor, Baltimore	.30	.50
UX137	15¢ Bridge, New York	.30	.50
UX138	15¢ Capitol, Washington	.30	.50
	#UX139-42 issued in sheets of 4 plus 2 inscribed labels, rouletted 9¹/₂ on 2 or 3 sides.		
UX139	15¢ (UX135)	2.00	.90
UX140	15¢ The White House	2.00	.90
UX141	15¢ (UX137)	2.00	.90
UX142	15¢ (UX138)	2.00	.90
a	Sheet of 4, #UX139-42	8.00	
UX143	15¢ The White House	1.00	1.00
UX144	15¢ Jefferson Memorial	1.00	1.00
UX145	15¢ Papermaking	.30	.30
UX146	15¢ World Literacy Year	.30	.50

UX79

UX70

UX81

UX83

UX94

UX109

UX112

UX113

UX115

UX116

UX118

UX119

UX131

UX143

UX144

UX143 (picture side)

UX144 (picture side)

UX174

UX175

UX176

UX177

UX198

UX199

UX220

UX241

UX262

UX263

UX280

UX282

UX283

UY12

UY41

UXC1

UXC2

Issues of 1990-95	Un	U
UX147 15¢ George Caleb Bingham	1.00	*1.00*
UX148 15¢ Isaac Royall House	.30	*.50*
UX150 15¢ Stanford University	.30	*.50*
UX151 15¢ Constitution Hall	1.00	1.00
UX152 15¢ Chicago Orchestra Hall	.30	*.50*
UX153 19¢ Flag	.40	*.50*
UX154 19¢ Carnegie Hall	.40	*.50*
UX155 19¢ Old Red, UT-Galveston	.40	*.50*
UX156 19¢ Bill of Rights	.40	*.50*
UX157 19¢ Notre Dame	.40	*.50*
UX158 30¢ Niagara Falls	.75	*1.40*
UX159 19¢ The Old Mill	.40	*.50*
UX160 19¢ Wadsworth Atheneum	.40	*.50*
UX161 19¢ Cobb Hall	.40	*.50*
UX162 19¢ Waller Hall	.40	*.50*
UX163 19¢ America's Cup	1.00	*1.75*
UX164 19¢ Columbia River Gorge	.40	*.50*
UX165 19¢ Ellis Island	.40	*.50*
UX166 19¢ National Cathedral	.40	*.50*
UX167 19¢ Wren Building	.40	*.50*
UX168 19¢ Holocaust Memorial	1.00	*1.75*
UX169 19¢ Fort Recovery	.40	*.50*
UX170 19¢ Playmakers Theatre	.40	*.50*
UX171 19¢ O'Kane Hall	.40	*.50*
UX172 19¢ Beecher Hall	.40	*.50*
UX173 19¢ Massachusetts Hall	.40	*.50*
UX174 19¢ Lincoln's Home	.40	*.50*
UX175 19¢ Wittenberg University	.40	*.50*
UX176 19¢ Canyon de Chelly	.40	*.50*
UX177 19¢ St. Louis Union Station	.40	*.50*
UX198 20¢ Red Barn	.40	.40
UX199 20¢ Old Glory	.40	.40
UX220 20¢ American Clipper Ships	.40	.40

Issues of 1996-97	Un	U
UX241 20¢ Winter Scene	.40	.40
UX262 20¢ St. John's College	.40	.40
UX263 20¢ Princeton University	.40	.40
UX280 20¢ City College of New York	.40	.40
UX281 20¢ Bugs Bunny	.40	.40
UX282 20¢ Pacific 97 Golden Gate Bridge in Daylight	.40	.40
UX283 50¢ Pacific 97 Golden Gate Bridge at Sunset	1.00	1.00
20¢ Fort McHenry		
Issues of 1892-1995		
Paid Reply Postal Cards		
Prices are: Un=unsevered, U=severed card.		
UY1 1¢ + 1¢ black Grant	35.00	7.50
UY6 1¢ + 1¢ green G. and M. Washington, double frame line around instructions	140.00	22.50
UY7 1¢ + 1¢ green G. and M. Washington, single frame line	1.25	.50
UY12 3¢ + 3¢ red McKinley	9.00	25.00
UY18 4¢ + 4¢ Lincoln	3.00	2.50
UY23 6¢ + 6¢ John Adams	.90	2.00
UY31 "A" (12¢ + 12¢) Eagle	.75	2.00
UY39 15¢ + 15¢ Bison and Prairie	.75	1.00
UY40 19¢ + 19¢ Flag	.75	1.00
UY41 20¢ Red Barn	.80	1.25
Issues of 1949-60, Airmail Postal Cards		
UXC1 4¢ orange Eagle	.50	.75
UXC2 5¢ red Eagle (C48)	1.75	.75
UXC3 5¢ UXC2 redrawn—"Air Mail-Postal Card" omitted	6.00	2.00

Red barns part of America's rural landscape

A common building found on America's farms, traditional barns were two stories, built of wood and painted red. Toward the end of the 20th century, more barns have been constructed of sheet metal or aluminum and are one story. Used to store animals, farming materials and equipment, barns have also provided a place for children to play. Dotting the rural landscape of the U.S., a red barn adds a rustic beauty to many farming communities. **(#UX198)**

Issues of 1963-1981	Un	U
UXC4 6¢ red Eagle	.60	*.75*
UXC5 11¢ Visit The USA	.60	*12.50*
UXC6 6¢ Virgin Islands	.40	*6.00*
a Red, yellow omitted	*1,700.00*	
UXC7 6¢ Boy Scout World Jamboree	.40	*6.00*
UXC8 13¢ blue & red (UXC5)	1.25	*8.00*
UXC9 8¢ Stylized Eagle	.60	*2.00*
UXC10 9¢ red & blue (UXC5)	.50	*1.00*
UXC11 15¢ Travel Service	1.75	*12.50*
UXC12 9¢ black Grand Canyon	.50	*8.00*
UXC13 15¢ black Niagara Falls	.65	*15.00*
UXC14 11¢ Stylized Eagle	.70	*2.00*
UXC15 18¢ Eagle Weather Vane	.85	*7.00*
UXC16 21¢ Angel Weather Vane	.80	*7.50*
UXC17 21¢ Curtiss Jenny	.75	*6.00*
UXC18 21¢ Olympic Gymnast	1.00	*10.00*
UXC19 28¢ First Transpacific Flight	.90	*4.00*

Issues of 1982-95	Un	U
UXC20 28¢ Gliders	.90	*3.00*
UXC21 28¢ Olympic Speed Skater	.90	*2.00*
UXC22 33¢ China Clipper	.90	*2.00*
UXC23 33¢ AMERIPEX '86	.65	*2.00*
UXC24 36¢ DC-3	.70	*1.00*
UXC25 40¢ Yankee Clipper	.80	*1.00*
UXC26 50¢ Soaring Eagle	1.00	*1.50*
Issues of 1913-95 Official Mail Postal Cards		
UZ1 1¢ black Numeral	325.00	150.00
UZ2 13¢ blue Great Seal	.60	*35.00*
UZ3 14¢ blue Great Seal	.60	*35.00*
UZ4 15¢ blue Great Seal	.60	*35.00*
UZ5 19¢ blue Great Seal	.55	*30.00*
UZ6 20¢ Official Mail	.40	—

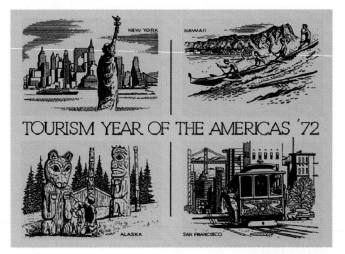

Back of UXC12

JXC4

UXC5

JXC6

UXC7

JXC8

UXC9

UXC10

JXC11

UXC12

UXC13

JXC19

UXC20

UXC23

Souvenir Pages

With First Day Cancellations

The Postal Service offers Souvenir Pages for new stamps. The series began with a page for the Yellowstone Park Centennial stamp issued March 1, 1972. The Pages feature one or more stamps tied by the first day cancel, along with technical data and information on the subject of the issue. More than just collectors' items, Souvenir Pages make wonderful show and conversation pieces. Souvenir Pages are issued in limited editions. Number in parentheses ( ) indicates the number of stamps on page if there are more than one.

1972

72-00	Family Planning	750.00
72-01	Yellowstone Park	130.00
72-01a	Yellowstone Park with DC cancel	500.00
72-02	2¢ Cape Hatteras	100.00
72-03	14¢ Fiorello LaGuardia	110.00
72-04	11¢ City of Refuge Park	110.00
72-05	6¢ Wolf Trap Farm Park	40.00
72-06	Colonial Craftsmen (4)	20.00
72-07	15¢ Mount McKinley	30.00
72-08	6¢-15¢ Olympic Games (4)	12.50
72-08E	Olympic Games with broken red circle on 6¢ stamp	1,000.00
72-09	PTA	7.50
72-10	Wildlife Conservation (4)	10.00
72-11	Mail Order	7.75
72-12	Osteopathic Medicine	7.50
72-13	Tom Sawyer	7.50
72-14	7¢ Benjamin Franklin	9.25
72-15	Christmas (2)	9.00
72-16	Pharmacy	7.50
72-17	Stamp Collecting	7.50

1973

73-01	$1 Eugene O'Neill	17.50
73-01E	$1 Eugene O'Neill picture perf. error	750.00
73-02	Love	10.00
73-03	Pamphleteer	6.75
73-04	George Gershwin	7.75
73-05	Broadside	8.00
73-06	Copernicus	7.50
73-07	Postal Employees	7.50
73-08	Harry S. Truman	6.25
73-09	Post Rider	8.00
73-10	21¢ Amadeo Gianninni	6.25
73-11	Boston Tea Party (4)	8.25
73-12	6¢-15¢ Electronics (4)	10.00
73-13	Robinson Jeffers	6.00
73-14	Lyndon B. Johnson	5.25
73-15	Henry O. Tanner	7.50
73-16	Willa Cather	5.00
73-17	Colonial Drummer	5.75
73-18	Angus Cattle	5.00
73-19	Christmas (2)	9.00
73-20	13¢ Winged Envelope airmail	4.00
73-21	10¢ Crossed Flags	4.00
73-22	10¢ Jefferson Memorial	4.00
73-23	13¢ Winged Envelope airmail coil (2)	4.00

1974

74-01	26¢ Mount Rushmore airmail	7.50
74-02	ZIP Code	4.75
74-02E	ZIP Code with date error 4/4/74	500.00
74-03	18¢ Statue of Liberty airmail	7.50
74-04	18¢ Elizabeth Blackwell	3.25
74-05	VFW	3.25
74-06	Robert Frost	3.50
74-07	Expo '74	3.25
74-08	Horse Racing	6.00
74-09	Skylab	5.00
74-10	UPU (8)	6.50
74-11	Mineral Heritage (4)	7.50
74-12	Fort Harrod	3.25
74-13	Continental Congress (4)	6.00
74-14	Chautauqua	2.75
74-15	Kansas Wheat	2.75
74-16	Energy Conservation	2.75
74-17	6.3¢ Liberty Bell coil (2)	4.00
74-18	Sleepy Hollow	4.00
74-19	Retarded Children	3.25
74-20	Christmas (3)	7.50

1975

75-01	Benjamin West	3.25
75-02	Pioneer/Jupiter	7.50
75-03	Collective Bargaining	3.50
75-04	8¢ Sybil Ludington	3.25
75-05	Salem Poor	3.25
75-06	Haym Salomon	4.00
75-07	18¢ Peter Francisco	5.00
75-08	Mariner 10	6.00
75-09	Lexington & Concord	3.50
75-10	Paul Dunbar	5.00
75-11	D.W. Griffith	4.00
75-12	Bunker Hill	3.50
75-13	Military Uniforms (4)	7.50
75-14	Apollo Soyuz (2)	7.50
75-15	International Women's Year	3.25
75-16	Postal Service Bicentennial (4)	5.25
75-17	World Peace Through Law	3.25
75-18	Banking & Commerce (2)	3.25
75-19	Christmas (2)	4.25
75-20	3¢ Francis Parkman	4.00
75-21	11¢ Freedom of the Press	3.00
75-22	24¢ Old North Church	2.75
75-23	Flag over Independence Hall (2)	2.75
75-24	9¢ Freedom to Assemble (2)	3.00
75-25	Liberty Bell coil (2)	2.75
75-26	Eagle & Shield	4.00

1976

76-01	Spirit of '76 (3)	5.00
76-01E	Spirit of '76 with cancellation error Jan. 2, 1976 (3)	1,000.00
76-02	25¢ and 31¢ Plane and Globes airmails (2)	4.00
76-03	Interphil '76	4.00
76-04	State Flags, DE to VA (10)	10.00
76-05	State Flags, NY to MS (10)	10.00
76-06	State Flags, IL to WI (10)	10.00
76-07	State Flags, CA to SD (10)	10.00

76-08	State Flags, MT to HI (10)	10.00
76-09	9¢ Freedom to Assemble coil (2)	2.50
76-10	Telephone Centennial	2.75
76-11	Commercial Aviation	3.00
76-12	Chemistry	2.75
76-13	7.9¢ Drum coil (2)	2.75
76-14	Benjamin Franklin	2.75
76-15	Bicentennial souvenir sheet	12.50
76-15E	13¢ Bicentennial souvenir sheet with perforation and numerical errors	1,000.00
76-16	18¢ Bicentennial souvenir sheet	12.50
76-17	24¢ Bicentennial souvenir sheet	12.50
76-18	31¢ Bicentennial souvenir sheet	12.50
76-19	Declaration of Independence (4)	6.00
76-20	Olympics (4)	6.25
76-21	Clara Maass	2.50
76-22	Adolph S. Ochs	2.50
76-23	Christmas (3)	4.25
76-24	7.7¢ Saxhorns coil (2)	2.50

1977

77-01	Washington at Princeton	2.75
77-02	Flag over Capitol booklet pane (9¢ and 13¢) Perf. 10 (8)	25.00
77-03	Sound Recording	2.50
77-04	Pueblo Pottery (4)	3.50
77-05	Lindbergh Flight	4.00
77-06	Colorado Centennial	3.00
77-07	Butterflies (4)	3.25
77-08	Lafayette	2.50
77-09	Skilled Hands (4)	3.25
77-10	Peace Bridge	2.50
77-11	Battle of Oriskany	2.50
77-12	Alta, CA, First Civil Settlement	2.50
77-13	Articles of Confederation	2.50
77-14	Talking Pictures	4.00
77-15	Surrender at Saratoga	3.75
77-16	Energy (2)	2.50
77-17	Christmas, Mailbox and Christmas, Valley Forge, Omaha cancel (2)	3.00
77-18	Same, Valley Forge cancel	3.00
77-19	10¢ Petition for Redress coil (2)	4.00

| 77-20 | 10¢ Petition for Redress sheet (2) | 3.25 |
| 77-21 | 1¢-4¢ Americana (5) | 3.25 |

1978

78-01	Carl Sandburg	3.00
78-02	Indian Head Penny	3.00
78-03	Captain Cook, Anchorage cancel (2)	3.25
78-04	Captain Cook, Honolulu cancel (2)	3.25
78-05	Harriet Tubman	5.00
78-06	American Quilts (4)	4.00
78-07	16¢ Statue of Liberty sheet and coil (2)	2.75
78-08	29¢ Sandy Hook Lighthouse	2.75
78-09	American Dance (4)	4.00
78-10	French Alliance	3.00
78-11	Early Cancer Detection	4.00
78-12	"A" (15¢) sheet and coil (2)	7.50
78-13	Jimmie Rodgers	4.75
78-14	CAPEX '78 (8)	10.00
78-15	Oliver Wendell Holmes coil	2.75
78-16	Photography	3.00
78-17	Fort McHenry Flag sheet and coil (2)	3.25
78-18	George M. Cohan	2.50
78-19	Rose booklet single	4.00

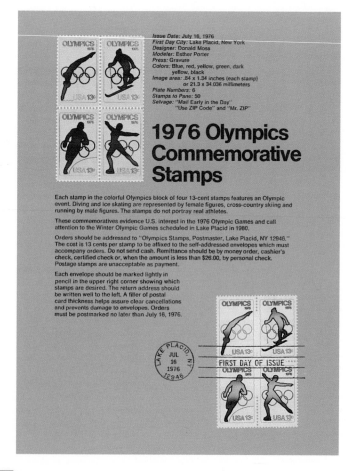

Issue Date: July 16, 1976
First Day City: Lake Placid, New York
Designer: Donald Moss
Modeler: Esther Porter
Press: Gravure
Colors: Blue, red, yellow, green, dark yellow, black
Image area: .84 x 1.34 inches (each stamp) or 21.3 x 34.036 millimeters
Plate Numbers: 6
Stamps to Pane: 50
Selvage: "Mail Early in the Day" "Use ZIP Code" and "Mr. ZIP"

1976 Olympics Commemorative Stamps

Each stamp in the colorful Olympics block of four 13-cent stamps features an Olympic event. Diving and ice skating are represented by female figures, cross-country skiing and running by male figures. The stamps do not portray real athletes.

These commemoratives evidence U.S. interest in the 1976 Olympic Games and call attention to the Winter Olympic Games scheduled in Lake Placid in 1980.

Orders should be addressed to "Olympics Stamps, Postmaster, Lake Placid, NY 12946." The cost is 13 cents per stamp to be affixed to the self-addressed envelopes which must accompany orders. Do not send cash. Remittance should be by money order, cashier's check, certified check or, when the amount is less than $26.00, by personal check. Postage stamps are unacceptable as payment.

Each envelope should be marked lightly in pencil in the upper right corner showing which stamps are desired. The return address should be written well to the left. A filler of postal card thickness helps assure clear cancellations and prevents damage to envelopes. Orders must be postmarked no later than July 16, 1976.

78-20	8.4¢ Piano coil (2)	3.25
78-21	Viking Missions	6.00
78-22	28¢ Remote Outpost	3.25
78-23	American Owls (4)	4.00
78-24	31¢ Wright Brothers airmails (2)	4.00
78-25	American Trees (4)	4.00
78-26	Christmas, Madonna	3.00
78-27	Christmas, Hobby Horse	3.00
78-28	$2 Kerosene Lamp	7.50

1979

79-01	Robert F. Kennedy	3.00
79-02	Martin Luther King, Jr.	5.00
79-03	International Year of the Child	3.00
79-04	John Steinbeck	3.00
79-05	Albert Einstein	3.50
79-06	21¢ Octave Chanute airmails (2)	4.00
79-07	Pennsylvania Toleware (4)	4.00
79-08	American Architecture (4)	4.00
79-09	Endangered Flora (4)	4.00
79-10	Seeing Eye Dogs	3.00
79-11	$1 Lamp & Candle	6.00
79-12	Special Olympics	2.75
79-13	$5 Lantern	15.00
79-14	30¢ Schoolhouse	4.75
79-15	10¢ Summer Olympics (2)	4.25
79-16	50¢ Whale Oil Lamp	5.00
79-17	John Paul Jones	3.25
79-18	Summer Olympics (4)	5.50
79-19	Christmas, Madonna	4.00
79-20	Christmas, Santa Claus	4.00
79-21	3.1¢ Guitar coil (2)	5.75
79-22	31¢ Summer Olympics airmail	6.25
79-23	Will Rogers	2.75
79-24	Vietnam Veterans	2.75
79-25	25¢ Wiley Post airmails (2)	5.00

1980

80-01	W.C. Fields	3.00
80-02	Winter Olympics (4)	7.50
80-03	Windmills booklet pane (10)	6.00
80-04	Benjamin Banneker	5.00
80-05	Letter Writing (6)	3.50
80-06	1¢ Ability to Write (2)	2.25
80-07	Frances Perkins	2.25
80-08	Dolley Madison	5.00
80-09	Emily Bissell	3.00
80-10	3.5¢ Violins coil (2)	4.00
80-11	Helen Keller/ Anne Sullivan	3.00
80-12	Veterans Administration	2.25
80-13	General Bernardo de Galvez	2.25
80-14	Coral Reefs (4)	2.75
80-15	Organized Labor	5.00
80-16	Edith Wharton	5.00
80-17	Education	5.00
80-18	Indian Masks (4)	4.00
80-19	American Architecture (4)	3.00
80-20	40¢ Philip Mazzei airmail	4.00
80-21	Christmas, Madonna	4.00

80-22	Christmas, Antique Toys	4.00
80-23	Sequoyah	2.25
80-24	28¢ Blanche Scott airmail	2.25
80-25	35¢ Glenn Curtiss airmail	2.25

1981

81-01	Everett Dirksen	2.25
81-02	Whitney M. Young	5.00
81-03	"B" (18¢) sheet and coil (3)	4.00
81-04	"B" (18¢) booklet pane (8)	3.50
81-05	12¢ Freedom of Conscience sheet and coil (3)	2.75
81-06	Flowers block (4)	3.00
81-07	Flag and Anthem sheet and coil (3)	4.00
81-08	Flag and Anthem booklet pane (8 - 6¢ and 18¢)	3.50
81-09	American Red Cross	2.25
81-10	George Mason	2.25
81-11	Savings & Loans	2.25
81-12	Wildlife booklet pane (10)	5.00
81-13	Surrey coil (2)	4.00
81-14	Space Achievement (8)	10.00
81-15	17¢ Rachel Carson (2)	2.25
81-16	35¢ Charles Drew, MD	4.00
81-17	Professional Management	2.25
81-18	17¢ Electric Auto coil (2)	4.50
81-19	Wildlife Habitat (4)	2.75
81-20	International Year of the Disabled	2.25
81-21	Edna St. Vincent Millay	4.00
81-22	Alcoholism	4.00
81-23	American Architecture (4)	4.00
81-24	Babe Zaharias	7.50
81-25	Bobby Jones	7.50
81-26	Frederic Remington	2.50
81-27	"C" (20¢) sheet and coil (3)	5.00
81-28	"C" (18¢) booklet pane (10)	4.25
81-29	18¢ and 20¢ Hoban (2)	2.50
81-30	Yorktown/ Virginia Capes (2)	3.00
81-31	Christmas, Madonna	5.00
81-32	Christmas, Bear on Sleigh	5.00
81-33	John Hanson	2.25
81-34	Fire Pumper coil (2)	7.50
81-35	Desert Plants (4)	4.00
81-36	9.3¢ Mail Wagon coil (3)	6.00
81-37	Flag over Supreme Court sheet and coil (3)	6.00
81-38	Flag over Supreme Court booklet pane (6)	5.00

1982

82-01	Sheep booklet pane (10)	3.50
82-02	Ralph Bunche	6.00
82-03	13¢ Crazy Horse (2)	2.25
82-04	37¢ Robert Millikan	2.00
82-05	Franklin D. Roosevelt	2.25

82-06	Love	2.25
82-07	5.9¢ Bicycle coil (4)	9.00
82-08	George Washington	5.00
82-09	10.9¢ Hansom Cab coil (2)	6.00
82-10	Birds & Flowers, AL-GE (10)	15.00
82-11	Birds & Flowers, HI-MD (10)	15.00
82-12	Birds & Flowers, MA-NJ (10)	15.00
82-13	Birds & Flowers, NM-SC (10)	15.00
82-14	Birds & Flowers, SD-WY (10)	15.00
82-15	USA/Netherlands	2.25
82-16	Library of Congress	2.25
82-17	Consumer Education coil (2)	5.00
82-18	Knoxville World's Fair (4)	2.50
82-19	Horatio Alger	2.25
82-20	2¢ Locomotive coil (2)	5.25
82-21	Aging Together	2.25
82-22	The Barrymores	3.75
82-23	Mary Walker	2.25
82-24	Peace Garden	2.25
82-25	America's Libraries	2.25
82-26	Jackie Robinson	20.00
82-27	4¢ Stagecoach coil (3)	6.00
82-28	Touro Synagogue	2.25
82-29	Wolf Trap Farm Park	2.25
82-30	American Architecture (4)	3.00
82-31	Francis of Assisi	2.25
82-32	Ponce de Leon	2.25
82-33	13¢ Kitten & Puppy (2)	4.00
82-34	Christmas, Madonna	4.00
82-35	Christmas, Seasons Greetings (4)	4.00
82-36	2¢ Igor Stravinsky (2)	3.25

1983

83-01	1¢, 4¢, 13¢ Penalty Mail (5)	4.00
83-02	17¢ Penalty Mail (4)	3.25
83-03	Penalty Mail coil (2)	5.00
83-04	$1 Penalty Mail	6.00
83-05	$5 Penalty Mail	12.50
83-06	Science & Industry	2.50
83-07	5.2¢ Antique Sleigh coil (4)	7.50
83-08	Sweden/USA Treaty	3.00
83-09	3¢ Handcar coil (3)	5.00
83-10	Balloons (4)	2.75
83-11	Civilian Conservation Corps	2.00
83-12	40¢ Olympics airmails (4)	3.50
83-13	Joseph Priestley	2.50
83-14	Volunteerism	2.50
83-15	Concord/German Immigration	2.50
83-16	Physical Fitness	2.50
83-17	Brooklyn Bridge	3.00
83-18	TVA	2.50
83-19	4¢ Carl Schurz (5)	2.50
83-20	Medal of Honor	4.00
83-21	Scott Joplin	5.00
83-22	Thomas H. Gallaudet	2.50
83-23	28¢ Olympics (4)	4.75
83-24	5¢ Pearl S. Buck (4)	2.50
83-25	Babe Ruth	15.00
83-26	Nathaniel Hawthorne	2.50
83-27	3¢ Henry Clay (7)	2.00
83-28	13¢ Olympics (4)	5.00

83-29	$9.35 Eagle booklet single	140.00
83-30	$9.35 Eagle booklet pane (3)	190.00
83-31	1¢ Omnibus coil (3)	5.00
83-32	Treaty of Paris	3.00
83-33	Civil Service	2.50
83-34	Metropolitan Opera	3.00
83-35	Inventors (4)	3.00
83-36	1¢ Dorothea Dix (3)	3.00
83-37	Streetcars (4)	3.50
83-38	5¢ Motorcycle coil (4)	7.50
83-39	Christmas, Madonna	3.00
83-40	Christmas, Santa Claus	3.00
83-41	35¢ Olympics airmails (4)	3.50
83-42	Martin Luther	4.00
83-43	Flag over Supreme Court booklet pane (10)	3.50

1984

84-01	Alaska Statehood	3.00
84-02	Winter Olympics (4)	4.00
84-03	FDIC	2.50
84-04	Harry S. Truman	2.00
84-05	Love	2.50
84-06	Carter G. Woodson	5.00
84-07	11¢ RR Caboose coil (2)	5.00
84-08	Soil & Water Conservation	2.50
84-09	Credit Union Act	2.50
84-10	40¢ Lillian M. Gilbreth	2.00
84-11	Orchids (4)	3.50
84-12	Hawaii Statehood	2.50
84-13	7.4¢ Baby Buggy coil (3)	5.00
84-14	National Archives	2.50
84-15	20¢ Summer Olympics (4)	5.00
84-16	New Orleans World's Fair	2.50
84-17	Health Research	2.50
84-18	Douglas Fairbanks	3.00
84-19	Jim Thorpe	12.50
84-20	10¢ Richard Russell (2)	2.00
84-21	John McCormack	3.50
84-22	St. Lawrence Seaway	2.50
84-23	Migratory Bird Hunting and Conservation Stamp Act	6.00
84-24	Roanoke Voyages	2.50
84-25	Herman Melville	2.50
84-26	Horace Moses	2.50
84-27	Smokey Bear	7.50
84-28	Roberto Clemente	17.50
84-29	30¢ Frank C. Laubach	2.00
84-30	Dogs (4)	5.00
84-31	Crime Prevention	3.00
84-32	Family Unity	3.75
84-33	Eleanor Roosevelt	4.00
84-34	Nation of Readers	4.00
84-35	Christmas, Madonna	4.00
84-36	Christmas, Santa Claus	4.00
84-37	Hispanic Americans	2.00
84-38	Vietnam Veterans Memorial	3.75

1985

85-01	Jerome Kern	4.00
85-02	7¢ Abraham Baldwin (3)	3.00
85-03	"D" (22¢) sheet and coil (3)	3.00
85-04	"D" (22¢) booklet pane (10)	5.00
85-05	"D" (22¢) Penalty Mail sheet and coil (3)	2.50
85-06	11¢ Alden Partridge (2)	2.50
85-07	33¢ Alfred Verville airmail	2.25
85-08	39¢ Lawrence & Elmer Sperry airmail	3.00
85-09	44¢ Transpacific airmail	3.00
85-10	50¢ Chester Nimitz	2.75
85-11	Mary McLeod Bethune	3.50
85-12	39¢ Grenville Clark	2.00
85-13	14¢ Sinclair Lewis (2)	2.00
85-14	Duck Decoys (4)	3.00
85-15	14¢ Iceboat coil (2)	5.00
85-16	Winter Special Olympics	3.00
85-17	Flag over Capitol sheet and coil (3)	3.50
85-18	Flag over Capitol booklet pane (5)	3.50
85-19	12¢ Stanley Steamer coil (3)	5.00
85-20	Seashells booklet pane (10)	5.00
85-21	Love	5.00
85-22	10.1¢ Oil Wagon coil (3)	4.00
85-23	12.5¢ Pushcart coil (2)	5.00
85-24	John J. Audubon	3.00
85-25	$10.75 Eagle booklet single	50.00
85-26	$10.75 Eagle booklet pane (3)	100.00
85-27	6¢ Tricycle coil (4)	5.00
85-28	Rural Electrification Administration	2.50
85-29	14¢ and 22¢ Penalty Mail sheet and coil (4)	5.00
85-30	AMERIPEX '86	2.50
85-31	9¢ Sylvanus Thayer (3)	3.00
85-32	3.4¢ School Bus coil (7)	6.00
85-33	11¢ Stutz Bearcat coil (2)	5.00
85-34	Abigail Adams	2.00
85-35	4.9¢ Buckboard coil (5)	6.00
85-36	8.3¢ Ambulance coil (3)	6.00
85-37	Frederic Bartholdi	5.00
85-38	8¢ Henry Knox (3)	2.00
85-39	Korean War Veterans	3.50
85-40	Social Security Act	3.00
85-41	44¢ Father Junipero Serra airmail	3.00
85-42	World War I Veterans	3.00
85-43	6¢ Walter Lippmann (4)	2.50
85-44	Horses (4)	5.00
85-45	Public Education	3.00
85-46	International Youth Year (4)	4.00
85-47	Help End Hunger	3.00
85-48	21.1¢ Letters coil (2)	4.00
85-49	Christmas, Madonna	3.00
85-50	Christmas, Poinsettias	4.00
85-51	18¢ Washington/ Washington Monument coil (2)	4.00

1986

86-01	Arkansas Statehood	2.25
86-02	25¢ Jack London	2.50
86-03	Stamp Collecting booklet pane (4)	6.00
86-04	Love	3.50
86-05	Sojourner Truth	4.50
86-06	5¢ Hugo L. Black (5)	3.25
86-07	Republic of Texas (2)	2.25
86-08	$2 William Jennings Bryan	5.00
86-09	Fish booklet pane (5)	5.00
86-10	Public Hospitals	1.75
86-11	Duke Ellington	5.00
86-12	Presidents, Washington- Harrison (9)	6.00
86-13	Presidents, Tyler-Grant (9)	6.00
86-14	Presidents, Hayes-Wilson (9)	6.00
86-15	Presidents, Harding-Johnson (9)	6.00
86-16	Polar Explorers (4)	5.00
86-17	17¢ Belva Ann Lockwood (2)	3.50
86-18	1¢ Margaret Mitchell (3)	3.00
86-19	Statue of Liberty	4.00
86-20	4¢ Father Flanagan (3)	2.50
86-21	17¢ Dog Sled coil (2)	4.00
86-22	56¢ John Harvard	2.75
86-23	Navajo Blankets (4)	4.00
86-24	3¢ Paul Dudley White, MD (8)	3.00
86-25	$1 Bernard Revel	2.75
86-26	T.S. Eliot	2.50
86-27	Wood-Carved Figurines (4)	2.75
86-28	Christmas, Madonna	3.50
86-29	Christmas, Village Scene	3.50
86-30	5.5¢ Star Route Truck coil (4)	5.00
86-31	25¢ Bread Wagon coil	5.00

1987

87-01	8.5¢ Tow Truck coil (5)	4.00
87-02	Michigan Statehood	4.00
87-03	Pan American Games	4.00
87-04	Love	5.00
87-05	7.1¢ Tractor coil (5)	4.00
87-06	14¢ Julia Ward Howe (2)	2.00
87-07	Jean Baptiste Pointe Du Sable	7.50
87-08	Enrico Caruso	3.00
87-09	2¢ Mary Lyon (3)	3.00
87-10	Reengraved 2¢ Locomotive coil (6)	4.00
87-11	Girl Scouts	5.00
87-12	10¢ Canal Boat coil (5)	5.00
87-13	Special Occasions booklet pane (10)	6.00
87-14	United Way	2.50
87-15	Flag with Fireworks	2.50
87-16	Flag over Capitol coil, prephosphored paper (2)	4.00
87-17	Wildlife, Swallow- Squirrel (10)	7.50
87-18	Wildlife, Armadillo- Rabbit (10)	7.50
87-19	Wildlife, Tanager- Ladybug (10)	7.50
87-20	Wildlife, Beaver- Prairie Dog (10)	7.50
87-21	Wildlife, Turtle-Fox (10)	7.50
87-22	Delaware Statehood	2.75
87-23	U.S./Morocco Friendship	2.50
87-24	William Faulkner	2.50
87-25	Lacemaking (4)	5.00
87-26	10¢ Red Cloud (3)	2.00

Copyright U.S. Postal Service 1996

Issue Date: March 13, 1997
First Day City: New York, New York
Designer: Richard Sheaff, Norwood, Massachusetts
Engraver: Armandina Lozano
Typographer: John Boyd, New York, New York
Modeler: Banknote Corporation of America
Manufacturing Process: Intaglio

Printer: Banknote Corporation of America
Colors: Modified PMS 206 (red) and PMS 301 (blue)
Image Area: 2.047 x 1.456 inches or 52 x 37 millimeters
Stamps per pane: 16
Plate Numbers: "B" followed by one single digit
Marginal Markings: © USPS 1996, plate position diagram, plate numbers, price, header text

Stagecoach and Ship

The first triangular stamps ever issued by the U.S. Postal Service feature period engravings portraying modes of transportation representative of 18th-century San Francisco.

The clipper ship, the Richard S. Ely, was originally pictured on a small advertising card handed out on the streets of eastern cities to entice travelers to sail to California. The ship was built in 1856 in East Boston, Massachusetts, and was registered in New York in 1859. The clipper ship stamp was printed from an engraving of the drawing.

The stagecoach image is believed to be based on a drawing of a U. S. Mail stagecoach by American artist Harrison Eastman. The engraving from which this stamp was taken is dated 1867. Eastman worked as a post office clerk and later established his reputation as a painter, engraver, lithographer, and illustrator.

These stamps were released at the Postage Stamp Mega-Event in New York, New York by the U.S. Postal Service.

FIRST DAY OF ISSUE

Souvenir Page © 1997 U.S. Postal Service

9/08

87-27	$5 Bret Harte	12.50	88-12	"E" (25¢) Earth booklet pane (10)	6.00	88-34	15¢ Tugboat coil (2) 3.00
87-28	Pennsylvania Statehood	3.00	88-13	"E" (25¢) Penalty Mail coil (2)	3.00	88-35	13.2¢ Coal Car coil (2) 5.00
87-29	Drafting of the Constitution booklet pane (5)	4.50	88-14	44¢ New Sweden airmail	3.00	88-36 88-37	New York Statehood 4.00 45¢ Love 3.00
87-30	New Jersey Statehood	4.00	88-15	Pheasant booklet pane (10)	6.00	88-38	8.4¢ Wheelchair coil (3) 4.00
87-31	Signing of Constitution	3.00	88-16	Jack London booklet pane (6)	4.50	88-39	21¢ Railroad Mail Car coil (2) 5.00
87-32	Certified Public Accountants	6.00	88-17	Jack London booklet pane (10)	5.75	88-40 88-41	Summer Olympics 3.00 Classic Cars
87-33	5¢ Milk Wagon and 17.5¢ Racing Car coils (4)	4.50	88-18 88-19	Flag with Clouds 45¢ Samuel Langley airmail	2.50 3.00	88-42 88-43	booklet pane (5) 7.00 7.6¢ Carreta coil (4) 5.00 Honeybee coil (2) 7.50
87-34	Locomotives booklet pane (5)	10.00	88-19A	20¢ Penalty Mail coil (2)	3.50	88-44	Antarctic Explorers (4) 4.00
87-35	Christmas, Madonna	3.00	88-20	Flag over Yosemite coil (2)	3.00	88-45	5.3¢ Elevator coil (5) 5.00
87-36	Christmas, Ornaments	2.50	88-21	South Carolina Statehood	3.00	88-46	20.5¢ Fire Engine coil (2) 5.00
87-37	Flag with Fireworks booklet-pair	4.00	88-22	Owl & Grosbeak booklet pane (10)	5.00	88-47 88-48	Carousel Animals (4) 5.00 $8.75 Eagle 25.00
	1988		88-23	15¢ Buffalo Bill Cody (2)	3.00	88-49 88-50	Christmas, Madonna 3.00 Christmas,
88-01	Georgia Statehood	3.00	88-24	15¢ and 25¢ Penalty Mail coils (4)	4.00	88-51	Snow Scene 3.00 21¢ Chester Carlson 2.50
88-02	Connecticut Statehood	3.00	88-25	Francis Ouimet	10.00	88-52	Special Occasions booklet pane (6),
88-03	Winter Olympics	2.50	88-26	45¢ Harvey			Love You,
88-04	Australia Bicentennial	2.75		Cushing, MD	2.50		Thinking of You 15.00
88-05	James Weldon Johnson	5.00	88-27	New Hampshire Statehood	3.00	88-53	Special Occasions booklet pane (6),
88-06	Cats (4)	5.00	88-28	36¢ Igor Sikorsky airmail	4.00		Happy Birthday, Best Wishes 25.00
88-07	Massachusetts Statehood	3.50	88-29	Virginia Statehood	3.00	88-54	24.1¢ Tandem Bicycle coil (2) 5.00
88-08	Maryland Statehood	3.50	88-30	10.1¢ Oil Wagon coil, precancel (3)	4.00	88-55	20¢ Cable Car coil (2) 5.00
88-09	3¢ Conestoga Wagon coil (8)	3.50	88-31	Love	3.50	88-56	13¢ Patrol Wagon coil (2) 5.00
88-10	Knute Rockne	7.50	88-32	Flag with Clouds booklet pane (6)	6.00	88-57	23¢ Mary Cassatt 3.00
88-11	"E" (25¢) Earth sheet and coil (3)	3.00	88-33	16.7¢ Popcorn Wagon coil (2)	4.00	88-58	65¢ H.H. "Hap" Arnold 3.50

1989

89-01	Montana Statehood	2.50
89-02	A. Philip Randolph	5.00
89-03	Flag over Yosemite coil, prephosphored paper (2)	3.50
89-04	North Dakota Statehood	3.00
89-05	Washington Statehood	3.00
89-06	Steamboats booklet pane (5)	5.00
89-07	World Stamp Expo '89	3.00
89-08	Arturo Toscanini	2.50
89-09	U.S. House of Representatives	3.00
89-10	U.S. Senate	3.00
89-11	Executive Branch	3.00
89-12	South Dakota Statehood	3.00
89-13	7.1¢ Tractor coil, precancel (4)	4.00
89-14	$1 Johns Hopkins	3.50
89-15	Lou Gehrig	15.00
89-16	1¢ Penalty Mail	4.50
89-17	45¢ French Revolution airmail	4.50
89-18	Ernest Hemingway	2.50
89-19	$2.40 Moon Landing	17.50
89-20	North Carolina Statehood	3.00
89-21	Letter Carriers	2.50
89-22	28¢ Sitting Bull	2.50
89-23	Drafting of the Bill of Rights	3.00
89-24	Prehistoric Animals (4)	12.50
89-25	25¢ and 45¢ PUAS-America (2)	3.50
89-26	Christmas, Madonna	10.00
89-27	Christmas, Antique Sleigh	10.00
89-28	Eagle and Shield, self-adhesive	3.50
89-29	World Stamp Expo '89 souvenir sheet	10.00
89-30	Classic Mail Transportation (4)	4.00
89-31	Future Mail Transportation souvenir sheet	8.00
89-32	45¢ Future Mail Transportation airmails (4)	8.00
89-33	Classic Mail Transportation souvenir sheet	9.00

1990

90-01	Idaho Statehood	3.00
90-02	Love sheet and booklet pane (10)	6.00
90-03	Ida B. Wells	6.00
90-04	U.S. Supreme Court	3.00
90-05	15¢ Beach Umbrella booklet pane (10)	5.00
90-06	5¢ Luis Munoz Marin (5)	3.00
90-07	Wyoming Statehood	3.00
90-08	Classic Films (4)	7.50
90-09	Marianne Moore	3.00
90-10	$1 Seaplane coil (2)	9.00
90-11	Lighthouses booklet pane (5)	7.50
90-12	Plastic Flag stamp	5.00
90-13	Rhode Island Statehood	4.00
90-14	$2 Bobcat	7.50
90-15	Olympians (5)	8.00
90-16	Indian Headdresses booklet pane (10)	9.00
90-17	5¢ Circus Wagon coil (5)	5.00
90-18	40¢ Claire Lee Chennault	4.50
90-19	Federated States of Micronesia/ Marshall Islands (2)	4.00
90-20	Creatures of the Sea (4)	7.50
90-21	25¢ and 45¢ PUAS/America (2)	4.50

90-22	Dwight D. Eisenhower	3.50
90-23	Christmas, Madonna, sheet and booklet pane (11)	7.50
90-24	Christmas, Yule Tree, sheet and booklet pane (11)	7.50

1991

91-01	"F" (29¢) Flower sheet and coil (3)	5.00
91-02	"F" (29¢) Flower booklet panes (20)	15.00
91-03	4¢ Makeup	3.50
91-04	"F" (29¢) ATM booklet single	4.00
91-05	"F" (29¢) Penalty Mail coil (2)	4.00
91-06	4¢ Steam Carriage coil (7)	5.00
91-07	50¢ Switzerland	4.00
91-08	Vermont Statehood	4.00
91-09	19¢ Fawn (2)	4.00
91-10	Flag over Mount Rushmore coil (2)	4.00
91-11	35¢ Dennis Chavez	4.00
91-12	Flower sheet and booklet pane (10)	9.00
91-13	4¢ Penalty Mail (8)	4.00
91-14	Wood Duck booklet panes (10)	15.00
91-15	23¢ Lunch Wagon coil (2)	4.00
91-16	Flag with Olympic Rings booklet pane (10)	9.00
91-17	50¢ Harriet Quimby	4.00
91-18	Savings Bond	3.00
91-19	Love sheet and booklet pane, 52¢ Love (12)	12.50
91-20	19¢ Balloon booklet pane (10)	6.00
91-21	40¢ William Piper airmail	4.00
91-22	William Saroyan	4.00
91-23	Penalty Mail coil and 19¢ and 23¢ sheet (4)	5.00
91-24	5¢ Canoe and 10¢ Tractor Trailer coils (4)	5.00
91-25	Flags on Parade	4.00
91-26	Fishing Flies booklet pane (5)	7.50
91-27	52¢ Hubert H. Humphrey	4.00
91-28	Cole Porter	4.00
91-29	50¢ Antarctic Treaty airmail	4.00
91-30	1¢ Kestrel, 3¢ Bluebird and 30¢ Cardinal (3)	4.00
91-31	Torch ATM booklet single	4.00
91-32	Desert Shield/ Desert Storm sheet and booklet pane (11)	10.00
91-33	Flag over Mount Rushmore coil, gravure printing (darker, 3)	4.00
91-34	Summer Olympics (5)	8.00
91-35	Flower coil, slit perforations (3)	4.00
91-36	Numismatics	4.00
91-37	Basketball	8.00
91-48	19¢ Fishing Boat coil (3)	4.00
91-49	Comedians booklet pane (10)	10.00
91-50	World War II miniature sheet (10)	10.00
91-51	District of Columbia	4.00
91-52	Jan Matzeliger	7.50
91-53	$1 USPS/ Olympic Logo	5.00
91-54	Space Exploration booklet pane (10)	10.00
91-55	50¢ PUASP/America airmail	4.00
91-56	Christmas, Madonna sheet and booklet pane (10)	12.00

91-57	Christmas, Santa Claus sheet and booklet pane (11)	20.00
91-58	5¢ Canoe coil, gravure printing (red, 6)	5.00
91-59	29¢ Eagle and Shield, self-adhesive (3)	7.50
91-60	23¢ Flag presort	4.00
91-61	$9.95 Express Mail	30.00
91-62	$2.90 Priority Mail	10.00
91-63	$14.00 Express Mail International	40.00

1992

92-01	Winter Olympic Games (5)	6.00
92-02	World Columbian Stamp Expo '92	3.50
92-03	W.E.B. DuBois	10.00
92-04	Love	4.00
92-05	75¢ Wendell Willkie	5.00
92-06	29¢ Flower coil, round perforations (2)	4.00
92-07	Earl Warren	6.00
92-08	Olympic Baseball	20.00
92-09	Flag over White House, coil (2)	4.00
92-10	First Voyage of Christopher Columbus (4)	6.00
92-11	New York Stock Exchange	4.00
92-18	Space Adventures (4)	6.00
92-19	Alaska Highway	4.00
92-20	Kentucky Statehood	4.00
92-21	Summer Olympic Games (5)	6.00
92-22	Hummingbirds booklet pane (5)	7.50
92-23	Wildflowers (10)	10.00
92-24	Wildflowers (10)	10.00
92-25	Wildflowers (10)	10.00
92-26	Wildflowers (10)	10.00
92-27	Wildflowers (10)	10.00
92-28	World War II miniature sheet (10)	10.00
92-30	Dorothy Parker	4.00
92-31	Theodore von Karman	7.50
92-33	Minerals (4)	7.50
92-35	Juan Rodriguez Cabrillo	4.00
92-36	Wild Animals booklet pane (5)	7.50
92-38	Christmas Contemporary, sheet and booklet pane (8)	10.00
92-39	Christmas Traditional, sheet and booklet pane (11)	12.50
92-40	Pumpkinseed Sunfish	4.00
92-41	Circus Wagon	5.00
92-42	Year of the Rooster	10.00

1993

93-01	Elvis	15.00
93-02	Space Fantasy (5)	10.00
93-03	Percy Lavon Julian	7.50
93-04	Oregon Trail	5.00
93-05	World University Games	5.00
93-06	Grace Kelly	7.50
93-07	Oklahoma!	5.00
93-08	Circus	7.50
93-09	Thomas Jefferson	5.00
93-10	Cherokee Strip	5.00
93-11	Dean Acheson	5.00
93-12	Sporting Horses	7.50
93-13	USA Coil	5.00
93-14	Garden Flowers, booklet pane (5)	7.50
93-15	Eagle and Shield, coil	5.00
93-16	World War II miniature sheet (10)	7.50
93-17	Futuristic Space Shuttle	12.50
93-18	Hank Williams, sheet	7.50
93-19	Rock & Roll/Rhythm & Blues, sheet single, booklet pane (8)	12.50
93-20	Joe Louis	12.50
93-21	Red Squirrel	5.00
93-22	Broadway Musicals, booklet pane (5)	10.00
93-23	National Postal Museum, strip (4)	6.00

93-24	Rose	5.00
93-25	American Sign Language, pair	5.00
93-26	Country & Western Music, sheet and booklet pane (4)	15.00
93-27	African Violets, booklet pane (10)	7.50
93-28	10¢ Official Mail	4.00
93-29	Contemporary Christmas, booklet pane (10), sheet and self-adhesive stamps	12.00
93-30	Traditional Christmas, sheet, booklet pane (4)	7.50
93-31	Classic Books, strip (4)	7.50
93-32	Mariana Islands	5.00
93-33	Pine Cone	5.00
93-34	Columbus' Landing in Puerto Rico	6.00
93-35	AIDS Awareness	10.00

1994

94-01	Winter Olympics	7.50
94-02	Edward R. Murrow	5.00
94-03	Love, self-adhesive	5.00
94-04	Dr. Allison Davis	7.50
94-05	29¢ Eagle, self-adhesive	7.50
94-06	Year of the Dog	7.50
94-07	Love, booklet pane (10), single sheet stamp	10.00
94-08	Postage and Mailing Center	5.00
94-09	Buffalo Soldiers	10.00
94-10	Silent Screen Stars	10.00
94-11	Garden Flowers, booklet pane (5)	12.00
94-12	Victory at Saratoga	10.00
94-13	10¢ Tractor Trailer gravure printing	7.50
94-14	World Cup Soccer	12.50
94-15	World Cup Soccer souvenir sheet	12.50
94-16	World War II miniature sheet (10)	7.50
94-17	Love, sheet stamp	7.50
94-18	Statue of Liberty	7.50
94-19	Fishing Boat, reissue	7.50
94-20	Norman Rockwell	12.50
94-21	$9.95 and 29¢ Moon Landing	17.50
94-22	Locomotives (5)	10.00
94-23	George Meany	7.50
94-24	$5.00 Washington/ Jackson	15.00
94-25	Popular Singers (5)	12.50
94-26	James Thurber	7.50
94-27	Jazz Singers/Blues Singers (10)	17.50
94-28	Wonders of the Sea (4)	12.50
94-29	Chinese/Joint Issue (2)	7.50
94-30	Holiday Traditional (10)	17.50
94-31	Holiday Contemporary (4)	15.00
94-32	Holiday, self-adhesive	15.00
94-33	20¢ Virginia Apgar	12.50
94-34	BEP Centennial	25.00
94-35	Year of the Boar	15.00
94-G1	G1 (4)	15.00
94-G2	G2 (6)	15.00
94-G3	G3 (5)	15.00
94-G4	G4 (2)	15.00

1995

95-01	Love (2)	15.00
95-02	Florida State	15.00
95-03	Butte (7)	15.00
95-04	Automobile (4)	15.00
95-05	Flag Over Field, self-adhesive	15.00
95-06	Juke Box (2+2)	15.00
95-07	Tail Fin (2+2)	15.00
95-08	Circus Wagon (7)	7.50
95-09	Kids Care (4)	15.00
95-10	Richard Nixon	15.00
95-11	Bessie Coleman	15.00
95-12	Official Mail	15.00
95-13	Kestrel with cent sign	10.00
95-14	Love 1 oz. and 2 oz.	15.00
95-15	Flag Over Porch	15.00
95-16	Recreational Sports (5)	15.00
95-17	POW & MIA	15.00

95-18	Marilyn Monroe	15.00
95-19	Pink Rose	10.00
95-20	Ferry Boat (3)	10.00
95-21	Cog Railway Car (3)	10.00
95-22	Blue Jay (10)	10.00
95-23	Texas Statehood	15.00
95-24	Great Lake Lighthouses (5)	15.00
95-25	Challenger Shuttle	15.00
95-26	United Nations	15.00
95-27	Civil War (front and back)	20.00
95-28	Two Fruits	15.00
95-29	Alice Hamilton	15.00
95-30	Carousel Horses	15.00
95-31	Endeavor Shuttle	30.00
95-32	Alice Paul	15.00
95-33	Women's Suffrage	15.00
95-34	Louis Armstrong	15.00
95-35	World War II	15.00
95-36	Milton Hershey	15.00
95-37	Jazz Musicians	17.50
95-38	Fall Garden Flowers (5)	15.00
95-39	Eddie Rickenbacker (airmail)	15.00
95-40	Republic of Palau	15.00
95-41	Holiday Contemporary/ Santa (4)	17.50
95-42	American Comic Strips	25.00
95-43	Naval Academy	15.00
95-44	Tennessee Williams	15.00
95-45	Holiday Children Sledding	15.00
95-46	Holiday Traditional sheet and booklet pane (10)	17.50
95-47	Holiday Midnight Angel	15.00
95-48	Ruth Bendict	15.00
95-49	James K. Polk	15.00
95-50	Antique Automobiles, strip (5)	17.50

1996

96-01	Utah Statehood	15.00
96-02	Garden Flowers	17.50
96-03	Love/Kestrel	20.00
96-04	Postage and Mailing Center (3)	5.00
96-05	Ernest J. Just	15.00
96-06	Woodpecker	17.50
96-07	Smithsonian Institution	15.00
96-08	Year of the Rat	15.00
96-09	Pioneers of Communication	17.50
96-10	Fulbright Scholarships	15.00
96-11	Jacqueline Cochran	15.00
96-12	Mountain	15.00
96-13	Bluebird	6.00
96-14	Marathon	6.00
96-15	Flag over Porch/ Eagle & Shield	7.50
96-16	Cal Farley	6.00
96-17	Classic Olympic Collection	—
96-18	Georgia O'Keefe Art	6.00
96-19	Tennessee	6.00
96-20	American Indian Dances	9.00
96-21	Prehistoric Animals	9.00
96-22	Breast Cancer Awareness	6.00
96-23	Flag over Porch/ Juke Box/Butte/Tail Fin Automobile/Mountain	9.00
96-24	James Dean	6.00
96-25	Folk Heroes	9.00
96-26	Olympic/Discus	—
96-27	Iowa	6.00
96-28	Blue Jay	6.00
96-29	Rural Free Delivery	6.00
96-30	Riverboats	9.00
96-31	Big Band Leaders	9.00
96-32	Songwriters	9.00
96-33	F. Scott Fitzgerald	6.00
96-34	Endangered Species	10.00
96-35	Computer Technology	6.00
96-36	Family Scenes	—
96-37	Skaters	—
96-38	Hanukkah	—
96-39	Madonna and Child	—
96-40	Yellow Rose	—
96-41	Cycling	—

1997

97-01	Year of the Ox	—
97-02	Flag Over Porch/ Juke Box/Mountain	—
97-03	Benjamin O. Davis Sr.	—
97-04	Statue of Liberty	—
97-05	Love Swans	—
97-06	Helping Children Learn	—
97-07	Merian Botanical Plants	—
97-08	Pacific 97 - Stagecoach and Ship	—
97-09	Linerless Flag Over Porch/Juke Box	—
97-10	Thornton Wilder	—
97-11	Raoul Wallenberg	—
97-12	Dinosaurs	—
97-13	Pacific '97 - Franklin	—
97-14	Pacific '97 - Washington	—
97-15	Bugs Bunny	—
97-16	The Marshall Plan	—
97-17	Humphrey Bogart	—
97-18	Classic Aircraft	—
97-19	Classic American Dolls	—
97-20	Football Coaches	—
97-20A	George Halas	—
97-20B	Vince Lombardi	—
97-20C	Pop Warner	—
97-20D	Bear Bryant	—
97-21	Yellow Rose	—
97-22	"Stars and Stripes Forever"	—
97-23	Padre Félix Varela	—
97-24	Composers and Conducters	—
97-25	Opera Singers	—
97-26	Air Force	—
97-27	Movie Monsters	—
97-28	Supersonic Flight	—
97-29	Women in Military	—
97-30	Kwanzaa	—
97-31	Holiday Traditional, Madonna and Child	—
97-32	Holly	—
97-33	Mars Pathfinder	—

1998

98-01	Year of the Tiger	—
98-02	Winter Sports	—
98-03	Madame C. J. Walker	—
98-04	Spanish American War	—
98-05	Flowering Trees	—
98-06	Calder	—
98-07	Luce	—
98-08	Cinco De Mayo	—
98-09	Sylvester & Tweety	—
98-10	Wisconsin	—
98-11	Trans-Mississippi Reissue of 1898	—
98-12	Trans-Mississippi (single stamp)	—
98-13	Folk Singers	—
98-14	Berlin Airlift	—
98-15	Diner/Wetlands Coil	—
98-16	Spanish Settlement of the Southwest	—
98-17	Gospel Singers	—
98-18	The Wallaces	—
98-19	Benet	—
98-20	Tropical Birds	—
98-21	Alfred Hitchcock	—
98-22	Organ Donations	—
98-23	Bright Eyes	—
98-24	Klondike Gold Rush	—
98-25	American Art	—
98-26	Ballet	—
98-27	Space Fantasy	—
98-28	Philanthropy	—
98-29	Holiday Traditional	—
98-30	Holiday Contemporary	—
98-31	Hospice	—

Note: Numbers and prices may be changed without notice, due to additional USPS stamp issues and/ or different information that may become available on older issues.

American Commemorative Panels

The Postal Service offers American Commemorative Panels for each new commemorative stamp and special Christmas and Love stamp issued. The series began in 1972 with the Wildlife Commemorative Panel. The panels feature mint stamps complemented by fine reproductions of steel line engravings and the stories behind the commemorated subjects.

	1972	
1	Wildlife	8.00
2	Mail Order	7.50
3	Osteopathic Medicine	7.50
4	Tom Sawyer	6.25
5	Pharmacy	7.50
6	Christmas, Angels	11.00
7	Christmas, Santa Claus	11.00
7E	Same with error date (1882)	750.00
8	Stamp Collecting	7.00
	1973	
9	Love	9.50
10	Pamphleteers	8.00
11	George Gershwin	8.25
12	Posting a Broadside	8.00
13	Copernicus	8.00
14	Postal People	7.25
15	Harry S. Truman	11.00
16	Post Rider	10.00
17	Boston Tea Party	24.00
18	Electronics	8.00
19	Robinson Jeffers	8.00
20	Lyndon B. Johnson	10.00
21	Henry O. Tanner	8.00
22	Willa Cather	8.00
23	Drummer	12.00
24	Angus Cattle	8.00
25	Christmas, Madonna	12.50
26	Christmas Tree, Needlepoint	12.50
	1974	
27	VFW	8.00
28	Robert Frost	8.00
29	Expo '74	9.00
30	Horse Racing	10.00
31	Skylab	12.50
32	Universal Postal Union	10.00
33	Mineral Heritage	10.00
34	First Kentucky Settlement	8.00

35	Continental Congress	10.00
35A	Same with corrected logo	150.00
36	Chautauqua	8.00
37	Kansas Wheat	8.00
38	Energy Conservation	8.00
39	Sleepy Hollow	8.00
40	Retarded Children	8.00
41	Christmas, Currier & Ives	12.00
42	Christmas, Angel Altarpiece	12.00
	1975	
43	Benjamin West	8.00
44	Pioneer	12.00
45	Collective Bargaining	8.00
46	Contributors to the Cause	8.00
47	Mariner 10	11.00
48	Lexington & Concord	9.00
49	Paul Laurence Dunbar	10.00
50	D.W. Griffith	8.00
51	Bunker Hill	9.00
52	Military Uniforms	9.00
53	Apollo Soyuz	12.00
54	World Peace Through Law	8.00
54A	Same with August 15, 1975 date	150.00
55	Women's Year	8.00
56	Postal Service Bicentennial	10.00
57	Banking and Commerce	10.00
58	Early Christmas, Card	11.00
59	Christmas, Madonna	11.00
	1976	
60	Spirit of '76	12.00
61	Interphil 76	11.00
62	State Flags	25.00

63	Telephone	10.00
64	Commercial Aviation	13.00
65	Chemistry	12.00
66	Benjamin Franklin	11.00
67	Declaration of Independence	10.50
68	12th Winter Olympics	15.00
69	Clara Maass	10.00
70	Adolph S. Ochs	12.50
70A	Same with charter logo	18.00
71	Christmas, Winter Pastime	12.00
71A	Same with charter logo	21.00
72	Christmas, Nativity	12.00
72A	Same with charter logo	21.00
	1977	
73	Washington at Princeton	17.50
73A	Same with charter logo	18.00
74	Sound Recording	25.00
74A	Same with charter logo	33.00
75	Pueblo Art	75.00
75A	Same with charter logo	110.00
76	Solo Transatlantic Lindbergh Flight	80.00
77	Colorado Statehood	20.00
78	Butterflies	19.00
79	Lafayette	20.00
80	Skilled Hands	20.00
81	Peace Bridge	20.00
82	Battle of Oriskany	20.00
83	Energy	20.00
84	Alta, CA, Civil Settlement	20.00

228	Dogs	10.00
229	Crime Prevention	7.50
230	Hispanic Americans	8.00
231	Family Unity	8.00
232	Eleanor Roosevelt	8.00
233	Nation of Readers	8.00
234	Christmas, Madonna	10.00
235	Christmas, Santa Claus	10.00
236	Vietnam Veterans Memorial	12.00

1985

237	Jerome Kern	8.00
238	Mary McLeod Bethune	10.00
239	Duck Decoys	10.00
240	Winter Special Olympics	8.50
241	Love	10.00
242	Rural Electrification Administration	7.00
243	AMERIPEX '86	9.50
244	Abigail Adams	6.50
245	Frederic Auguste Bartholdi	12.50
246	Korean War Veterans	9.00
247	Social Security Act	7.00
248	World War I Veterans	8.00
249	Horses	12.50
250	Public Education	6.50
251	Youth	10.00
252	Help End Hunger	7.00
253	Christmas, Madonna	12.50
254	Christmas, Poinsettias	12.50

1986

255	Arkansas Statehood	7.50
256	Stamp Collecting Booklet	9.50
257	Love	10.00
258	Sojourner Truth	9.50
259	Republic of Texas	8.00
260	Fish Booklet	9.50
261	Public Hospitals	6.00
262	Duke Ellington	11.00
263	U.S. Presidents' Sheet #1	9.00
264	U.S. Presidents' Sheet #2	9.00
265	U.S. Presidents' Sheet #3	9.00
266	U.S. Presidents' Sheet #4	9.00
267	Polar Explorers	9.50
268	Statue of Liberty	9.50
269	Navajo Blankets	9.50
270	T.S. Eliot	9.00
271	Wood-Carved Figurines	9.00
272	Christmas, Madonna	8.00

| 273 | Christmas, Village Scene | 8.00 |

1987

274	Michigan Statehood	9.00
275	Pan American Games	8.00
276	Love	9.00
277	Jean Baptiste Pointe Du Sable	9.00
278	Enrico Caruso	9.00
279	Girl Scouts	9.00
280	Special Occasions Booklet	9.00
281	United Way	7.00
282	#1 American Wildlife	9.00
283	#2 American Wildlife	9.00
284	#3 American Wildlife	9.00
285	#4 American Wildlife	9.00
286	#5 American Wildlife	9.00

1987-90

287	Delaware Statehood	9.00
288	Pennsylvania Statehood	8.00
289	New Jersey Statehood	9.00
290	Georgia Statehood	9.00
291	Connecticut Statehood	9.00
292	Massachusetts Statehood	9.00
293	Maryland Statehood	9.00
294	South Carolina Statehood	9.00
295	New Hampshire Statehood	9.00
296	Virginia Statehood	9.00
297	New York Statehood	9.00
298	North Carolina Statehood	9.00
299	Rhode Island Statehood	10.00

1987

300	Morocco/U.S. Diplomatic Relations	7.00
301	William Faulkner	7.00
302	Lacemaking	7.00
303	Constitution Booklet	7.00
304	Signing of the Constitution	7.00
305	Certified Public Accountants	8.00
306	Locomotives Booklet	8.00
307	Christmas, Madonna	9.00
308	Christmas, Ornaments	8.00

1988

309	Winter Olympics	9.00
310	Australia	8.00
311	James Weldon Johnson	9.00
312	Cats	11.00
313	Knute Rockne	12.50
314	New Sweden	8.00
315	Francis Ouimet	20.00
316	Love	10.00
317	Summer Olympics	9.00
318	Classic Cars Booklet	9.00
319	Antarctic Explorers	9.00
320	Carousel Animals	10.00
321	Special Occasions Booklet	9.00
322	Christmas, Madonna, Sleigh	9.00

1989

323	Montana Statehood	9.00
324	A. Philip Randolph	12.50
325	North Dakota Statehood	9.00
326	Washington Statehood	9.00
327	Steamboats Booklet	12.50
328	World Stamp Expo '89	9.00
329	Arturo Toscanini	9.00

1989-90

330	U.S. House of Representatives	11.00
331	U.S. Senate	11.00
332	Executive Branch	11.00
333	U.S. Supreme Court	11.00

1989

334	South Dakota Statehood	9.00
335	Lou Gehrig	25.00
336	French Revolution	11.00
337	Ernest Hemingway	11.00
338	Letter Carriers	11.00
339	Drafting of the Bill of Rights	11.00
340	Prehistoric Animals	15.00
341	25¢ and 45¢ America/PUAS	11.00
342	Christmas, Traditional and Contemporary	12.50
343	Classic Mail Transportation	11.00
344	Future Mail Transportation	12.50

1990

345	Idaho Statehood	11.00
346	Love	11.00
347	Ida B. Wells	18.00

348	Wyoming	
	Statehood	9.00
349	Classic Films	15.00
350	Marianne Moore	9.00
351	Lighthouses	
	Booklet	15.00
352	Olympians	15.00
353	Indian	
	Headdresses	
	Booklet	12.50
354	Micronesia/	
	Marshall Islands	12.50
355	Creatures	
	of the Sea	20.00
356	25¢ and 45¢	
	America/PUAS	14.00
357	Eisenhower	12.50
358	Christmas,	
	Traditional and	
	Contemporary	14.00
	1991	
359	Switzerland	12.50
360	Vermont	
	Statehood	11.00
361	Savings Bonds	9.00
362	29¢ and 52¢	
	Love	11.00
363	Saroyan	11.00
364	Fishing Flies	
	Booklet	12.50
365	Cole Porter	11.00
366	Antarctic Treaty	11.00
367	Desert Shield/	
	Desert Storm	30.00
368	Summer	
	Olympics	12.50
369	Numismatics	12.50
370	World War II	
	Miniature Sheet	19.00
371	Basketball	15.00
372	District of	
	Columbia	11.00
373	Comedians	
	Booklet	15.00
374	Jan Matzeliger	14.00
375	Space Exploration	
	Booklet	16.00
376	America/PUAS	11.00
377	Christmas,	
	Traditional and	
	Contemporary	14.00
	1992	
378	Winter Olympics	15.00
379	World Columbian	
	Stamp Expo '92	12.50
380	W.E.B. Du Bois	12.50
381	Love	12.50
382	Olympic Baseball	25.00
383	Columbus' First	
	Voyage	20.00
384	Columbian	
	Souvenir Sheets	30.00
385	Columbian	
	Souvenir Sheets	30.00
386	Columbian	
	Souvenir Sheets	30.00
387	New York Stock	
	Exchange	17.50
388	Space	
	Adventures	17.00
389	Alaska Highway	12.50

390	Kentucky	
	Statehood	12.50
391	Summer	
	Olympics	15.00
392	Hummingbirds	
	Booklet	17.00
393	World War II	
	Miniature Sheet	15.00
394	Wildflowers #1	15.00
395	Wildflowers #2	15.00
396	Wildflowers #3	15.00
397	Wildflowers #4	15.00
398	Wildflowers #5	15.00
399	Dorothy Parker	12.50
400	Theodore	
	von Karman	15.00
401	Minerals	14.00
402	Juan Rodriguez	
	Cabrillo	15.00
403	Wild Animals	
	Booklet	14.00
404	Christmas,	
	Traditional and	
	Contemporary	12.50
405	Happy New Year	15.00
	1993	
406	Elvis	30.00
407	Space Fantasy	17.50
408	Percy Julian	20.00
409	Oregon Trail	15.00
410	World Univ.	
	Games	15.00
411	Grace Kelly	20.00
412	Oklahoma!	17.50
413	Circus	17.50
414	Cherokee Strip	12.50
415	Dean Acheson	15.00
416	Sport Horses	20.00
417	Garden Flowers	20.00
418	World War II	20.00
419	Hank Williams	20.00
420	Rock & Roll/R&B	25.00
421	Joe Louis	21.00
422	Broadway	
	Musicals	22.50
423	National Postal	
	Museum	17.50
424	Deaf	
	Communication	17.50
425	Country Western	21.00
426	Christmas,	
	Traditional	20.00
427	Youth Classics	20.00
428	Mariana Islands	17.50
429	Columbus Landing	
	In Puerto Rico	15.00
430	AIDS Awareness	17.50
	1994	
431	Winter Olympics	15.00
432	Edward R.	
	Murrow	12.50
433	Dr. Allison Davis	17.50
434	Year of the Dog	21.00
435	Love	20.00
436	Buffalo Soldiers	25.00
437	Silent Screen	
	Stars	18.00
438	Garden Flowers	15.00
439	World Cup	
	Soccer	15.00
440	World War II	20.00

441	Norman Rockwell	20.00
442	Moon Landing	25.00
443	Locomotives	20.00
444	George Meany	20.00
445	Popular Singers	20.00
446	James Thurber	20.00
447	Jazz/Blues	25.00
448	Wonders of	
	the Sea	20.00
449	Birds (Cranes)	20.00
450	Christmas,	
	Madonna	20.00
451	Christmas,	
	Stocking	20.00
	1995	
452	Year of the Boar	20.00
453	Florida	
	Statehood	20.00
454	Bessie Coleman	20.00
455	Kids Care!	20.00
456	Richard Nixon	20.00
457	Love	20.00
458	Recreational	
	Sports	20.00
459	POW & MIA	20.00
460	Marilyn Monroe	25.00
461	Texas Statehood	20.00
462	Great Lakes	
	Lighthouses	25.00
463	United Nations	20.00
464	Carousel Horses	25.00
465	Jazz Musicians	25.00
466	Women's	
	Suffrage	20.00
467	Louis Armstrong	20.00
468	World War II	20.00
469	Fall Garden	
	Flowers	20.00
470	Republic of Palau	20.00
471	Christmas,	
	Contemporary	25.00
472	Naval Academy	20.00
473	Tennessee	
	Williams	20.00
474	Christmas,	
	Traditional	20.00
475	James K. Polk	20.00
476	Antique	
	Automobiles	25.00
	1996	
477	Utah Statehood	20.00
478	Winter Garden	
	Flowers	25.00
479	Ernest E. Just	20.00
480	Smithsonian	
	Institution	20.00
481	Year of the Rat	20.00
482	Pioneers of	
	Communication	20.00
483	Fulbright	
	Scholarships	20.00
484	Olympics	20.00
485	Marathon	20.00
486	Georgia O'Keefe	20.00
487	Tennessee	
	Statehood	20.00
488	James Dean	20.00
489	Prehistoric	
	Animals	20.00
490	Breast Cancer	
	Awareness	20.00

491	American Indian Dances	20.00
492	Folk Heroes	20.00
493	Centennial Games (Discus)	20.00
494	Iowa Statehood	20.00
495	Rural Free Delivery	20.00
496	Riverboats	20.00
497	Big Band Leaders	20.00
498	Songwriters	20.00
499	Endangered Species	25.00
500	Family Scenes (4 designs)	20.00
501	Hanukkah	20.00
502	Madonna and Child	20.00
503	Cycling	—
503A	F. Scott Fitzgerald	—
503B	Computer Technology	—

1997

504	Year of the Ox	—
505	Benjamin O. Davis	—
506	Love	—
507	Helping Children Learn	—
508	Pacific 97 Triangle Stamps	—
509	Thornton Wilder	—
510	Raoul Wallenberg	—
511	Dinosaurs	—
512	Bugs Bunny	—
513	Pacific 97 Franklin	—
514	Pacific 97 Washington	—
515	The Marshall Plan	—
516	Classic Aircraft	—
517	Football Coaches	—
518	Dolls	—
519	Humphrey Bogart	—
520	Stars and Stripes	—
521	Opera Singers	—
522	Composers and Conductors	—
523	Padre Varela	—
524	Air Force	—
525	Movie Monsters	—
526	Supersonic Flight	—
527	Women in the Military	—
528	Holiday Kwanzaa	—
529	Holiday, Traditional	—
530	Holiday Holly	—

1998

531	Year of the Tiger	—
532	Winter Sports	—
533	Madam C.J. Walker	—
534	Spanish American War	—
535	Flowering Trees	—
536	Alexander Calder	—
537	Cinco de Mayo	—
538	Sylvester & Tweety	—
539	Wisconsin Statehood	—
540	Trans-Mississippi	—
541	Folk Singers	—
542	Berlin Airlift	—
543	Spanish Settlement of the Southwest	—
544	Gospel Singers	—
545	Stephen Vincent Benet	—
546	Tropical Birds	—
547	Alfred Hitchcock	—
548	Organ Donations	—
549	Bright Eyes	—
550	Klondike Gold Rush	—
551	American Art	—
552	Ballet	—
553	Space Discovery	—
554	Philanthropy	—
555	Holiday, Traditional	—
556	Holiday, Contemporary	—

Note: 1998 issues subject to change.

Subject Index

The numbers listed next to the stamp description are the Scott numbers, and the numbers in parentheses are the numbers of the pages on which the stamps are listed.

I

Wood, Grant, *American Gothic*, (37)

Wooden Propeller, Airplane Radiator and, C4 (409)

Woodland Habitats, 1924 (252)

Woodson, Carter G., 2073 (271)

Wool Industry, American, 1423 (193)

Workmen's Compensation, 1186 (170)

World
Columbian Stamp Expo '92, 2616 (328), 2624-2629 (331)
Cup Soccer Championships, 1994, 2834-2837 (355)
Exposition, Louisiana, 2086 (271)
Forestry Congress, Fifth, 1156 (169)
Health Organization, 1194 (170)
of Dinosaurs, 3136a-o (392)
Peace Through Law, 1576 (210)
Peace Through World Trade, 1129 (165)
Refugee Year, 1149 (166)
STAMP EXPO '89, 2410 (311), 2433 (315)
STAMP EXPO '92, Columbian, 2616 (328), 2624-2629 (331)
University Games, 2748 (344)
War (355)
War I, (25), 537 (107), 2154 (280)
War II, 899-901 (139), 905 (139), 907-908 (139), 909-915 (140), 917-921 (140), 925-926 (140), 929 (143), 934-936 (143), 939-940 (143), 956 (146), 969 (149), 1026 (153), 1289 (178), 1424 (193), 1869 (247), 2186 (283), 2192 (283), 2559a-j (324), 2697 (339), 2765a-j (347), 2838a-j (355), 2981a-2981j (371)

World's
Fair '64, 1244 (174)
Fair Expo '74, 1527 (205)
Fair, Expo Seattle '62, 1196 (173)
Fair, Knoxville '82, 2006-2009 (263)
Fair, New York, 853 (135)

Wreath and Toys, 1843 (244)

Wreaths, (42)

Wright
Airplane, 649 (116), C45 (410), C47 (410), C91 (417)
Brothers, C45 (410), C47 (410), C91-C92 (417)
Frank Lloyd, 1280 (178), 2019 (263)

Wulfenite, 2703 (339)

Wyoming, 1676 (221), 2002 (260)
Statehood, 2444 (316)
Yellowstone National Park, 744 (124), 760 (127), 1453 (197),

Postmasters General of the United States

Appointed by the Continental Congress
1775 Benjamin Franklin, PA
1776 Richard Bache, PA
1782 Ebenezer Hazard, NY

Appointed by the President with the advice and consent of the Senate
1789 Samuel Osgood, MA
1791 Timothy Pickering, PA
1795 Joseph Habersham, GA
1801 Gideon Granger, CT
1814 Return J. Meigs, Jr., OH
1823 John McLean, OH
1829 William T. Barry, KY
1835 Amos Kendall, KY
1840 John M. Niles, CT
1841 Francis Granger, NY
1841 Charles A. Wickliffe, KY
1845 Cave Johnson, TN
1849 Jacob Collamer, VT
1850 Nathan K. Hall, NY
1852 Samuel D. Hubbard, CT
1853 James Campbell, PA
1857 Aaron V. Brown, TN
1859 Joseph Holt, KY
1861 Horatio King, ME
1861 Montgomery Blair, DC
1864 William Dennison, OH
1866 Alexander W. Randall, WI
1869 John A.J. Creswell, MD
1874 James W. Marshall, NJ
1874 Marshall Jewell, CT
1876 James N. Tyner, IN
1877 David McK. Key, TN
1880 Horace Maynard, TN
1881 Thomas L. James, NY
1882 Timothy O. Howe, WI
1883 Walter Q. Gresham, IN
1884 Frank Hatton, IA
1885 William F. Vilas, WI
1888 Don M. Dickinson, MI
1889 John Wanamaker, PA
1893 Wilson S. Bissell, NY
1895 William L. Wilson, WV
1897 James A. Gary, MD
1898 Charles Emory Smith, PA
1902 Henry C. Payne, WI
1904 Robert J. Wynne, PA
1905 George B. Cortelyou, NY
1907 George von L. Meyer, MA
1909 Frank H. Hitchcock, MA
1913 Albert S. Burleson, TX
1921 Will H. Hays, IN
1922 Hubert Work, CO
1923 Harry S. New, IN
1929 Walter F. Brown, OH
1933 James A. Farley, NY
1940 Frank C. Walker, PA
1945 Robert E. Hannegan, MO
1947 Jesse M. Donaldson, IL
1953 Arthur E. Summerfield, MI
1961 J. Edward Day, CA
1963 John A. Gronouski, WI
1965 Lawrence F. O'Brien, MA
1968 W. Marvin Watson, TX
1969 Winton M. Blount, AL

Selected by the Presidentially appointed U.S. Postal Service Board of Governors
1971 Elmer T. Klassen, MA
1975 Benjamin Franklin Bailar, MD
1978 William F. Bolger, CT
1985 Paul N. Carlin, WY
1986 Albert V. Casey, MA
1986 Preston R. Tisch, NY
1988 Anthony M. Frank, CA
1992 Marvin Runyon, TN
1998 William J. Henderson, NC